Instructor's Manual
with Test Bank

for

Ingraham and Ingraham's Introduction to Microbiology

Third Edition

Jay M. Templin
Montgomery County Community College

THOMSON

BROOKS/COLE

Australia • Canada • Mexico • Singapore • Spain • United Kingdom • United States

Printed in the United States of America
1 2 3 4 5 6 7 07 06 05 04 03

Printer: Victor Graphics, Inc.

ISBN 0-534-39467-1

For more information about our products,
contact us at:
Thomson Learning Academic Resource Center
1-800-423-0563

For permission to use material from this text,
contact us by:
Phone: 1-800-730-2214
Fax: 1-800-731-2215
Web: http://www.thomsonrights.com

Brooks/Cole—Thomson Learning
10 Davis Drive
Belmont, CA 94002-3098
USA

Asia
Thomson Learning
5 Shenton Way #01-01
UIC Building
Singapore 068808

Australia/New Zealand
Thomson Learning
102 Dodds Street
Southbank, Victoria 3006
Australia

Canada
Nelson
1120 Birchmount Road
Toronto, Ontario M1K 5G4
Canada

Europe/Middle East/South Africa
Thomson Learning
High Holborn House
50/51 Bedford Row
London WC1R 4LR
United Kingdom

Latin America
Thomson Learning
Seneca, 53
Colonia Polanco
11560 Mexico D.F.
Mexico

Spain/Portugal
Paraninfo
Calle/Magallanes, 25
28015 Madrid, Spain

Contents

Preface

To the instructor:
This instructor's manual offers several features to assist you when teaching your course in microbiology. Several course outlines are suggested to complement the sequence of topics you choose for your course. Each chapter of the instructor's manual provides the following:

learning goals
chapter outline
teaching tips
discussion topics
answers to review questions, essay questions, and correlation questions from the textbook plus answers to discussion topics and correlation questions stated in the instructor's manual

In addition, the test bank offers a variety of questions on the content of each chapter. Questions are at the knowledge, comprehension, and application levels. Answers are provided for all of the questions. This bank of questions will be useful as you compose the exams for your microbiology course.

Jay Templin
Montgomery County Community College
Pottstown, PA

Suggested Course Outlines

Outline I

The following outline is for a one-semester course in microbiology based on 40 lectures, each one running for 50 minutes. The outline presents the topics in the order as presented in the textbook. Use the textbook's table of contents as a more detailed outline of these topics.

Topics	*Number of Lectures*
Introduction/The Science of Microbiology	1
Basic Chemistry	4
Methods of Studying Microorganisms	1
Prokaryotic and Eukaryotic Cells	3
Metabolism of Microorganisms	2
The Genetics of Microorganisms	1.5
Recombinant DNA Technology	0.5
The Growth of Microorganisms	1
Controlling Microorganisms	1
Classification	2
The Prokaryotes	2
Eukaryotic Microorganisms, Helminths, and Arthropod Vectors	1
The Viruses	
Microorganisms and Human Health	1.5
Microorganisms and Human Disease	1.5
The Body's Three Lines of Defense Against Infection	1
The Immune System: Innate Immunity	1
Immunologic Disorders	1
Diagnostic Immunology	0.5
Preventing Disease	1.5
Pharmacology	2
Infections of the Respiratory System	1
Infections of the Digestive System	2
Infections of the Genitourinary System	1
Infections of the Nervous System	1
Infections of the Body's Surfaces	1
Systemic Infections	2
Microorganisms and the Environment	2
Microbial Biotechnology	

Outline II

This outline uses a taxonomic approach. Use Chapters 1-4 for background and then emphasize the types of microorganisms.

Topics	*Number of Lectures*	
Introduction/The Science of Microbiology	1	Chapter 1
Basic Chemistry	2	Chapter 2
Methods of Studying Microorganisms	2	Chapter 3
Prokaryotic and Eukaryotic Cells Structure and Function: The Prokaryotic Cell The Eukaryotic Cell Passage of Molecules Across Cell Membranes	2	Chapter 4
Classification Principles of Biological Classification Microorganisms and Higher Levels of Classification Methods of Microbial Classification	3	Chapter 10
Prokaryotes Identifying Bacteria/Bacterial Taxonomy	4	Chapter 11
Eukaryotic Microorganisms/Introduction	2	Chapter 12
Eukaryotic Microorganisms/Fungi	2	
Algae	2	
Lichens	1	
Protozoa	2	
The Slime Molds	2	
Helminths	2	
Arthropod Vectors	1	
The Viruses	2	Chapter 13
Classification of Viruses	1	
Bacteriophages	1	
Animal Viruses	1	
Plant Viruses	1	
Viruses of Eukaryotic Microorganisms	2	
Infectious Agents That Are Simpler that Viruses	1	
The Origin of Viruses	1	
Microorganisms and the Environment Life and the Evolutin of Our Environment Microorganisms in the Biosphere The Cycles of Matter Treatment of Waste Water Escape from the Carbon Cycle	2	Chapter 28

Outline III

This outline emphasizes environmental and public safety issues.

Topics	*Number of Lectures*	
Introduction/The Science of Microbiology	1	Chapter 1
Basic Chemistry	2	Chapter 2
Methods of Studying Microorganisms	2	Chapter 3
Prokaryotic and Eukaryotic Cells	2	Chapter 4
Metabolism of Microorganisms	2	Chapter 5
The Growth of Microoganisms Populations What Microorganisms Need to Grow Measuring the Numbers of Microorganisms	5	Chapter 8
Controlling Microorganisms The Way Microorganisms Die Physical Controls on Microorganisms Chemical Controls on Microorganisms Preserving Food	5	Chapter 9
Pharmacology	4	Chapter 21
Infections of the Digestive System The Digestive System Infections of the Oral Cavity and Salivary Glands Infections of the Intestinal Tract Infections of the Liver	4	Chapter 23
Infections of the Genitourinary System The Genitourinary System Urinary Tract Infections Sexually Transmissible Diseases Female Reproductive Tract Infections Male Reproductive Tract Infections	4	Chapter 24
Infections of the Nervous System The Nervous System Infections of the Meninges Neural Tissue Infections	3	Chapter 25
Infections of the Body's Surfaces The Body's Surfaces	3	Chapter 26
Skin Infections		

Eye Infections

Systemic Infections
The Cardiovascular System
The Lymphatic System
Infections of the Heart
Infections of the Lymphatic System

Chapter 27

Chapter 1
The Science of Microbiology

Learning Goals

To understand:

    The impact of microorganisms on human affairs

    Advances and challenges in applied microbiology

    Careers available to trained microbiologists

    The scope of microbiology and why it is a separate science

    The development of microbiology as a science

    Microbiology today and where it is headed in the future

Chapter Outline

The Unseen World and Ours
    Microbes, Diseases, and History
    Microbes and Life Today
    Careers in Microbiology
The Scope of Microbiology
    Bacteria
    Archaea
    Algae
    Fungi
    Protozoa
    Viruses
    Helminths
A Brief History of Microbiology
    Leeuwenhoek's "Animalcules"
    Spontaneous Generation
    The Germ Theory of Disease
    Koch's Postulates
    Immunity
    Public Hygiene
Microbiology Today
    Chemotherapy
    Immunology
    Virology
    Basic Biology
    Genetic Engineering and Genomics
    The Future
Summary

Chapter 1

Teaching Tips

1. Invite a representative from a local hospital or public health department to visit your students as as a guest lecturer. As this person addresses your students, they should gain additional perspectives about the applications of microbiology in their future careers.

2. Does your course have a lab component accompanying the lecture? Introduce the lab activities briefly in lecture as a lead-in to the scheduled lab period. Relate the discussions of the topics in Chapter 1 and lecture to studies in the lab. One appropriate topic is microbial metabolism. Show your students the results when bacteria metabolize a carbohydrate in a Durham tube. What caused the color change and gas accumulation in the nutrient broth in this tube?

3. Show your students other examples of the nutrient broth and culture tubes. They were used in experiments to disprove spontaneous generation. Describe the normal composition of nutrient broth.

4. Biological supply houses sell special attachments for microscopes that will enlarge and project the images of prepared slides onto a screen. This instructional tool will reinforce the explanations of microbial structure discussed in Chapter 1. It will also introduce the students to the slides of the different subgroups of microbes that they will study in the lab.

5. Relate some of the concepts stated in Chapter 1 to human structure and function. Use a human torso model to illustrate these concepts. Where is insulin normally produced in the human body? Where does *E. coli* normally inhabit the human body?

6. The discovery of new facts and concepts in microbiology has always drawn from advances in technology. For example, the knowledge of viral structure expanded rapidly with the development of the electron microscope. Improvements in microscopy continue to open avenues for learning more about microbial structure. Current examples of the link between microbiology and technological advances are cited in this chapter and throughout the text. A Case Study in Chapter 1 cites the advances in genomics for diagnosing a STD in a patient. Use these examples to show your students that microbiology is an exciting science with a growing body of knowledge, constantly drawing from breakthroughs in technology.

7. Use the Internet as a source to find additional examples of the relationship between microbiology and technology. Entering "genomics" as a keyword in a search engine will reveal other examples to build on the information about this topic in the textbook. Promote this search as a class project.

Discussion Topics

1. Microorganisms are the experimental organisms used for recombinant DNA studies. Aside from their advantages, can you see possible dangers to humans resulting from this kind of research? How can these potential dangers be prevented?

2. Many students take a course in microbiology after studying human anatomy and physiology. How can an understanding of your students' knowledge of human structure and function be applied to the concepts they will learn in microbiology? Start with a discussion of the human immune system.

3. Understanding microbiology depends on relating this information to other branches of science. Courses in genetics and ecology offer students the opportunities to increase their background in biology. What they learn in these courses can enhance their grasp of the facts and concepts that they study in microbiology. Students can discuss how their biology courses are interrelated.

4. Discussing the interrelatedness of courses can expand to the link between microbiology and courses in chemistry or physics. How does a knowledge of chemistry aid in the understanding of microbial metabolism? How does a knowledge of physics contribute to an understanding of microscopy?

5. Most biologists point to evidence that life did arise spontaneously on the earth over three billion years ago. There is evidence from fossil imprints that these first organisms resembled bacteria. Could this event occur today? How were conditions on the earth different billions of years ago if the spontaneous generation of microorganisms did occur then?

Correlation Questions

1. The first Case Study at the beginning of this chapter cites the symptoms of a patient visiting an urgent care clinic. An examination of the patient includes facts about the following: body temperature, body areas where pain is occurring, pelvic discharge, and results from a test on a blood sample. Could other tests have been conducted for a more thorough examination? For example, blood tests can include a red blood cell count and a platelet count in addition to a total white blood cell count. Also, a differential white blood cell count lists the percentage of each kind of white blood cell in the total (e.g., neutrophils are normally about 65% of the total). Are these additional tests valuable for diagnosing the health of this patient? Red blood cells carry oxygen in the circulation. How is a knowledge of their changing concentration in the body valuable?

2. For the patient in the Case Study cited in question #1, what is the advantage of knowing about the percentages of different kinds of white blood cells in the total? For example, is the human body reacting to the same kind of microorgansim when the percentage of neutrophils changes as opposed to changes in the percentage of other white blood cell types? These other types include: basophils, eosinophils, lymphocytes, and monocytes. Look ahead to the textbook chapters on immunity (Chapters 16-18) for additional background.

Answers: Review Questions

The Unseen World and Ours

1. Microorganisms are organisms that generally cannot be seen without the use of magnification. They are usually observed through a microscope. Pathogenic species have caused major human diseases and plagues throughout the world. Although their impact has often been harmful to humans, microorganisms also have many positive effects on humans. They are the organisms of decay in the environment. They decompose organic matter into simpler substances, often producing elements such as carbon that can recycle in ecosystems. Microorganisms, such as <u>E. coli</u> are used in recombinant DNA research to make useful products such as insulin.

2. Advances in medical microbiology include the development of vaccines and production of antibiotics. Research in this area has improved our understanding of the immune system. Challenges include finding cures and effective treatments for human diseases, such as AIDS.

3. Environmental microbiology is the study of how microorganisms affect the earth and its atmosphere. This branch of microbiology has been used to produce water supplies that are safe for human consumption.

4. Microorganism-dependent industries include those producing food, beverages, vitamins, antibiotics, pharmaceuticals, hormones (e.g., insulin, human growth hormone), and an antiviral substance, interferon. The major challenges for industrial microbiology is applying genetic engineering to solve problems in other branches of microbiology.

5. Advances in agricultural microbiology include using microorganisms as pesticides to kill insects and using other microorganisms to make soil fertile. Future challenges in this branch include producing food supplements for humans and animals. Increased productivity for crops remains a major goal.

The Scope of Microbiology

6. The six subgroups of microorganisms are the bacteria, archaea, algae, fungi, protozoa, and viruses.

7. Small size is the single property that links all microorganisms. Microbiology is a cohesive science because of its methodology and approach to solving problems, regardless of the microorganisms studied. This includes identifying, cultivating, and studying microorganisms. Steps of the scientific method are used in research with these organisms.

8. Prokaryotes lack a true nucleus and other membrane-bound structures in cells such as the ER and mitochondrion. Eukaryotes have a true nucleus, with chromosomes and a double membrane, and membrane-bound, cellular structures. You will study these differences more in Chapter 4.

9. Archaea resemble the bacteria superficially. They are small, unicellular, and prokaryotic. However, they are distantly related to bacteria and live in hostile environments where many kinds of bacteria cannot live.

10. Bacteria show diversity in cell shape, cell structure, motility, metabolism, nutritional requirements, temperature tolerance, pH tolerance, salinity tolerance, and environmental preferences.

11. Algae are eukaryotic organisms. Their cells contain chloroplasts. Therefore, they conduct photosynthesis. Some are microscopic such as phytoplankton. Others are macroscopic such as the kelps. The multicellular algae superficially resemble higher plants but lack their specific structures. They are important as food producers and for global ecology.

12. The fungi are eukaryotic and nonphotosynthetic. Some are microscopic such as yeasts. Others are macroscopic such as mushrooms. Most are scavengers. Along with the bacteria, the fungi are important ecologically as decomposers. Decomposers are important for the release and recycling of substances in the environment. Some fungi are pathogens. One example is the fungus that causes corn smut.

13. Protozoa are eukaryotic, nonphotosynthetic, and usually motile. They are animal-like. Familiar forms are the amoeba and paramecium. Most protozoans are microscopic. Various species move by cilia, flagella, and pseudopodia. Some are pathogens. Parasitology is the study of diseases caused by protozoa and helminths.

14. Viruses are acellular. This means they lack a cellular structure. As intracellular parasites, they require host cells to survive. Outside the host they consist of a core of nucleic acid surrounded by a protein coat. They are studied biochemically and through the electron microscope. Causing major diseases (e.g., AIDS), they are medically important.

15. Prions are proteins acting as infectious agents. Prions are simpler than viruses.

16. Helminths are studied in microbiology because many of the stages in their life cycle are microscopic. Well-known members are the flatworms and roundworms.

A Brief History of Microbiology

17. Leeuwenhoek first studied microorganisms through the microscope in 1674. He described and drew them accurately.

18. By spontaneous generation living organisms arise from a nonliving source. Needham conducted an experiment that appeared to support this idea, but Redi and Spallanzani designed and performed experiments that disproved the theory of spontaneous generation. They used microorganisms in their experiments.

19. Pasteur finally disproved the theory of spontaneous generation by showing that microorganismsm could not be produced from a nutrient broth solution that lacked microorganisms. Therefore, life can only be produced from pre-existing life.

20. Well-designed experiments using microorganisms disproved the theory of spontaneous generation. All experimenters applied the steps of the scientific method.

21. Pasteur's contributions to microbiology include disproving the theory of spontaneous generation. By his work, microbiology became grounded in scientific reality. He proved that microorganisms could be studied by rational scientific means.

22. According to the germ theory of disease, specific microorganisms cause specific diseases. Robert Koch established this connection.

23. Koch developed four postulates to prove that a given microorganism causes a specific disease. He also developed a technique to obtain and cultivate bacteria in a pure culture.

24. An infectious disease is caused by a microorganism. By immunity the body is stimulated to develop its own ability to combat infection. Through immunization the body becomes immune to a disease by reacting to a weakened (attenuated) form of the microorganism, or its product, that does not cause the disease. This altered organism, or product, can be found in a vaccine and is introduced into the body by vaccination. The weakened microbe is not potent enough to cause the disease when introduced into the body of an organism. However, it can stimulate the immune system to react in the body. A killed vaccine contains dead cells of a microorganism. This form of the microorganism can also stimulate a subject's immune system. It is not possible to develop vaccines with attenuated form of a microorganism.

25. Jenner developed a vaccine for introduction into the body to stimulate immunity. Lister promoted asepsis through the use of phenol in operating rooms, killing the microbes before they could invade the human body.

26. Public hygiene attempts to prevent the growth and spread of harmful microbial populations in the environment. Improving water supplies for consumption and safely degrading sewage are some of the successful results.

Microbiology Today

27. Chemotherapy is the treatment of disease with chemicals called drugs. By selective toxicity a drug must kill an infecting microorganism but not harm the infected human cells. Antibiotics, such as penicillin, can be produced from microorganisms rather than manufactured synthetically in the lab. Many additional antibiotics, such as the sulfa drugs, have been discovered since.

28. By the founding efforts of Pasteur and Koch, immunology was initially viewed as the study of vaccines and the immune system. Continued study and research on the immune system makes this an expanding field. Many vaccines oppose viruses. Vaccines may hold the key for protection against the common cold and AIDS, both viral diseases.

29. Virology is the study of viruses. Iwanowsky isolated the first-discovered viruses from the juices of plants having the tobacco mosaic disease. He noted that viruses were small enough to pass through filters that normally trap bacteria.

30. Through genetic engineering DNA is obtained from one the cells of one organism and manipulated in a lab. This modified DNA is then introduced into another cell where it has an effect. *E. coli* is the most common cell to have DNA that is studied and used for this outcome. Products of genetic engineering include insulin. There are many other examples. Other advances are discussed throughout the text.

31. The cells of microorganisms are simple in structure and easily studied. Many species are easily cultivated. Many cells can be produced in a short span of time. This is an advantage for statistical analysis. All of these attributes are advantages for experimentation.

Answers: Essay Questions

1. Start with the idea that Pasteur was ahead of his time as he designed experiments using microorganisms to test theories. Unlike many of his colleagues, he used the scientific method to uncover many breakthroughs.

2. Microorganisms can mutate and evolve rapidly. This leads to the quick establishment of new microbial strains that are resistant to the antibiotics already used. This trend may leave fewer antibiotics available for discovery and successful use. Also the use of an antibiotic starts a selection process that eliminates some microbial mutants, preserving mutants that can resist the antibiotic. These selected, surviving mutants can produce asexually through binary fission and increase their exact, genetic types. This produces a population with a higher percentage of bacterial strains that can resist the antibiotic.

3. If a bacterium were as small as a virus, it would probably be as simple in structure as well. Viruses lack the comparatively detailed structures of a bacterial cell. To package these structures in a viral-sized particle is unlikely. However, the rickettsiae were once thought to be viruses. They are now known to be very small bacteria.

Answers: Discussion Topics

1. New mutant strains of microbes can evolve that can overcome the human immune system. Accurate, thorough testing of these new microbes are needed.

2. The immune system provides both cellular immunity and humoral immunity through the production of antibodies. Look ahead to the chapters on immunity in the textbook (Chapters 16-18).

3. Studying genetics can help one understand recombinant DNA technology. Studying ecology can help one to understand environmental microbiology.

4. Studying chemistry can help to understand the structure of the carbohydrates, lipids, and proteins that microbes metabolize. Studying physics can help one understand the behavior of light as it passes through regions of different densities. It also is applicable for topics of heat and temperature.

5. The climate of the earth was different three billion years ago. The temperature was higher. This factor and other forms of energy (e.g., light) facilitated the bonding of smaller molecules into macromolecules of life.

Answers: Correlation Questions

1. A normal, adult red cell count is about 5,000,000 per cubic millimeter. A low red blood cell count can indicate anemia, meaning that the oxygen-carrying power of the blood is diminished. At maturity, a red blood cell is mainly hemoglobin, consisting of protein and iron. Suggesting a dietary supplement, for example with a source of iron, could possibly correct this anemic condition in the patient and promote better health. A dietary supplement can provide the body with the raw materials to build more red blood cells.

2. Different kinds of white blood cells attack different kinds of microorganisms. For example, a lymphocyte may be more likely to attack one kind of virus. Its increased activity could indicate a viral disease. Eosinophils tend to increase in amount during allergies or parasitic infections.

Chapter 2
Basic Chemistry

Learning Goals

To understand:

The basic building blocks of matter-subatomic particles, atoms, elements, and molecules

The ways in which atoms bond to make molecules and compounds

What a chemical reaction is, what determines whether a reaction occurs, and what determines the rate of a chemical reaction

The unique chemical properties of water

The structure of organic molecules

The structure of the macromolecules-proteins, nucleic acids, carbohydrates, and lipids—from which all cellular microorganisms are built

Chapter Outline

The Basic Building Blocks
    Atoms
    Elements
    Molecules
Chemical Bonds and Reactions
    Covalent Bonds
    Ionic Bonds
    Hydrogen Bonds
    Chemical Reactions
Water
    Special Properties of Water
    Water as a Solvent
Organic Molecules
    Carbon Atoms
    Functional Groups
Macromolecules
    Proteins
    Nucleic Acids
    Polysaccharides
    Lipids
Summary

Teaching Tips

1. Use the periodic table as you teach the atomic numbers and atomic weights for the biologically important elements. As you display the table, explain the arrangement of the elements in vertical families and horizontal rows.

2. Use three-dimensional, stickball models to illustrate the bonding patterns of atoms in biologically important molecules. Ask your students to take the models apart and put the atoms back together. This will improve their understanding of bonding patterns in molecules.

3. Worksheets, circulated in class and completed by students, offer students a chance to apply concepts learned in any course. The reinforcement provided by these exercises facilitates mastery of the information students need to know. Use this worksheet approach for the class you are teaching. Write some practice problems on the calculation of molecular weights and pH values. Copy these problems and distribute them in class for practice. Can your students calculate the molecular weight of glucose? What is the pH of a solution with a hydrogen ion concentration of 0.000001 grams per liter?

4. Continue the worksheet-practice approach with this idea: Display a list of numbers such as the following: 1, 2, 3, 4, 5, 6, 12, 24, 45, etc. Let each number represent an answer to a possible question that can be written from Chapter 2. For example, questions for the number 6 can be: What is the approximate pH of milk? How many electrons are in the outer energy shell of oxygen? How many carbon atoms are in a molecule of glucose? Theses exercises challenge students to think about the course content in a different way. In addition, these exercises emphasize the quantitative-based concepts stated throughout the chapter.

5. Show your students that chemistry has wide applicability to upcoming topics in microbiology. How does a bacterium ferment glucose? Where is peptidoglycan found in the bacterial cell? What is the genetic significance of the structure of DNA?

6. A study of chemistry has an obvious link to nutrition. Use information about the carbohydrates, lipids, and proteins to show this. Study the labels of some well-known food products. What is their percentages for the different kinds of organic molecules. In addition to the tie-in to human nutrition, show the relevance of these macromolecules to bacterial nutrition. Let students study the makeup of nutrient agar and other kinds of media they will use to culture microorganisms in the lab.

Discussion Topics

1. Life consists of complex molecules. However, these molecules consist of the simplest elements. How did life evolve from this pattern?

2. How are the principles of this chapter important to the topics of bacterial genetics, metabolism, and nutrition?

3. Chemistry courses are prerequisites for courses in microbiology. Specifically, how does background information from these chemistry courses help students understand the concepts in this and other chapters. How does the chemistry -related topics in this course build on students' background and extend their knowledge?

4. The facts and concepts of chemistry have wide applications to other branches of science. Consider the topic of pH. How do buffers in the human body stabilize the pH of the blood or stomach? How do buffers in the bottom of a limestone stream stabilize the pH of this waterway, maintaining a pH that is optimal to support the various kinds of organisms living there? How does a highly-acidic rainfall threaten the ability of buffers to work in this stream?

Correlation Questions

1. The atomic weight of carbon in the periodic table is listed as 12.001. Why is this value not 12.000?

2. How does the computation of a pOH depend on the changing concentration of a free ion in solution?

3. Explain how one isotope of hydrogen has the same atomic number and atomic mass.

4. Potassium has an atomic number of 19. Will it tend to form cations or anions in solution?

Answers: Review Questions

The Basic Building Blocks

1. An atom consists of a nucleus composed of densely packed protons and neutrons. A cloud of electrons surrounds the nucleus. Either a proton or neutron has a mass of one atomic weight unit. The proton is positive and the neutron is neutral. An electron is negative. Its mass is negligible.

2. The valence electrons are located in the outermost shell of the atom. They determine the reactivity and bonding capability of an atom.

3. The atomic number is either the number of protons or number of electrons in an atom. The atomic weight is the number of protons plus the number of neutrons in an atom.

4. Elements are the simplest chemical substances.

5. A molecule is a particle of matter consisting of two or more atoms chemically bonded. A macromolecule is a very large molecule. A compound is a substance composed of molecules with more than one kind of atom. Organic compounds are carbon-containing compounds. They also contain hydrogen. Therefore, carbon dioxide is not an organic compound.

6. The molecular formula of water is two hydrogen atoms followed by one oxygen atom. By knowing the number of atoms of each kind in a molecule, and the atomic weight of each atom, you can compute the molecular weight of a substance. For example, water is 2 (2 x 1 for hydrogen) plus 16 (1 x 16 for oxygen) for a molecular weight of 18.

7. Avogadro's number is 6.02 times 10 raised to the 23rd power. One mole of substance with covalent bonding has this number of molecules. One mole of an ionic substance, such as NaCl, has this number of particles before dissociation.

Chemical Bonds and Reactions

8. Chemical bonds are the forces that hold atoms together in molecules. Chemical bonds form if the molecule produced has a lower energy state than the atoms originally reacting to form it. The valence electrons determine an atom's ability to form chemical bonds.

9. A covalent bond holds atoms together by the sharing of valence electrons. When these electrons are shared equally, and therefore equally spaced in a molecule, a nonpolar covalent bond is produced. With a polar covalent bond, the valence electrons are not shared equally and are not equally spaced in the molecule. Therefore, the molecule has a positive and negative end. Water is the most important polar molecule of life.

10. Ions are atoms that have acquired a complete valence shell by gaining or losing electrons. A cation is a positive ion. An anion is a negative ion.

11. The functions of ions in organisms include signaling environmental changes, serving as intermediates in the cycle of elements in the environment, neutralizing the charges of molecules, and balancing solute concentrations.

12. An ionic bond is a force holding ions or molecules together by the opposite charges of these particles. In NaCl, sodium ions are attracted to chloride ions by ionic bonds.

13. A hydrogen bond forms when a hydrogen atom interacts between two different molecules or between different parts of the same molecule. They stabilize the structure of many large, biologically important molecules such as DNA.

14. Covalent bonds are most stable. Hydrogen ions are least stable.

15. In a chemical reaction atoms or molecules, the reactants, collide and are transformed into new combinations of atoms or molecules, the products.

16. When chemical bonds are broken, energy is released; when chemical bonds are formed, energy is stored.

17. The concentration of reactants, the reaction temperature, and the presence of enzymes are all factors affecting the rate of chemical reactions.

18. Enzymes are important because they speed up chemical reactions to a rate where they support life.

19. A ribozyme is an RNA molecule with enzymatic properties. Whereas a large part of an enzyme molecule is usually a protein, in a ribozyme it is a nucleic acid.

Water

20. Because it forms hydrogen bonds between molecules, water has a high specific heat and heat of vaporization. It is cohesive and can therefore be drawn through distances. As a solid, water has a more open structure, making ice less dense than liquid water. Therefore, ice floats. This affects the melting pattern of lakes. In addition, water is a solvent for many substances.

21. By its polarity, water can attract positive and negative particles of a solute, promoting their dissociation. Water serves as a solvent.

22. Hydrophobic groups are repelled by water. They separate from water, forming important biological barriers. Hydrophilic groups are attracted to water. They dissolve in water.

23. A colloid is a tiny solid particle that draws ions, which in turn attract water molecules. This result forms colloidal dispersions, which are cloudy. Gels are concentrated colloidal dispersions.

24. Hydrogen or hydroxide ions participate in every chemical reaction of living things. The concentration of these free ions in solution determine the pH of a solution. The pH of a solution controls the chemical properties and reactions of the solution.

25. An acid is a compound that dissociates into hydrogen ions in water. A base is a compound that dissociates into hydroxide ions or removes hydrogen ions in water. A salt is an ionic compound consisting of a positive ion, such as sodium, and a negative ion, such as chloride.

26. The pH scale is a numerical scale showing how acidic or basic a solution is. It is logarithmic because a change of one number on this scale represents a tenfold change in the hydrogen ion concentration of a solution. For example, a pH of 3 is ten times more acidic than a pH of 4.

27. Buffers are compounds that stabilize the pH of a solution. In living systems they resist changes in pH, holding the level of acidity to an optimal level. They are used in labs to stabilize the pH of reaction mixtures.

Organic Molecules

28. Biochemistry is the study of carbon-containing molecules of organisms.

29. A carbon atom has great bonding versatility, as it can form four covalent bonds. These bonds can be with other elements or other carbon atoms. This leads to a large variety of carbon compounds.

30. Functional groups are atoms other than carbon or hydrogen that bond to organic molecules. Examples include the carboxyl and amino groups.

Macromolecules

31. A polymer is a macromolecule consisting of repeating, bonded subunits called monomers. The monomers unite by the process of polymerization.

32. Macromolecules are formed by the bonding of subunits through dehydration synthesis. Each time a covalent bond is formed, a water molecule is lost. Hydrolysis is the reverse of this process. A water molecule added to the bond breaks the bond, making the subunits available in a cell.

33. Amino acids, through peptide bonds, form proteins. Functions of proteins include structural building, transport, movement, and enzymatic roles.

34. L-isomers and D-isomers are mirror-image structural forms of amino acids. Only the L-isomers are found in proteins in nature. D-isomers are found in the peptidoglycan molecules of bacterial cell walls.

35. The primary structure of a protein is the specific sequence of bonded amino acids. The secondary structure is the shape of the molecule, such as an alpha helix, from hydrogen bonding. The tertiary structure involves further folding by the interaction of R groups. In the quaternary structure, different protein chains fit together. Denaturation is the disrupting of the secondary, tertiary, and quaternary structures through intense heat and other physical changes.

36. DNA is the nucleic acid encoding genetic information. RNA is the nucleic acid that builds proteins in a cell.

37. Nucleotides are the building blocks of nucleic acids. They are joined by phosphodiester bonds.

38. DNA and RNA are both nucleic acids consisting of bonded nucleotides. DNA is double-stranded. RNA is usually single-stranded. The sugar in the nucleotide of DNA is deoxyribose; it is ribose in RNA. The different nucleotides of DNA and RNA share three common bases: adenine, cytosine, and guanine. In DNA the fourth base is thymine. In RNA it is uracil.

39. ATP is the universal energy currency in the cell. cAMP is a messenger molecule in the cell. NAD and FAD are hydrogen carriers.

40. The carbohydrates are a class of organic compounds. Monosaccharides are the building blocks. Polysaccharides are macromolecules consisting of bonded monosaccharides. Important monosaccharides include glucose and fructose, which serve as a direct source of energy for cells.

41. Glycoside bonds link monosaccharides in a polysaccharide. Cellulose is a structural component in the cell wall of plants and bacteria. Starch is a molecule storing energy in plants and bacteria. Glycogen stores energy in animals. Polysaccharides are important for structure and energy storage in bacteria.

42. Lipids are defined as any nonpolar molecule. Three fatty acids bond to glycerol by ester linkages in triglycerides.

43. One of the three fatty acids bonded to glycerol is replaced by a phosphate group in a phospholipid.

44. Peptidoglycan is a macromolecule. Its configuration resembles an endless sheet forming a hollow structure. It has protein and polysaccharide components and confers strength to the cell wall of the bacterial cell.

Answers: Correlation Questions in the Textbook

1. Each element consists of one, unique kind of atom. Therefore, the number of different kinds of elements or atoms is the same. However, considering isotopes of an element, this makes the number of kinds of atoms greater than the number of elements. For example, the element hydrogen has three different isotopes. Oxygen has two isotopes.

2. Hydrogen is the smallest, simplest atom. This makes it easier to bond with other atoms that have unbonded electron pairs.

3. At a pH of 7 the hydroxide ion concentration is ten to the negative seven or 0.0000001 grams per liter. At a pH of 10, the hydroxide ion concentration is ten to the negative four or 0.0001 grams per liter. The difference between these two concentrations is three decimal places or a one thousandfold difference.

4. The atomic number for an element is its number of protons. The atomic weight of that element is the number of protons plus the number of neutrons. One isotope of hydrogen has one proton and lacks neutrons. In this isotope the atomic number and atomic weight each have a value of one. In other isotopes of hydrogen, and in other elements, adding the number of neutrons to the number of protons makes the atomic weight a higher number than the atomic number.

5. Sketch the structural formula for formic acid.

6. The electron arrangement of magnesium is 2 - 8 - 2. It can lose two outer-shell electrons and become plus two as an ion.

Answers: Essay Questions

1. Hydrogen bonds add stability to the structure of many different macromolecules. Without this bonding these molecules would not have the stability to carry out their biological functions.

2. Catalysts speed up the rate of chemical reactions. Without this increased speed these reactions could not support life processes.

Answers: Discussion Topics

1. Start with the idea that simple atoms can be assembled into more complex subunits. It is the arrangement and repeating pattern of these subunits that led to the formation of the complex macromolecules of life.

2. Examples to use are protein synthesis, starch hydrolysis, and the fermentation of various sugars. Although these topics will be studied in more depth, students will have enough background from this chapter to start understanding the bridge between chemistry and nutrition.

3. Students should have learned about the basic bonding properties of atoms before entering a course in microbiology. However, in microbiology they will be applying fundamental principles in new contexts. For example, students will now study simple atoms they have learned about previously—they will learn about them now in a peptidoglycan molecule. Nitrogen forms three covalent bonds in a molecule of ammonia or in a complex protein molecule.

4. In any buffer system, a buffer releases or takes up free hydrogen ions. By controlling the concentration of free hydrogen ions in solution, they control the pH value of that solution. In the case of acid rain in a stream, a point can be reached when there is insufficient buffer to bind and release hydrogen ions. Uncontrolled at this point, the pH can change. For example, an increase of free hydrogen ions (unbuffered) can make the stream more acidic.

Correlation Questions in the Instructor's Manual

1. The value of 12.001 is a weighted average of all carbon atoms in a sample. Although most of the atoms have an atomic weight of 12, a few have atomic weights of 13 or 14.

2. The pOH is depends on the concentration of hydroxide ions in solution. For example, if the concentration of this ion is 0.00000001, its concentation is 10 to the negative 8 power. This exponent, minus eight, converts to a pOH of 8.

3. The most common isotope of hydrogen has one proton and one electron. It lacks a neutron. Therefore, the atomic number (number of protons) and atomic weight (number of protons plus the number of neutrons) have the same value in this isotope.

4. The electron arrangement in potassium, from the inside energy level to the outermost energy level, is 2 - 8 - 8 -1. With one electron in its outermost energy shell, potassium tends to lose this one negative charge and form a positive ion, a cation.

Chapter 3
Methods of Studying Microorganisms

Learning Goals

To understand:

The fundamental properties of light: reflection, transmission, absorption, diffraction, and refraction

The principles of microscopy: how magnification, contrast, and resolution are achieved

The preparations necessary to view microorganisms by microscopy

How the compound light microscope works

How the phase-contrast, darkfield, fluorescence, and Nomarsky modifications of the light microscope increase contrast

How transmission and scanning electron microscopy work

How channeling tunneling and atomic force microscopes work

The advantages and uses of various microscopes

What pure cultures are, why they are important, and how they are obtained

How to cultivate a pure culture: types of media and the laboratory environment

How cultures are preserved

Chapter Outline

Viewing Microorganisms
    Properties of Light
    Microscopy
    The Compound Light Microscope
    Wet Mounts
    Stains
    Light Microscopy: Other Ways to Achieve Contrast
    Light Microscopy: Scanning Microscopes
    Other Light Microscopes
    Electron Microscopy
    Scanned-proximity Probe Microscopes: Viewing Atoms and Molecules
    Molecules
    Uses of Microscopy
Culturing Microorganisms
    Obtaining a Pure Culture
    Isolation
    Growing a Culture
    Preserving Cultures
Summary

Teaching Tips

1. Encourage outside readings on the topics of microbiology that you teach. Start with the Internet as a source of these outside readings. Use the boldfaced key terms (e.g., microscopy) from the chapter to begin the search for topics relevant to this chapter and other chapters.

2. Bring a compound light microscope to lecture. Briefly name the parts of the microscope and explain their functions. This can also be done in a short, introductory talk for the scheduled lab period of microscopy.

3. Schedule a short trip with some of your students to a local clinical lab or university. Arrange for them to see other kinds of microscopes (e.g., electron microscope) in action.

4. Continue to use part of your lecture as a bridge to the laboratory component of your course. Emphasize to your students that the lab classes offer the hands-on opportunities to reinforce and extend the concepts begun in lecture. As a prelude to lab show the students items such as petri dishes and transfer loops. You can illustrate the steps for transferring microorganisms by sterile technique for the streak-plate method. This can also be done in your introductory talk that begins the lab period.

5. Have you decided to project prepared microscope slides of microbes in you lecture? You can either make these slides (e.g., Gram stain of *B. subtilis* and *E. coli*) or purchase them from biological supply houses. These suppliers also sell 35 mm slides for viewing with a carousel projector. By either approach show your students the results of a successful wet mount, Gram stain, acid-fast stain, etc. Students need to see correct results before making their own slides.

6. Continue to relate the concepts of your course to human anatomy and physiology. Many students have taken two courses, each with a lecture and lab, on this subject before enrolling in microbiology. Where does *Mycobacterium tuberculosis* infect the human body? How do species of *Salmonella* or *Shigella* produce pathogenic effects in the human body?

Discussion Topics

1. Physics, chemistry, and biology are divisions of science. Microbiology is one field where all of these divisions are integrated. How?

2. Make a list of the various pathogens discussed in Chapter 3. Explain where each one infects the human body.

3. Many microorganisms are easy to culture and have many advantages for use in laboratory studies. What are some of these advantages?

4. A microbiology course usually has a lab component along with the lecture/discussion part of the course. What are the advantages of the lab experience accompanying the lecture? What drawbacks could develop in the teaching/learning process of the course if the lab were not a part of the course instruction?

Correlation Questions:

1. Challenge the students to apply the concept of osmosis (Chapter 4) to this chapter. How does the volume of cells change in a hypertonic or hypotonic extracellular environment? How do these changes outside the cells change the density of that area or the density of the cells? How do these changes affect phase-contrast microscopy when the cells are viewed through this kind of microscope?

2. Present the students with a bacterial cell population of 10,000 cells per milliliter. Outline one serial dilution that will not produce workable cell counts. Outline one serial dilution that will produce workable results.

3. How does a knowledge of microbial metabolism and nutrition pertain to the growth requirements of microorganisms on various kinds of nutrient media?

4. A given antibiotic can have different effects on a Gram negative bacterium and a Gram positive species. Explain the correlation between this effectiveness and the type of bacterium.

Answers: Review Questions

Viewing Microorganisms

1. Light provides the source of illumination for viewing microorganisms through certain kinds of microscopes (e.g., compound light microscope). Light also makes microorganisms visible by creating contrast through differences in light intensity. Light is the visible part of the continuous spectrum of electromagnetic waves.

2. Light striking an object can be reflected, transmitted, or absorbed.

3. By reflection light bounces off a smooth surface. When passing through a small opening or the edge of an opaque object, light rays are diffracted. Refraction takes place when light meets an object of a different density at an angle. The refractive index is the ratio of the velocity of light traveling through a particular kind of substance (e.g., water or air) to the velocity of light traveling through a vacuum.

4. Magnification is the enlargement of an image by a microscope. As a power it is the product of the ocular and objective lens used (e.g., 10 x 40 = 400). Contrast is the difference in light intensity, used to distinguish part of an image from its surroundings. Variations in contrast allow some parts of an image to be seen apart from others. Resolution means perceiving two adjacent points of an image as separate. It is important for seeing the fine detail of an image.

5. The resolving power of a microscope is a measure of resolution. It can be increased by increasing the size of lenses, by illuminating a specimen with shorter wavelengths of light, and by using materials with a higher refractive index. Shorter blue waves have greater resolving power than red waves. Immersion oil has a higher refractive index than air. The numerical aperture is the measurement of the lens size and the use of immersion oil with a lens. The text shows a formula relating numerical aperture to resolution.

6. The ocular lens is on top of the body tube. Several objective lenses are mounted on a revolving nosepiece at the bottom of the body tube. The condenser is under the stage for directing and concentrating light through the stage.

7. As one example of a lens system, the compound light microscope has an ocular lens and several different objective lenses. Corrected lenses are several lenses bonded together, eliminating the aberrations of a simpler lens system. Brightfield illumination produces a brightly-lit background, as light passes through the specimen. The specimen is seen by the contrast of light.

8. A simple wet mount involves a drop of liquid on a slide with microorganisms. A cover slip is placed over the drop on the slide. A hanging wet mount involves placing a drop of liquid with microorganisms on a cover slip and suspending it in a depression slide. Petroleum jelly seals the margin of this mount. It resists drying and can be observed longer.

9. Staining a sample improves contrast. However, it distorts the appearance of the cell.

10. A basic dye has positively charged ions. An acid dye has negatively charged ions. A mordant is a substance that increases the cell's affinity for a dye.

11. A simple stain uses one basic dye, such as methylene blue, on cells. A differential stain distinguishes among microorganisms by using primary staining and counterstaining. The Gram stain is a differential stain involving four steps: the primary stain, the iodine mordant, a decolorizing agent, and a counterstain. Bacteria are classified into two major groups, Gram positive and Gram negative, by this stain. The acid-fast stain is a differential stain that reveals bacteria of the genus *Mycobacterium*.

12. A special stain heightens the contrast within a microbe cell. The Leifson flagellar stain reveals the long, threadlike flagella from cells. The negative stain reveals the capsule around a cell.

13. Brightfield microscopy uses the advantages of illumination and staining to create contrast to study cells. It also depends on different materials absorbing light differently to create contrast. Phase-contrast microscopy depends on the different refractive indexes of materials to create contrast. Cells do not need to be distorted by fixation and staining. By darkfield microscopy a bright image is created against a dark background by the principle of scattering. This is effective for many external cell structures. In fluorescent microscopy certain materials absorb light at one wavelength and give off light at another. The use of UV light and fluorescent dyes promotes this fluorescence for effective viewing. Nomarsky microscopy produces contrast by interference. Three-dimensional images with fine detail are produced using complementary pairs of prisms.

14. By freeze-fracturing, the sample is frozen into a block of ice and fractured by a sharp blow by a knife. By freeze etching the fractured sample is put in a vacuum and water is removed by sublimation This causes structures to protrude. By ultra-thin sectioning, a specimen is cut no thicker than 0.1 micrometer for viewing by the TEM. By freeze-drying, a specimen is dessicated in a vacuum when frozen. The specimen is then coated with a heavy metal. It is viewed with an SEM.

15. A scanning tunneling microscope is used to view surfaces that conduct electricity. It uses a metal probe that carries a slight electrical charge. The flow of electrons to the tip of this probe produces a signal. Signal transmission varies depending on the concentration of electrons in an area.

16. The image in the atomic force microscope depends on the attractive and repulsive forces between molecules. A probe scans a specimen, detecting these forces. A beam coupled to this probe bends in response to these forces. This bending is detected by a laser beam, generating a signal and creating an image.

17. Light microscopes are used in everyday labs for studying cell details. Magnification and resolution are limited. Electron microscopes are used in research, offering greater magnification and resolution for viewing cell details.

Cultivating Microorganisms

18. A pure culture contains one species of microorganism. To make a pure culture, all materials must first be sterilized. Then one microorganism must be isolated to produce the culture. The streak plate method is often used to isolate separate cells on a nutrient agar surface to produce pure cultures.

19. Sterilization means eliminating all microorganisms. Heat sterilization in the lab includes moist heat under pressure in an autoclave. Materials must be exposed for certain minimum times and temperatures in an autoclave. One example is 121 degrees Celsius for 15 minutes at 15 pounds per square inch. The moist heat can permeate all regions of materials if they are properly exposed. Boiling is another form of moist heat sterilization. Boiling, however, does not kill bacteria that can form endospores. Therefore, it does not kill species of *Clostridium* and *Bacillus*.

    An open flame and other forms of dry heat, such as the use of an oven, can be used as a direct, intense type of sterilization.

20. Filtration removes cells from substances by trapping them based on their size. The pores of the filter must be small enough to remove all microbes. Filtration does not sterilize but is practical for removing most cells where other means are not practical. It is preferable for treating heat-sensitive solutions.

21. To inoculate is to introduce a single microbial cell into a sterilized liquid or gel medium.

    A clone is a population of cells descended from one cell. Arising from the same, original cell, all cells produced from this cell are genetically identical. A clone grows on a solid medium as a visible colony.

    To incubate is to grow microbial cultures in a warm place. An incubator provides such an environment.

    To dilute a microbial population is to decrease its concentration of cells in nutrient liquid. In serial dilution this is done through a series of steps. Each step reduces the cell concentration tenfold. This process reduces the cell number to a countable size when one ml of a culture is grown on nutrient agar.

22. By the streak plate method a sterile wire inoculating loop spreads a mixed culture over a nutrient agar surface. Done several successive times, this separates cells from one another on the surface. By the pour plate and spread plate methods, suspensions of microbial cells are diluted before they are put on the nutrient surface. They are diluted through the steps of a serial dilution.

23. a. A defined medium has an exact known chemical composition. One example is a minimal medium.

    b. In a complex media the exact chemical composition is not known. It is made from extracts of natural materials.

    c. A selective medium favors the growth of only certain microbe species through its unique chemical makeup. Only one type, for example, supports *Salmonella typhi*.

    d. A differential medium is used to identify colonies of certain species by the unique chemical change produced in it.

    e. A selective-differential medium combines the properties of both types of media. For example, there is a selective-differential medium for *Salmonella*.

    f. An enrichment culture isolates particular kinds of microorganisms because only they can grow on it.

24. Each kind of microorganism has an optimal temperature, pH, and oxygen level at which it grows best. Many bacterial species grow best at a temperature of 37 degrees Celsius and at a pH range of 6.5 to 7.5.

25. Strict aerobes require oxygen for growth. Strict anaerobes require the absence of oxygen to grow. Facultative anaerobes can grow in the presence or absence of oxygen. Aerotolerant anaerobes cannot use oxygen, but its presence does not hinder them. Microaerophiles need low concentrations of oxygen.

26. A culture can be preserved by dessication by removing the water from the cells and medium. Placing the culture in a refrigerator places cells in a temperature that is too low for effective metabolism. This also preserves the culture.

27. Many microorganisms cannot be cultivated in the lab because their growth requirements are not known or they are dangerous to work with in the lab. One example is *Mycobacterium leprae*.

Answers: Correlation Questions from the Textbook

1. The salinity in the water would increase the contrast of the solution in the background of the microorganisms. However, it could also threaten the volume of the cells osmotically. Their density can also change, affecting their contrast with their extracellular environment. This affects light passage through the cells compared to the environment outside them.

2. A higher numerical aperture decreases the distance at which two points can be distinguished as separate when seen under the microscope. Therefore as the numerical aperture is greater, this distance becomes smaller, indicating a greater resolving power. Resolution is more important at lower magnifications, where the low power does not reveal the details of higher powers.

3. Separate cells for a pure culture can be obtained by creating conditions (e.g., for temperature or pH) that will remove other competing kinds of cells.

4. Although both can survive with many nutrients available, one kind of microorganism may not be able to synthesize all nutrients independently in a minimal medium. This one will be eliminated in the minimal medium.

5. A selective medium favors the growth of one microorganism over another. It presents characteristics that one organism can tolerate and another cannot. Differential media exploit the ability of one microbe to change the appearance of the medium when another cannot.

6. The microorganisms from the soil could be difficult to cultivate. They can be viewed and quantified more easily through microscopy.

Answers: Essay Questions

1. Start with the idea that the compound light microscope has wide applicability.

2. Start with the idea that you would test the ability of the organism to survive in a wide variety of physical and chemical conditions. By a process of elimination, determine the ones that are unique for this microorganism's survival.

Answers: Discussion Topics

1. Discuss with the students the relevancy of physics to understanding light and microscopy. Discuss how chemistry is relevant to the steps of the different staining procedures.

2. Start with species of *Mycobacterium* and *Staphylococcus*.

3. Many microorganisms are easy and inexpensive to cultivate. They reproduce rapidly. Their haploid structure makes them easier to analyze genetically, compared to diploid organisms.

4. The lab part of the course offers the hands-on opportunity for the students to learn about microorganisms. Without the lab experience the chance to reinforce lecture-base principles would be missing. An important part of the overall teaching-learning experience would be lacking.

Answers: Correlation Questions from the Instructor's Manual

1. The size of the cells will shrink with a hypertonic environment outside the cells. In the hypotonic setting the cell size may increase slightly. However, due to the presence of the bacterial cell wall, these cells should not burst. However, in either case, the cell density will change. From shrinking, the bacterial cell will be more dense. Changes in the cell density, and the density of the environment outside the cells, will change the contrast between these two areas and alter the effectiveness of phase-contast microscopy.

2. For example, a total dilution of 1/100 will yield a concentration of 100 cells per ml. This is not a countable number. A total dilution of 1/1000 will produce a concentration of 10 cells. This is a countable number.

3. The biochemical ability of a microorganism determines what molecules it can make on its own and what chemical substances (e.g., vitamins, minerals) are required in its diet. A bacterium that makes more chemical components on its own, through its own metabolism, is capable of living on a more minimal medium. It is less dependent on a nutrient-rich medium fortified with vitamins and minerals.

4. The Gram reaction is based on the ability of a bacterium to retain or not retain crystal violet in its cell wall. Some antibiotics vary in effectiveness, depending on the makeup of the cell wall of a bacterium. Therefore, cell wall composition is related to both the Gram reactions and the effectiveness of antibiotics.

Chapter 4
Prokaryotic and Eukaryotic Cells

Learning Goals

To understand:

The principal differences between prokaryotic and eukaryotic cells

The structural differences between Gram-positive bacteria, Gram-negative bacteria, and mycoplasmas

The structural and chemical differences between bacteria and archaea

The structure of eukaryotic cells and the functions of the organelles

How molecules cross cell membranes: simple diffusion, osmosis, facilitated diffusion, active transport, group translocation, and engulfment

Chapter Outline

Structure and Function
The Prokaryotic Cell
    Structure of the Bacterial Cell
    Structures Outside the Envelope
    Cytoplasm
    Endospores
The Eukaryotic Cell
    Structure
Membrane Function
    Simple Diffusion
    Osmosis
    Facilitated Diffusion
    Active Transport
    Group Translocation
    Engulfment
Summary

Teaching Tips

1. Sketch a prokaryotic cell, unlabeled, and copy this sketch for distribution in class. As an activity at the end of one class period, ask your students to label the structures of this cell.

2. Sketch a eukaroytic cell for student labeling. Emphasize the differences between this cell type and the prokaryotic cell.

3. As a continuation of #1 and #2, ask your students to describe a function for each eukaryotic cell structure. They can organize this information on the other side of the sketch in two columns:

        Structures   Functions

Ask your students to explain how some of this information can be applied to a description of the prokaryotic cell.

4. Biological supply houses sell special attachments for microscopes that will enlarge and project the images of microscope slides onto the screen. You can use slides that you prepared in lab to portray endospores, capsules, etc. or purchase these from supply houses. Another option is to show 35 mm slides of specialized cellular structures with the carousel projector.

5. Explore the possibilities of using a Smart Board for projection of bacterial structure in your classroom.

6. Students need to understand simple diffusion through examples rather than by memorizing definitions and descriptions of this process. You can use several kinds of demonstrations to illustrate diffusion. For example, perfume from an open bottle spreads throughout an entire room. How? A drop of purple food coloring in a beaker of water uniformly colors the entire beaker. How?

7. You can also plan a demonstration of osmosis in action. Saltwater in a bag, made from tied-off dialysis tubing, gains water when placed in a beaker of pure water. How did it gain water? A cloudy suspension of mammalian blood clears in a 0.5% saltwater solution (hypotonic) in a test tube. Why? Why does the blood suspension not clear in a 1.5% saltwater suspension (hypertonic)? As you demonstrate these examples, ask your students how osmosis applies in each case.

Discussion Topics

1. Many of the principles for the physical and chemical control methods of bacteria use the information in this chapter. Emphasize these principles to your students. Why, for example, does the salting of meat slow down its rate of decomposition? Why is autoclaving necessary to sterilize material from certain species of bacteria? How do antibiotics work on the cell wall or protein synthesis of bacterial cells?

2. There is evidence that eukaryotic cells evolved from prokaryotic cells. Are there any patterns in this chapter to offer support to this model?

Correlation Questions

1. What adaptations in a white blood cell allow it to carry out engulfment? How does this characteristic allow it to protect the human body?

2. Present several preserved slides of cells, eukaryotic and prokaryotic, to students in your lab for observation. In each case, challenge your students to label each viewed cell as eukaryotic or prokaryotic. Let students explain their choice for each viewed cell.

3. A student you teach is suffering from an upper respiratory tract infection. The student wants treatment and the prescription of an antibiotic. Will this treatment be successful? Tell your students to read more about the structure of viruses in Chapter 13.

4. How does the surface to volume ratio of a cell limit the size of a cell?

Answers: Review Questions

The Prokaryotic Cell

2. The eukaryotic cell has many kinds of organelles. Its nucleus has a well-defined, double membrane with a chromosome number for each species. The prokaryotic cell has few organelles and, usually, one circular chromosome in an irregular-shaped region, the nucleoid. Most prokaryotic cells have a cell wall with peptidoglycan. Not all eukaryotic cells have a cell wall and, if present, it does not have peptidoglycan. The eukaryotic cell is about 10 times larger than the prokaryotic cell.

3. Cell appendages are outward extensions of the cell envelope. The three types of prokaryotic appendages are the pilus, flagellum, and axial filament.

4. Pili attach bacteria to other cells. One type transmits genetic material from a donor to recipient cell. Flagella create motion and currents that propel their cells through the environment.

5. Use Figures 4-10 and 4-11 in the text as a guide to sketch the flagellum of a bacterium. It turns by rotating as a propeller. The four types of flagella arrangement are monotrichous, amphitrichous, lophotrichous, and peritrichous.

6. A taxis is a movement toward a favorable environment. By chemotaxis, *E. coli* moves toward a favorable environment, often with nutrients.

7. Axial filaments are bundles of flagella covered with protein. They are well fortified to pass through thick fluids.

8. Use Figure 4-4 in the text as a guide to sketch the prokaryotic cell envelope. Only Gram-negative bacteria have the complete, three-part cell envelope: the outer membrane, inner membrane, and the compartment between the two membranes.

9. The capsule is a slimy, thick outer covering. Its thickness provides protection for the cell. Some capsules are several times as thick as the rest of the cell.

10. The outer membrane is a bilayer, mainly lipopolysaccharide. This LPS is found only in the outer membrane of Gram-negative bacteria. Only water and a few gases pass through this membrane. Porins are channels through this membrane that allow the diffusion of small molecules. The LPS is an endotoxin, as it harms human and animal cells.

11. The periplasm is the region between the outer membrane and cytoplasmic membrane. It is filled with gelatinous material and two proteins. One breaks down nutrients for passage into the cell.

The other facilitates the passage of nutrients across the outer membrane and cytoplasmic membrane.

12. All bacteria except the mycoplasmas have a cell wall.

13. Peptidoglycan is the main chemical component of the bacterial cell wall. It consists of long chains of polysaccharides cross-linked by peptides. The cell wall confers shape to the bacterial cell. It also contains the turgor pressure that develops in the cell. Murein is the specific name for the peptidoglycan in the bacterial cell wall.

14. The cell wall of Gram-negative bacteria has a peptidoglycan mesh that is one cell layer thick. It is many layers thick in Gram-positive bacteria. It also has teichoic acid. Mycoplasmas lack a cell wall.

15. The three most common shapes of bacteria are the bacillus, coccus, and spirillum.

16. If lysozyme destroys the bacterial cell wall, it loses its former shape.

17. Turgor pressure is the internal fluid pressure that builds up inside the bacterial cell. The bacterial cell is very hypertonic to its extracellular environment. It draws water inside by osmosis. Water accumulation leads to a tremendous pressure buildup. Mycoplasmas offset turgor pressure by pumping sodium out of their cells. Therefore, water cannot follow sodium osmotically into these cells.

18. L forms are strains of bacteria that sometimes lose their ability to make cell walls. They can grow and multiply with osmotic protection. Protoplasts lack all traces of a cell wall. Spheroplasts lack most of it.

19. In the cytoplasmic membrane the hydrophilic heads of two rows of phospholipids are attracted to water. Therefore they face inward and outward where water is found. The inwardly directed hydrophobic tails face each other. There is a space between the two layers of this bilayer.

20. Permeases in the cell membrane are molecules that transport molecules through the cell membrane.

21. In eukaryotic and prokaryotic cells the cytoplasmic membrane regulates the passage of substances into and out of the cell. Bacterial cell membranes also have proteins for energy function. Their membranes also have inward folds with electron transport chains for generating energy.

22. The prokaryotic cell lacks most organelles. It is mostly water and protein. It has a nuclear region, the nucleoid, and ribosomes along with some inclusions.

23. The nucleoid is the region with chromosomal DNA in the prokaryotic cell. It is not defined by a membrane and usually contains one circular molecule of DNA. A plasmid is a very small segment of extrachromosomal DNA.

24. Ribosomes are the site of protein synthesis. Antibiotics affect the action of the 70S ribosomes in prokaryotic cells and do not affect the activity of the 80S ribosome in eukaryotic cells. Therefore

an antibiotic that destroys the 70S ribosomes of bacteria will not interfere with the function of the 80S ribosomes in the human host cells infected with the bacteria.

25. Inclusions are visible structures in the prokaryotic cytoplasm other than the nuclear region and ribosomes. They can store, for example, gases and waste products.

26. Endospores are resistant, latent structures produced by bacterial cells of *Clostridium* and *Bacillus*. By sporogenesis vegetative cells will form endospores under harsh conditions. These structures are smaller than the cells and contain very little water. When environmental conditions improve, the endospore will germinate into a vegetative cell.

27. The archaeon cell lacks peptidoglycan in the cell wall. Some members lack a cell wall. The composition of their cytoplasmic membrane is also different.

The Eukaryotic Cell

28. Eukaryotic cells include those found in the algae, fungi, protozoa, animals, and humans. In prokaryotic cells the nuclear region is not defined by a membrane. Their ribosomes are 70S and not 80S as found in eukaryotic cells. The cell membrane of prokaryotes has proteins involved in the electron transport chain and photosynthesis. Otherwise, the other eukaryotic organelles are lacking in prokaryotic cells.

29. The appendages of eukaryotic cells are flagella and cilia. Eukaryotic cells do not have pili or axial filaments. Prokaryotic cells lack cilia. Eukaryotic flagella also function for motility. However, they are longer and they do not turn but undulate to create the currents for motion. Eukaryotic flagella have a 9 + 2 arrangement of microtubules.

30. Fungi and algae are eukaryotes that have cell walls. Human cells lack a cell wall. The pellicle is a flexible structure outside the plasma membrane of some protozoa.

31. The cell wall of plants, most algae, and some fungi have cellulose and not peptidoglycan. Some primitive fungi have chitin in their cell wall.

32. Both eukaryotes and prokaryotes have cytoplasmic membranes of phospholipids with embedded proteins. The proteins are mobile in each. In each cell type the cytoplasmic membrane regulates the passage of materials. However, the prokaryotic cytoplasmic membrane has proteins that function in the electron transport chain. The eukaryotic cell membrane contains sterol lipids.

33. The cytoskeleton is a lattice network of proteins in the cytoplasm. It offers strength and support for the cytoplasm of larger, eukaryotic cells.

34. The nuclear envelope is a double-walled membrane defining the eukaryotic nucleus. This envelope has pores. The nucleus is filled with a gelatinous matrix, the nucleoplasm. The nucleolus stores RNA.

35. Eukaryotic DNA is associated with histone proteins and organized into chromosomal pairs. Prokaryotic DNA does not have this association and is usually organized into one circular chromosome. The DNA is chemically identical in both kinds of cells.

36. Use Figure 4.19 in the text to sketch mitosis. By mitosis one parent cell divides into two daughter cells, each one genetically identical to the parent cell. From the parent cell duplicates of each chromosome are separated into the daughter cells by an orderly process. This process occurs through the events of interphase, prophase, metaphase, anaphase, and telophase.

37. Mitosis produces diploid body cells for growth and development. Meiosis produces haploid gametes.

38. The cytomembrane system in the eukaryotic cell is a series of biological membranes in the cytoplasm that is continuous with the nuclear envelope. This system divides the cytoplasm into compartments with specific functions.

39. The ER is a double membrane in the cytoplasm that folds back on itself, producing a series of channels. The rough ER is covered with ribosomes. The smooth ER is not covered with ribosomes.

40. The SER produces the components for building and repairing membranes. It is also the site of phospholipid synthesis. The rough ER functions for protein synthesis.

41. The Golgi apparatus is a stack of flattened membranes. It is the site where vesicles are repackaged in the cell and used at other cellular sites. The lysosomes are packets of enzymes that destroy molecules in the cell.

42. Mitochondria and chloroplasts are both bounded by double membranes. Both are involved in energy metabolism.

43. By the endosymbiont theory, mitochondria and chloroplasts may have evolved from prokaryotic cells that became intracellular structures of eukaryotic cells.

Passage of Molecules Across Cell Membranes

44. Some molecules pass through cytoplasmic membranes. Others cannot. Therefore these membranes are semipermeable. Gases can pass through the phospholipids of these membranes. Water and hydrophilic substances cannot. However, water and ions can pass through pores in the membranes.

45. Simple diffusion is the movement of molecules from a region of higher concentration to a region of lower concentration.

46. Osmosis is the diffusion of water through a semipermeable membrane. The osmotic strength is the concentration of solute molecules in a membrane-bound space. The turgor pressure is the internal pressure in this space. If water is in higher concentration outside a cell, it moves into the cell by osmosis and increases the pressure in the cell.

47. By facilitated diffusion, molecules spread out, but they require carrier molecules to do this.

48. Active transport is the movement of molecules from a region of lower concentration to a region of higher concentration with the cell expending energy for this process.

49. Group translocation is a variation of active transport whereby the molecule transported is also charged.

50. By engulfment the plasma membrane folds in on itself, surrounds a foreign particle, brings it into the cell, and forms a vacuole around it. Endocytosis engulfs solid material. It is called phagocytosis if performed by a white blood cell. If liquid is engulfed, the process is called pinocytosis. Exocytosis is the expulsion of material from the cell.

51. Active transport, group translocation, facilitated diffusion, and engulfment require energy. Simple diffusion, osmosis, active transport, and facilitated diffusion occur in prokaryotic and eukaryotic cells. Group translocation occurs only in prokaryotic cells. Engulfment occurs in some kinds of eukaryotic cells.

Answers: Correlation Questions from the Textbook

1. Prokaryotic cells are covered with a rigid cell wall and lack the flexibility to engulf particles. Intracellularly they lack the organelles, such as lysosomes, to process engulfed particles.

2. The flagellum of the bacterium will rotate rapidly. It will undulate slowly in the eukaryotic cell.

3. The flagellum will rotate and propel the cell. The pilus will lack this action and function for cell attachment.

4. Gas vesicles allow bacteria to float to optimal environments. Therefore, to reach optimal environments, flagellar action and the presence of flagella unnecessary.

5. Penicillin attacks the cell wall of bacteria. The cell wall is missing in mycoplasmas, making this antibiotic useless.

6. An analysis of the chemical makeup of the captured organism is necessary. For example, if the mitochondrion had peptidoglycan, it would point to a bacterial origin.

Answers: Essay Questions

1. A major change in larger evolving cells was the presence of a cytoskeleton to reinforce the cell and provide the adaptations for the necessary kinds of cell movement to support the cell. A larger cell was also a more complex cell. It needed more structures with specialized functions.

2. Mitochondria have many similarities to prokaryotic cells, supporting the endosymbiont hypothesis. They are similar in size to these cells and are organelles containing DNA. Both mitochondria and prokaryotic cells have 70S ribosomes and multiply by binary fission.

Answers: Correlation Questions from the Instructor's Manual

1. A white blood cell has a flexible cytoplasmic membrane. Its movement is not inhibited by an external cell wall. By extensions of its cytoplasmic membrane, a white blood cell can form outward cell extensions, pseudopodia, allowing it to surround other cells such as bacterial cells.

Once engulfed, the bacterium is digested inside the white blood cell. If the bacterium is an invading pathogen, this process defeats the pathogen and protects the human body.

2. Emphasize the facts that prokaryotic cells are smaller and less complex, with few organelles and lacking a defined nucleus.

3. Viruses lack ribosomes. As most antibiotics microorganisms, by destroying 70S ribosomes, the use of an antibiotic will not inhibit viruses.

4. Start with a cube-shaped cell as an example. If one edge of this cell equals 1, the area equals 6 (6 x 1). The volume of this cell is 1 x 1 x 1 The surface to volume ratio is 6 to 1. However, if the edge is 2, the area of the cell is 24 (6 x 4). However the volume is 2 x 2 x 2 which equals 8. The surface to volume ratio is now 3 (24 to 8). If the edge of the cell is 3, the ratio becomes 2 to 1 (54 to 27). Therefore, as a cell becomes larger it does not have sufficient area (cytoplasmic membrane) to support its volume.

Chapter 5
Metabolism of Microorganisms

Learning Goals

To understand:

The function and importance of metabolism

How the five sequential steps in metabolism—bringing nutrients into the cell, catabolic reactions, biosynthesis, polymerization, and assembly—synthesize all the cell's components

How ATP is formed through substrate level phosphorylation and chemiosmosis and the role it plays in metabolism

How reducing power is formed and the role it plays in metabolism

How glycolysis, the TCA cycle, and the pentose phosphate cycle proceed and how they form the 12 precursor metabolites, ATP, and reducing power

How anaerobic metabolism proceeds by way of anaerobic respiration or fermentation

How photoautotrophs carry out metabolism through light-driven processes

How chemoautotrophs carry out metabolism by oxidizing inorganic compounds

How metabolism is regulated so the proper amounts of products are made efficiently

Chapter Outline

Metabolism: An Overview
Aerobic Metabolism
    Catabolism
    Catabolic Pathways
    Biosynthesis
    Polymerization
    Assembly
Anaerobic Metabolism
    Anaerobic Respiration
    Fermentation
Nutritional Requirements of Microorganisms
    Formation of Precursor Metabolites by Autotrophs
    Formation of ATP and Reducing Power by Photoautotrophs
    Formation of ATP and Reducing Power by Chemoautotrophs
Regulation of Metabolism
    Purpose
    Types
Summary

Teaching Tips

1. Encourage your students to answer the several types of questions, including the review questions, at the end of each chapter. Use some time at the end of your class periods to discuss the answers with your students.

2. Is it important that students memorize the detailed steps of glycolysis, aerobic respiration, and photosynthesis? Consider outlining only the broad patterns of these processes in lecture and discuss their significance biologically.

3. One way to summarize the events of anaerobic and aerobic respiration is to total the formation of ATP molecules from each series of events: glycolysis, substrate level phosphorylation, etc.

    Discuss the efficiency of each phase of respiration. If one mole of glucose yields 680 kilocalories of energy, and each mole of ATP yields 7 kilocalories, how efficient is glycolysis? What is 14 (2ATPs) divided by 680? How do the aerobic events change this efficiency?

4. Continue to relate the lessons of lecture to the lab. How does a bacterium ferment glucose in a Durham tube? Why does the growth medium change from red to yellow (pH change)? Why is there some gas accumulation in the inverted part of the tube?

5. Do your students understand the practical applications for learning metabolism? Invite a guest speaker from industry or the medical field to address some practical applications. For example, how has the production of ethyl alcohol been used commercially? What is the source of muscle fatigue in an athlete?

6. Show your students how the facts and concepts of this chapter relate to their lab experiences. For example, can a microbe studied in lab ferment glucose in a Durham tube? What products will accumulate in the nutrient broth of this tube from the fermentation? How will you test for their presence in the growth medium in the lab?

Discussion Topics

1. How does a knowledge of cell structure facilitate the understanding of the information in this chapter?

2. How are the broad patterns of photosynthesis and cellular respiration similar? How are they different?

Correlation Questions

1. Ask students to explain how a microorganism with a specific relationship to oxygen (e.g., strict aerobe or strict anaerobe) grows in two settings that differ in the availability of this gas. As a start consider two petri dishes with identical growth media. However one dish has plenty of oxygen. The other is isolated from it. How will the growth rate of the microbe compare in these two settings if the bacterium is a strict anaerobe? How will it change if the bacterium is a strict aerobe?

2. Ask more questions emphasizing the comparison from question #1. Make a comparison for a facultative anaerobe. Make another one for an aerotolerant microbe.

3. A bacterium is studied for its ability to synthesize a given substance that is part of coenzyme structure. Microorganism A cannot make it. Microorganism B can make it. Why is it considered a vitamin in A and not in B?

4. How is the genetics of microorganisms, presented in the next chapter (Chapter 6) related to their metabolism?

Answers: Review Questions

Metabolism

1. Metabolism is collectively all chemical reactions occurring in the cell.

2. *E. coli* is a well-understood organism because it has been used extensively in studies of genetics and metabolism.

3. *E. coli* is a normal floral species of the human large intestine. It is also found in aquatic environments. It has evolved metabolic specializations to survive in each type of environment.

4. Cellular metabolism is like a factory because it uses raw materials to make new materials. These new materials constitute the makeup of the cell, therefore serving to make new cells.

5. Cells store energy in the high-energy phosphate bonds of ATP. The breakdown of these bonds releases energy for cell activities.

6. The source of a cell's reducing power resides in molecules that can furnish hydrogen atoms to reduce other molecules. These molecules are usually in the form of NAD(P)H.

7. The five steps are bringing nutrients into the cell, catabolism, biosynthesis, polymerization, and assembly.

8. Catabolism converts a single organic molecule, such as glucose, into many kinds of organic molecules. Precursor metabolites are used to make small molecules through synthesis. Polymerization is bonding the products of biosynthesis into macromolecules.

9. Most of the ATP is formed by the aerobic steps of the electron transport chain that uses oxygen as the final electron acceptor. Most reducing power arises from the loss of hydrogens from compounds of the TCA.

10. Most ATP is consumed in biosynthesis and polymerization, as both require energy to make molecules. Most reducing power is required to carry hydrogens into the electron transport chain to make ATP.

Aerobic Metabolism

11. Aerobic metabolism is the group of cellular reactions that requires oxygen to take place.

12. During the entry mechanisms of aerobic metabolism, raw materials enter the cell. Some raw material molecules diffuse through porins in the cytoplasmic membrane. Permeases are carrier proteins that bring substrates into the cell. These carrier proteins use ATP as an energy requirement to concentrate the substrates into the cell.

13. The substrate is the molecule that an enzyme binds to and converts in a chemical reaction. Precursor metabolites are key substances needed for cell metabolism. They are formed through a series of metabolic intermediates in a metabolic pathway.

14. The three primary catabolic pathways are glycolysis, the TCA cycle, and the pentose phosphate pathway. Glycolysis makes six of the twelve precursor metabolites. The TCA makes four. The pentose phosphate pathway makes two.

15. In an oxidation-reduction reaction, one compound is oxidized as another is reduced. The oxidized substance loses electrons or hydrogen atoms or both. The reduced substance receives these substances.

16. In dehydrogenation reactions, protons are removed along with electrons in the oxidation. In hydrogenation reactions, reduction occurs with protons and electrons being added together. The reducing power is stored in NAD(P)H.

17. The energy-storing capacity of ATP is in its two terminal bonds joining phosphate groups to the molecule.

18. Phosphorylation is important because it forms the high-energy bonds joining phosphate groups to ATP.

19. ATP is formed by adding a single phosphate group to ADP.

20. By substrate level phosphorylation, a phosphate group belonging to a metabolic intermediate is added to ADP to make ATP.

21. Chemiosmosis forms ATP from ADP. The chemical energy from this production comes from a concentration gradient of protons across membranes.

22. Aerobic respiration is the process of transporting electrons through a chain of acceptors, with oxygen as the terminal electron acceptor. The chain of acceptors is the electron transport chain.

23. The interconvertible part of chemiosmosis is the shuttling of protons back and forth across the membranes in the cell. A difference in concentration establishes a proton gradient and a chemical energy potential. This energy is released as protons flow across the membrane. It is reestablished when protons are pumped back across the membrane.

24. Glycolysis begins with the substrate glucose and proceeds through a series of anaerobic steps to form two molecules of pyruvate. Each molecule of glucose produces four ATP molecules by glycolysis. However, two are used in the process. Therefore, there is a net yield of two ATP molecules per glucose molecule.

25. After pyruvate is converted to acetyl CoA, acetyl CoA enters the TCA cycle. This circular series of compounds forms more precursor metabolites—ATP by substrate phosphorylation, and carbon dioxide.

26. The pentose phosphate pathway produces two precursor metabolites that cannot be produced any other way in the cell. It begins with glucose-6-phosphate and produces three molecules of carbon dioxide, two molecules of NADPH, and one molecule of phosphoglyceraldehyde.

27. The first step of biosynthesis converts precursor metabolites into the building blocks of macromolecules. The next step is making larger molecules. Enzymes are organic catalysts that speed up the rate of the steps in the metabolic pathways. The coenzyme is the nonprotein part of the enzyme. The vitamin is a part of the coenzyme.

28. The major polymerization reactions of the cell are DNA replication, RNA synthesis, protein synthesis, and polysaccharide synthesis.

29. DNA contains the encoded information to direct the steps of polymerization reactions.

30. The polymerization of glycogen requires that the building blocks be activated by an ATP-utilizing reaction. The activated building blocks enter into the enzyme-catalyzed polymerization.

31. Assembly can be self-assembly, occurring spontaneously, or by reactions catalyzed by enzymes.

Anaerobic Metabolism

32. The anaerobic reactions of catabolism do not require oxygen. The aerobic reactions do require oxygen.

33. In the absence of oxygen nonphotosynthetic cells can make ATP by anaerobic respiration and by fermentation.

34. Aerobic and anaerobic respiration both maintain a functioning electron transport chain, generating energy by chemiosmosis. Oxygen is the terminal electron acceptor aerobically. There are many electron acceptors anaerobically. The ATP yield is also different in the two processes.

35. If glucose is metabolized to pyruvate, two net molecules of ATP are produced. The pyruvate is fermented if insufficient oxygen is available for entrance of pyruvate into the TCA. Fermentation pathways require substrates in an intermediate state of oxidation. Only sugars can provide this.

36. Aerobic respiration yields more ATP per glucose molecule and is therefore more efficient than fermentation and anaerobic respiration, where the ATP yield is low.

37. Lactic acid fermentation proceeds through the glycolysis pathway, producing two molecules of pyruvate, two molecules of ATP, and two molecules of reduced NAD from one glucose molecule. The pyruvate is reduced and the reduced NAD is reoxidized.

Nutritional Classes of Microorganisms

38. Nutritional class depends on the source of carbon atoms used to make precursor metabolites and how ATP plus reducing power is generated. A chemoautotroph uses carbon dioxide as a carbon source and uses chemical reactions as a source of energy to make ATP. Chemoheterotrophs use organic compounds as a carbon source and use chemical reactions as a source of energy to make ATP. Photoautotrophs use carbon dioxide as a carbon source and light reactions to make ATP. Photoheterotrophs use organic compounds as a carbon source and light reactions to make ATP.

39. Autotrophs are the producers of food chains. In the Calvin-Benson cycle an autotroph makes precursor metabolites, and carbon dioxide. It leads to the formation of PGAL. PGAL flows into central metabolism to make other precursor metabolites.

40. Anoxygenic photosynthesis depends on light activating and liberating electrons from chlorophyll. These liberated electrons flow through an electron transport chain. At the end of this chain the electrons return to chlorophyll. The flow of electrons creates a proton gradient to generate ATP by passing protons through a transmembrane ATPase. This process makes ATP exclusively.

    Oxygenic photosynthesis utilizes two different photosystems, I and II. Light liberates electrons from photosystem II and the electrons flow through an electron transport chain. At the end, however, the flowing electrons join chlorophyll molecules in photosystem I, not II. Light activates these electrons, causing them to flow through a second electron transport chain. Finally these electrons join protons and are transferred to NADP+, producing NADPH. A proton gradient makes ATP but NADPH is also formed.

41. Chemoautotrophs form ATP and reducing power by oxidizing several inorganic compounds. Reverse electron transport is needed to reduce NAD(P) in iron-oxidizing chemoautotrophs.

Regulation of Metabolism

42. Metabolic regulation increases the efficiency of a cell to produce maximum amounts of end-products.

43. The two types of metabolic regulation are the regulation of gene expression and regulation by allosteric enzymes. Allosteric enzymes increase activity and cell efficiency when effectors bind to them.

44. By end-product inhibition the end product of a metabolic pathway binds to the first enzyme in the pathway, inhibiting its activity and slowing down the pathway. By allosteric activation, an effector increases in concentration in the cell and activates an allosteric protein, which is an enzyme in a pathway.

Answers: Correlation Questions from the Textbook

1. *E. coli* is a facultative anaerobe. The culture exposed to air should grow more biomass, as it can extract more energy from nutrients through aerobic metabolism.

2. Some substances from the outside of the cell cannot pass through the outer membrane and enter the periplasm.

3. Tryptophan addition causes it to feed back to the beginning of the metabolic pathway producing it, decreasing the rate of reactions in the pathway. This is feedback inhibition.

4. A chemoheterotroph requires more reducing power as it processes nutrients through a long series of metabolic reactions to extract energy from nutrients.

5. They use another source besides water to extract hydrogen for cycling. Oxygen is a breakdown product of water which is not used by these cyanobacteria.

6. They can derive hydrogens from novel sources and maintain a proton gradient for some ATP production. They probably do not have the more common electron transport and enzyme systems.

Answers: Essay Questions

1. You can view the extensive regulatory mechanism as adaptive. It therefore promotes survival for the competing microorganism.

2. Anaerobic respiration often leads into the aerobic steps if more oxygen is available in the environment. Fermentation is an alternative pathway leading from the steps of anaerobic respiration in an environment where oxygen is not available.

Answers: Discussion Topics

1. In eukaryotic cells, chemiosmosis occurs across the membranes of the mitochondrion. The different stages of photosynthesis take place in different regions of the chlorplasts. In the prokaryotic cell the events of these processes can be related to membranous areas of the cell.

2. Both processes make ATP through electron transport. However, compare the overall reactions of the two processes. Photosynthesis requires light and stores energy in a synthesized glucose molecule. Respiration releases energy from glucose.

Answers: Correlation Questions from the Instructor's Manual

1. For the strict anaerobe, there will be more growth in the setting without oxygen. The presence of oxygen is toxic to this kind of microbe. For the strict aerobe, there will be more growth in the setting with oxygen. It requires oxygen for growth.

2. A facultative anaerobe can grow in the presence or absence of oxygen. However, in the presence of oxygen its growth could be better with the potential to make more ATP. Aerotolerant microbes

cannot use oxygen. However, they are not harmed in its presence. There should not be a significant difference in the growth in the two settings for this kind of organism.

3. As a part of coenzyme structure, the substance is probably a vitamin. It is a vitamin for A because it cannot make it. A vitamin is required in the diet. If B can make it, the substance is not a dietary requirement. Therefore, it is not a vitamin.

4. Start with the idea that DNA makes RNA which makes protein, presented in the next chapter. All enzymes consist of protein. DNA, which dictates the structure of proteins through this process, also controls enzyme structure. Enzymes run metabolism and DNA determines the number and kinds of enzymes in a cell, therefore detemining the metabolic abilities of the cell.

Chapter 6
The Genetics of Microorganisms

Learning Goals

To understand:

The structure of DNA and how it is replicated

The two steps of gene expression: transcription and translation

The ways that gene expression is regulated at the levels of transcription and translation

The microbial genome and the difference between genotype and phenotype

How the microbial genome changes by mutation

How genetic information is transferred between prokaryotes through transformation, conjugation, and transduction

How genetic information is exchanged between eukaryotic microorganisms

How genetic change spreads through a population of bacteria

Chapter Outline

Structure and Function of Genetic Material
    The Structure of DNA
    Reactions of DNA
    Replication of DNA
    Gene Expression
Regulation of Gene Expression
    Regulation of Transcription
    Regulation of Translation
    Global Regulation
    Two-component Regulatory Systems
Changes in a Cell's Genetic Information
    The Genome
    Mutations
    Selecting and Identifying Mutants
    Uses of Mutant Strains
    Genetic Exchange Among Bacteria
Genetic Exchange Among Eukaryotic Microorganisms
Population Dynamics
Summary

Teaching Tips

1. Continue to assign the several kinds of questions at the end of each chapter in the text. After the students have answered the questions, post the answers and use part of a class period to discuss the answers.

2. Use a take-apart model of DNA to teach its structure and to illustrate how it replicates.

3. Write some practice problems for the flow of genetic information in the cell. Copy these problems and distribute them in your class for practice. Use this sequence of DNA bases for one half of the DNA double helix. Read this sequence from left to right to answer all questions.

   ATA-TCA-GGC-GTA-TTA

   Ask these questions:

   What is the complementary sequence of bases in the other DNA strand of the double helix?

   What is the sequence of mRNA bases transcribed by the originally stated sequence of DNA bases?

   What is the sequence of amino acids transcribed by the five codons of mRNA?

   What is the anticodon of each tRNA that places its amino acid at each codon at the ribosome?

4. Change the base sequence of the originally stated DNA. Use a base substitution as one example. By this mutation, how does the flow of information change in the cell?

5. Try one more variation of questions #3 and #4. Pose these questions to your students. Start with a sequence of five amino acids. For example: phenylalanine - leucine - proline - histidine - valine. What is the sequence of codons of mRNA that determines this sequence of amino acids? From this sequence of mRNA bases, what is the sequence of DNA bases that made this mRNA by transcription? These questions challenge the students to "work backwards" compared to questions #3 and #4.

Discussion Topics

1. Much of our knowledge about molecular genetics in humans has developed from studying the genetics of microorganisms. What advantages for study do microorganisms offer? How can information about their genetics be applied to us? Are there concepts about them that are not applicable?

2. Most students in a microbiology course have also taken general biology courses. In general biology the genetics learned involves principles applicable to many species of organisms in addition to microorganisms. How is the genetics taught in general biology similar and different to the principles of microbial genetics presented in Chapter 6?

Correlation Questions

1. Some scientists originally thought that DNA lacked the complexity to encode genetic information. Proteins, they argued, were more likely to do this by their structure. Ask your students to support or refute the claim of these scientists.

2. Ask your students to read chapter 13, on viruses. How do some viruses have the ability to make DNA from RNA?

3. In early studies of the human genome, the estimated number of human genes was 100,000. How was this conclusion drawn?

4. The number of human genes is now estimated at about 40,000. Why are their fewer than originally thought?

Answers: Review Questions

1. The microorganism in question is a fungus that converts 5-FC to 5FU. It has an enzyme, cytosine deaminase, that catalyzes this conversion. FU disrupts gene expression in the fungus, killing it. The mutation destroys cytosine deaminase, blocking the formation of the lethal FU. Without the conversion of 5-FC to FU, the fungus survives.

Structure and Function of Genetic Material

2. Genetics is the study of the heredity and variation among organisms.

3. Nucleotides are the building blocks of DNA. The bases of the DNA nucleotides are adenine, cytosine, guanine, and thymine. In the DNA double helix the base pairs between complementary strands are adenine-thymine and guanine-cytosine.

4. DNA stores the genetic information that a cell needs to grow, reproduce, and maintain itself. A gene is a segment of DNA needed to manufacture a specific macromolecule.

5. Replication and gene expression are the two reactions that DNA enters into. By transcription, DNA makes RNA. By translation, RNA makes proteins.

6. DNA contains the information to direct all metabolism. By directing protein synthesis through transcription and translation, it directs the synthesis of enzymes that control the steps of cell metabolism.

7. Replication is the duplication of the DNA molecule.

8. The order of bases in one DNA strand dictates the order of bases in the newly-made other half of the molecule, the complementary strand, by rules of base pairing.

9. Replication of DNA requires energy furnished in the cell by ATP. ATP reacts with deoxyribonucleotides to form nucleoside triphosphates, chemically activated forms of nucleotide building blocks. The enzyme DNA polymerase joins the deoxyribonucleotides.

10. Each old strand of the DNA molecule serves as a template, or pattern, to guide the synthesis of a newly made complementary strand. The bubble that starts the replication of the bacterial chromosome occurs at a specific point called the origin. The replication forks are the two points where the original DNA double strand separates. From the origin the two replication forks travel in opposite directions around the chromosome. The terminus is the point where the two forks meet halfway around the chromosome. Here, two completed chromosomes (each a double helix) separate. Each new double helix, made by semiconservative replication, consists of one old strand and one newly made strand.

11. The replication apparatus is DNA polymerase and several other enzymes involved in replication. It moves the replication fork and synthesizes the two new strands of DNA.

12. The two strands of the DNA double helix are antiparallel because they are oppositely oriented. One ranges from the five prime end to the three prime end. The other ranges from the three prime end to the five prime end.

13. Primer DNA allows DNA polymerase III to synthesize new DNA in the five prime to three prime direction. The leading strand is the DNA strand exposed at the replication fork that presents a three prime carbon. The lagging strand is the DNA strand at the fork that presents a five prime carbon. Primase is the enzyme that synthesizes a short strand of RNA serving as a primer for DNA polymerase III. DNA polymerase I eventually destroys the RNA primer and replaces it with a DNA strand. DNA ligase seals a gap between a newly synthesized fragment of DNA and the continuous strand formed in front of it during replication.

14. By transcription the information in DNA is changed into information of RNA.

15. Replication is to DNA as transcription is to RNA. The sequence of bases in a transcribed strand of DNA dictates the order of bases in the synthesized RNA by rules of base pairing. A in DNA attracts U in RNA; C attracts G; G attracts C; and T attracts A. As with replication, transcription begins with the formation of a bubble. Nucleotides are ordered to make a new molecule. However, the nucleotides in transcription are ribonucleotides. Only one DNA strand is transcribed in one direction. A short, single strand of RNA is produced.

16. A promoter is the site on the genome where transcription begins. The terminator is where it ends. Only one of the DNA strands, the sense strand, is transcribed. The sequence of DNA bases of the sense strand directs the sequence of bases ordered in the synthesized RNA, which is a transcript of the DNA.

17. The three products of transcription are mRNA, rRNA, and tRNA.

18. By translation a sequence of nucleotide bases is changed into a specific sequence of amino acids that forms a protein for cell metabolism.

19. rRNA is a component of the ribosome, the site of translation. The order of bases in the mRNA is decoded at this site. tRNA brings the amino acids to the ribosome for ordering. This sequence is dictated by the order of bases on the mRNA.

20. tRNA is linked to a specific amino acid by activation, using ATP. The anticodon is a base triplet that is complementary to a codon, or base triplet, on mRNA. The tRNA transfers an amino acid to a complementary site on the mRNA. This meeting occurs at the ribosome.

21. The genetic code specifies which amino acids are encoded by the codons on the mRNA molecules. It is redundant because some amino acids have more than one codon. Nonsense codons do not specify an amino acid.

22. Translation of mRNA begins at the start codon. It is close to the Shine-Dalgarno sequence or the ribosome binding site. During translation the A site on the ribosome exposes successive codons on mRNA. An amino acid to be polymerized on a growing protein during translation is placed at the P site on the ribosome. Once the amino acid is bonded the ribosome moves to the next codon and the process is repeated.

Regulation of Gene Expression

23. Metabolic regulation is when a cell maximizes its efficiency of metabolism. It is important to meet the changing needs of the cell.

24. Regulation occurs by either modulating gene expression or changing the activity of enzymes.

25. Inducible enzymes are produced when a signal molecule is abundant in the environment. Repressible enzymes are made when a signal molecule is scarce in the environment. Glycolytic enzymes are constitutive, as they are produced at a constant rate.

26. Prokaryotes regulate transcription through operons. Allosteric proteins bind to DNA and change its activity.

27. An operon is a set of genes regulated and transcribed together. The lac operon encodes a series of enzymes that metabolize lactose in the cell. More of the enzymes are made in the presence of lactose. Less are made in its absence.

28. Attenuation is a means that regulates transcription without the participation of a DNA-binding protein.

29. The first gene of the histidine operon makes a leader protein that detects whether a sufficient supply of histidine is present. The attenuator loop is a short piece of RNA that folds to displace RNA polymerase and stop transcription. The antiterminator loop prevents the formation of the attenuator loop, allowing transcription to occur.

30. The translation of ribosomal proteins is controlled by operons with genes encoding for these proteins.

31. Global regulation involves general signals whereby any C source or shortage of amino acids can serve as a metabolic signal and affect metabolism.

32. By catabolite repression groups of genes encoding catabolism of a carbon source are not expressed when a better carbon source is available. cAMP is a signal molecule for catabolite repression. It signals the rate at which the reactions are occurring. CAP is a regulatory protein. It can bind with the signal affecting the operon.

33. There are two regulatory proteins: a sensory that detects an environmental signal and transmits it to another protein, a response regulator that alters gene expression.

Changes in a Cell's Information

34. Changes occur in a cell's genetic information by mutation or by receiving slightly different DNA from another microbial cell.

35. The genome is the sum total of DNA in any cell. It is much less in prokaryotes than in eukaryotes.

36. Plasmids are small structures of DNA. They encode functions not essential for growth or reproduction.

37. R factors are plasmids that encode enzymes that make a bacterium resistant to antibiotics. Some bacterial diseases can proliferate because the bacteria causing them cannot be treated with antibiotics.

38. Conjugative plasmids encode the ability to transfer a copy of themselves to another bacterial cell.

39. The genotype is the genes in the cell. The phenotype is the effect the genes have on the appearance and function of the cell.

40. By a base substitution, one base pair in DNA is replaced by a different pair. By deletion a segment of DNA is removed. By inversion the order of the segment of DNA is reversed. By transposition, a segment of DNA is moved to another site on the chromosome. By duplication, an identical segment of DNA is positioned next to the original one.

41. Mutation rates based on reproduction relate directly to the event and rates of chromosome reproduction.

42. Spontaneous mutations occur naturally without stimulus of mutagenic agents. They add to genetic variability and sometimes are beneficial.

43. Induced mutagens are caused by the stimulus of a mutagen, the agent causing them.

44. Chemical mutagens include nitrosoguanidine, hydroxylamine, and BU. UV light causes thymine dimers.

45. Transposable elements can move from one chromosome to another in the cell. Insertion elements encode only the ability to transpose. Transposons also carry genes.

46. The seriousness of a mutation depends on how much it changes a gene product. It also depends on how important the product is to the cell. A missense mutation changes the amino acid that is encoded. A nonsense mutation stops translation.

47. A lethal mutation destroys DNA polymerase. An auxotroph is a mutant strain with this type of mutation.

48. Conditionally expressed mutations are expressed only in certain environments, such as at particular temperatures or osmotic conditions.

49. Direct selection identifies mutant strains by creating conditions that foster their growth. Indirect selection creates conditions that prevent growth of the mutant in question. Brute strength involves finding a desired mutant from a large number of clones. Replica plating compares many clones in a particular growth environment.

50. The Ames test determines by direct selection the ability of a mutagen to cause reversions, mutations that reverse the original mutation causing auxotrophy.

51. Genetic exchange occurs in bacteria by transformation, conjugation, and transduction.

52. By transformation, DNA leaves one cell in an aqueous environment and enters another cell where it is incorporated into the genome. It can occur naturally in the environment or be stimulated artificially by treating chilled *E. coli* cells with a strong solution of calcium chloride.

53. By conjugation, a donor bacterial cell introduces a plasmid to a recipient cell across a cytoplasmic bridge. The plasmid DNA becomes part of the recipient cell DNA. HFr cells receive insertion sequences or transposons by conjugation.

54. A bacteriophage is a virus that infects bacteria. A virulent phage carries out generalized transduction. A temperate phage carries out specialized transduction. For specialized transduction a lytic or lysogenic cycle can ensue. In the lytic cycle the infected bacterial cell bursts, releasing many new phage particles from the infection. In the lysogenic cycle, the viral DNA becomes incorporated into the bacterial DNA but does not cause lysis of the host cell.

55. The recombination of meiotic products in baker's yeast is an example of genetic exchange in eukaryotes. Many rearrangements and recombinations are possible.

56. Transposons and the movement of plasmids from cell to cell can establish new genetic types of bacteria in hospitals that are resistant to antibiotics and other means of control.

Answers: Correlation Questions from the Textbook

1. A primase is an RNA polymerase. However, it is a short molecule and therefore could probably not do the complete job of the RNA polymerase functioning during transcription.

2. Replication is a very accurate process. There are more variables in the steps of gene expression, making it more likely to develop errors.

3. The occurrence of bacterial transformation could be proven by introducing a DNA fragment into the nutrient broth of the microbe. If it takes up this DNA directly and is changed from this environmental source, transformation has taken place. Conjugation could be observed by mixing two genetic strains of a bacterium and looking for genetic recombinants after the two strains have mated.

4. The frame shift could produce a single base change that produces a nonsense mutation. For example if AAA - UUU - AAA mutates to AAA - UUA - AA etc., the change of UUU to UUA (nonsense in a given species) could result in a new codon with a different meaning.

5. There is more energy efficiency at the level of transcription, as is has fewer steps and different kinds of molecules involved compared to translation. Also if translation occurs needlessly in a cell, wasted transcription also occurs. A block at the transcription level, prevents translation.

6. As many as six different codons of mRNA can attract the same amino acid, making it versatile and adaptive.

Answers: Essay Questions

1. A low, detectable rate of mutations regulating metabolic processes favors an acceptable amount of competition and natural selection to preserve the most successful mutants.

2. The mutant, resistant bacterial cell can increase its numbers asexually, dividing through binary fission. The mutant gene causing the resistance to the antibiotic can also be spread to other bacteria through conjugation or transduction.

Answers: Correlation Questions from the Instructor's Manual

1. DNA has four building blocks or nucleotides. Proteins, with a 20-subunit "alphabet" of amino acids, can form a larger vocabulary, namely protein "words." However, scientists did not originally know that DNA is decoded in groups of three nucleotides, greatly increasing the number of combinations of subunits during transcription. Four bases, read in groups of three, produces 64 combinations, increasing complexity.

2. These viruses have an enzyme that runs transcription in reverse when RNA makes DNA. Students should read ahead about viruses in Chapter 13 and learn about there unique metabolism.

3. Estimates were originally depended on a knowledge of the total number of DNA base pairs divided by the average number of base pairs per gene. For example, if an organism has one million base pairs, and the average gene length is 1000 base pairs, the organism has about 1000 genes by division.

4. One assumption made about the human genome was that all of the DNA is active in transcription. Actually there are regions of DNA, between actively transcribing regions of DNA, that are not genetically active.

Chapter 7
Recombinant DNA Technology

Learning Goals

To understand:

The nature of recombinant DNA technology and the potential it has to affect every aspect of out lives

The fundamental tool of recombinant DNA technology—gene cloning—and the five steps involved: obtaining DNA, splicing genes into a cloning vector, putting recombinant DNA into a host cell, testing, and propagating

The methods of finding the right gene for gene cloning

The uses of *Escherichia coli* as a host cell for recombinant DNA

Current applications of recombinant DNA technology in medicine, industry, agriculture, and criminal investigation and applications we can expect in the future

The methods of sequencing

The methods and information gained by genomics

The methods and information gained by microarray technology

Chapter Outline

Recombinant DNA Technology
Gene Cloning
    1.Obtaining DNA
    2.Splicing genes into a Cloning Vector
    3.Putting Recombinant DNA into a Host Cell
    4.Finding the Right Gene
Hosts for Recombinant DNA
Applications of Recombinant DNA Technology
Genomics
Sequencing
Assembling
Annotation
Benefits of Genomics
Summary

Teaching Tips

1. Encourage your students to answer the several kinds of questions at the end of the chapter. After the students have answered these questions, post the answers so they can check their results. Use part of one class period to discuss their answers.

2. Here is a list of genetically engineered products that have been used to treat human diseases. Assign one of these products as a topic to each student in your class. Each student can gather information on this topic through library research and a search on the Internet.

    erythropoietin

    clotting factors

    growth hormone

    insulin

    interferon

    surfactant

    tumor necrosis factor

    tPA

    vaccines for hepatitis

    Ask each student to report on his/her findings and share this information with the other class members. Ask each student to emphasize how the substance functions in the human body. How does a disease develop if this function is lost? For example, insulin lowers the concentration of glucose in the blood, converting it into glycogen for storage in the liver. The liver is the target organ for the hormone insulin. As a target organ, the liver responds to the signal of the hormone insulin. The lack of insulin in the body leads to Type I diabetes, an abnormally high concentration of glucose in the blood.

erythropoietin

clotting factors

growth hormone

insulin

interferon

surfactant

tumor necrosis factor

tPA

vaccines for hepatitis

3. Does recombinant DNA technology hold the key for the treatment of all human diseases? For example, another type of diabetes mellitus is Type II. This type of diabetes is not due to an insulin deficiency. It is due to the inability of receptor cells on target organs (e.g., the liver for blood sugar control) to respond to the hormone. Ask your students if they think recombinant DNA technology offers a key to treat this type of diabetes. For example, could liver cells be genetically instructed to make receptors that respond to insulin, potentially curing the disease?

4. This is the third edition of *Introduction to Microbiology*. Several new topics have been added to the topic of recombinant DNA technology in this chapter, such as genomics and annotation. Encourage your students to search the Internet for recent developments in these new branches of DNA technology.

5. Ask your students to solve this problem. A small amount of DNA, equivalent to one gene, is collected from a crime scene. For analysis by DNA fingerprinting, 75,000 copies of the gene are necessary. How many cycles of PCR are necessary to produce enough DNA for analysis?

Discussion Topics

1. Insertion of a gene for gene therapy in many animals works best at the one-cell stage. Why?

2. The progress of recombinant DNA technology and genetic engineering carries ethical implications. For example a latent gene, causing a disease, is discovered in a human subject on chromosome 18. Through gene therapy, treatment for this disease is possible. However, an insurance company denies coverage for the costly treatment. Without this advanced knowledge the company would not have made the decision. As symptoms developed, the subject would have received treatment.

   Was the technology an advantage or a drawback in this case?

Correlation Questions

1. A pair of homologous chromosomes is studied in a eukaryotic cell. On one homolog, the sequence of genes is ABCDE. On the other homolog the sequence of corresponding genes is abcde. Write two examples of how crossing over can change the identity of the gene sequences on these chromosomes.

2. The streak plate method, used to isolate different species of microorganisms, was discussed earlier in the text. How does the formation of isolated colonies by this method relate to the concept of cloning?

3. A salamander is cloned from a somatic (cell) of another salamander. Explain how this cloned salamander will be genetically identical to the salamander supplying the cell for cloning.

4. Returning to question #3, are the factors that will not make the cloned salamander identical, by genotype or phenotype, to the parent salamander?

Answers: Review Questions

Recombinant DNA Technology

1. Recombinant DNA technology is always recombining genes from different DNA molecules into a single molecule. However, it involves a vast array of different procedures.

2. Recombinant molecules produced naturally in the cell occur by crossing over between homologous DNA molecules. Recombinant molecules by DNA technology are made in vitro and do not necessarily involve homologous chromosomes.

Gene Cloning

3. DNA molecules are homologous if a single strand from one DNA molecule can form a hydrogen-bonded double strand with a single strand of the other DNA molecule, with only a few noncomplementary base pairs. Gene cloning is a process of obtaining identical copies of a gene. A clone is any identical group of progeny derived from an individual. A cloning vector is a DNA molecule that a cell will replicate.

4. The five steps of gene cloning are obtaining DNA that contains the gene to be cloned, splicing a piece of DNA containing the gene into a cloning vector, putting the cloning vector into an appropriate host cell, testing to assure that the described gene has been inserted into the host cell, and propagating the host cell to produce a clone of cells with the clones of genes.

5. DNA is obtained from the cell extract of ruptured cells. It is separated from other molecules in the presence of alcohol and wrapped around a glass rod. It is separated from other remaining molecules and purified.

6. Good cloning vectors need an origin of replication. They must be small and carry unique genes for identification. Cloning vectors are cut by enzymes called restriction endonucleases. A palindromic sequence has four to seven bases that read the complementary same direction on one DNA strand as the opposite direction on the other strand. Endonucleases cut asymmetrically in these sequences. The product of this has sticky ends. Sticky ends of cut DNA molecules can anneal or join together under certain conditions.

7. Gel electrophoresis is a technique that separates molecules by their ability to move in different directions and at different rates in a gel with an electrical field. It is used in gene cloning to separate different cut sequences of DNA.

8. Ligation is the sealing together of the sticky ends of cut pieces of DNA. If these ends were not sealed, the molecule would fall apart. Pieces of DNA without an extending single strand are blunt-ended and can be ligated. The DNA to be cloned can be cut mechanically by shearing. Also, the cloned gene and the vector can be cut by different restriction endonucleases.

9. By transformation, DNA is taken into the host cell from solution. By transfection, a virus is the cloning vector. By microinjection, the DNA is introduced into the cell by a pipette. By electroporation, cells incorporate DNA if they are exposed to high-voltage electrical impulses.

10. A gene for splicing can be tested by prior purification. Its degree of complementarity is compared to another gene. By subsequent identification, fragments of DNA are spliced into the cloning vector and inserted into cells that are plated and grow colonies. Colonies that produce the product of the desired gene are selected.

11. By shot gun cloning, an entire genome is cut into pieces, spliced into the molecules of the cloning vector, and transformed into bacterial cells. A gene bank is a set of bacterial clones for an entire genome. These are efficient ways to form and store large amounts of information.

12. A good recombinant DNA host must be easy to maintain and cultivate, must grow rapidly, and have well-known characteristics. *E. coli* has these advantages. Its disadvantages include forming inclusion bodies from abundant proteins. It also destroys some human proteins as foreign. CHO cells do not destroy human proteins, but they are expensive to cultivate and maintain.

Applications of Recombinant DNA Technology

13. Medically useful proteins from recombinant DNA technology include the human growth hormone and insulin.

14. PCR can pinpoint a single gene and multiply it to produce a pure solution of the gene. Amplifying it makes it easier to use and study. It will expand the possibilities for future research and medical diagnosis.

15. To genetically engineer an organism is to alter it genetically for specific purposes. By gene therapy good genes are introduced into cells to replace disease-producing genes. Genetic engineering could eventually be used to increase the productivity of microorganisms, increase the productivity of animals, and make disease-resistant plants.

Genomics

16. Genomics is the study of an organism as revealed by the sequence of bases in its DNA.

Sequencing

17. Sequencing is stating the correct order of all bases of all genes in an organism's genome.

18. They are the building blocks of an analogue used in the reaction mixture for DNA sequencing.

19. It is used to separate the various reaction products made from the reactions for DNA sequencing.

20. It detects different fluorescent dyes, a unique dye existing for each of the terminal bases.

Assembling

21. This links the short sequences of DNA, produced by DNA sequencing, into their correct overall order.

22. The sequences produced are short fragments of the entire gene under study and do not represent the entire DNA molecule studied.

Annotation

23. This process converts a group of DNA fragments, produced by sequencing, into useful information.

24. These are base sequences that are presumed to represent the beginning and end of a gene.

25. The base sequences of ORFs are compared with the sequences of genes with known functions.

26. It is the study of an organism as revealed by the complete set of proteins it contains.

27. Researchers can learn what a gene does even if the gene product is unknown.

28. Sequencing reveals the identity of the gene (base sequences) under study in microarray technology.

29. A fluorescent green dye tags genes that are studied during the hybridization steps of this process.

Answers: Correlation Questions from the Textbook

1. The sample of DNA does not have the palindromic sequence that can be cut by this particular restriction endonuclease.

2. The method of repeated heating and cooling of the enzyme would need to be changed.

3. DNA fragments of EcoRI anneal more readily.

4. The gene from another bacterium, *B subtilis*, would be more compatible with *E. coli* and easier to clone compared to a yeast cell.

Answers: Essay Questions

1. Some human proteins, particularly larger ones, do not fold properly in *E. coli*. This bacterium cell cannot modify some proteins for final production and actually treats some as foreign, destroying them.

2. Start with the idea that new strains of bacteria could be produced that are pathogenic and resistant to the human immune system.

Answers: Discussion Topics

1. It is easier to genetically change one cell compared to many cells. The change of the first, single cell will be copied and transferred to all subsequent cells as the first cell multiplies.

2. This is an ethical question to be debated. It does not have an easy answer. The technology offers the potential for treatment but also offers information that denies coverage for treatment.

Answers: Correlation Questions from the Instructor's Manual

1. If the homologs break and cross over after the first gene, the recombinants from crossing over will be: Abcde and aBCDE. If the cross over occurs after the middle gene, the recombinants will be ABCde and abcDE.

2. The streak plate method separates different cells from a mixture, allowing each isolated cell to produce its own local population of cells. This local population, or colony, is a clone. All of the cells are produced asexually from a common cell, without genetic recombination.

3. The cell taken for cloning should have a complete set of chromosomes with an entire genetic blue print of the salamander. By cloning, the body cells of the new salamander will be produced from this original cell. The cells are propagated asexually, without genetic recombination or chance for variation.

4. A cell of the cloned salamander could experience a somatic mutation, a change in the genetic blueprint of a body cell. If this occurs early in development, at the two-cell or four-cell stage, for example, all cells produced from that mutated cell will inherit this new genetic blueprint that is different from the salamander supplying the original cell. Also, if the cloned salamander keeps the same genetic blueprint as its parent (no somatic mutation), not all of the genes it inherits may be expressed as they were in the parent, producing a different phenotype in the cloned organism.

Chapter 8
The Growth of Microorganisms

Learning Goals

To understand:

How microorganisms grow

The meaning of doubling time and exponential growth

The phases of growth that microbial cultures pass through

The methods that can be used to keep microorganisms growing continuously

What kinds of nutrients microorganisms require for growth

The environmental conditions that permit microbial growth: temperature, hydrostatic pressure, pH, and osmotic strength

How to measure the size of a microbial population using indirect methods—measuring turbidity, dry weight, or metabolic activity

How to measure the size of a microbial population by direct count, plate count, most probable number, and filtration

Chapter Outline

Populations
The Way Microorganisms Grow
    Doubling Time and Growth Rate
    Exponential Growth
    Phases of Growth
    Continuous Culture of Microorganisms
    Growth of a Colony
    Biofilms
What Microorganisms Need to Grow
    Nutrition
    The Nonnuutrient Environment
Measuring Microbial Growth
    Measuring the Mass of Cells in a Population
    Counting the Number of Cells in a Population
    Measuring Metabolic Activity
Summary

Teaching Tips

1. Assign the review, correlation, and essay questions at the end of the chapter. After the students have answered them, take some time at the end of one class period to discuss the answers. Instead of posting an answer key, try a new approach. The students can break up into small groups and compare their answers. They can use this approach as a basis for discussion. Visit the groups and check the accuracy of the student answers when they are working in their groups.

2. Write some problems on the exponential growth of a microbial population. Copy these problems and distribute them in class for student practice. Use the following example as a start:

    Starting with one bacterial cell in a test tube of nutrient broth, what is the number of cells in the test tube after two hours? Assume synchronous growth and a doubling time of twenty minutes.

3. This chapter offers many principles that are also applicable to the lab. Are you doing serial dilutions in lab as one method to estimate the size of a bacterial population? Try this example in class with your students:

    In a test tube a bacterial population in nutrient broth has a cell concentration of 50,000 per ml. If one ml of this broth culture is pipetted into 9 ml of sterile nutrient broth in another test tube, what is the new concentration of cells?

    What is the concentration of cells after another one-tenth dilution?

    How many one-tenth dilutions are necessary to achieve a one ml suspension of cells that can be plated and easily counted?

4. Tie in other examples of lab to lecture. For example, how can the turbidity of a nutrient broth culture indicate population growth? Why, through a serial dilution, is choosing plates between 30 and 300 colonies a good compromise between speed and accuracy for counting? If a mixed culture has several colonies together, how can they be separated into pure cultures?

5. This chapter has many applications to the upcoming principles on the physical and chemical control of microorganisms. Many of these principles are described in the next chapter, Chapter 9. Make your students aware of this upcoming information and ask them to preview it.

6. Use the Internet as part of your instructional strategy. Tell your students to use the *Key Terms* in the textbook and study guide as search terms on the Internet to study the concepts of microbial growth. Examples of search terms from this chapter are *binary fission* and *exponential growth*.

Discussion Topics

1. Why is the projected size of a bacterial population by exponential growth not simply a matter of continually doubling the cell number? Keep in mind the idea of asynchronous growth and cell death.

2. What are some everyday, common examples of exponential growth in addition to the pattern of increase in population size?

Correlation Questions

1. Principles of population dynamics, applicable to all kinds of organisms, can be demonstrated as a bacterial population grows in a test tube of nutrient broth. What are these principles?

2. The principles from many branches of science support the information in this chapter on microbial growth. What are some of these principles?

3. The term *growth* has a different meaning for bacteria compared to multicellular organisms, such as plants or animals. What is the difference?

4. How can the increase in a limiting factor, such as phosphate ions in a stream, change the growth rate of the microorganisms in that waterway? How can these changes affect the population of plants and animals in the stream?

Answers: Review Questions

1. Microbial growth refers to the increase in the number of organisms in a population.

The Way Microorganisms Grow

2. Doubling time is the period needed for cells in a microbial population to grow, divide, and produce new cells from each original cell. Growth rate, which is doubling times per hour, is related to doubling time. A low value of doubling time yields a high growth rate. Growth rate more specifically states the rate of population increase.

3. During each doubling time the number of cells in the population increases by a factor of two. By this pattern the number of cells multiplies rapidly.

4. The phases of culture growth, in sequence, are lag, log, stationary, and death. During the lag phase, the population prepares for growth, but does not change cell numbers significantly. The log phase is the period of exponential growth. The mass of the culture stabilizes during the stationary phase due to the effect of some limiting nutrient or factor. During the death phase, the rate of cell death far exceeds the rate of any new cell production.

5. A continuous culture is maintained in the laboratory by keeping the concentration of one essential nutrient low enough that it limits the rate of population growth. By these conditions the number of cells in the population does not change.

6. In a natural population, the concentration of some limiting nutrient sets the growth rate.

7. A colony is a solid mass of cells derived from one cell. It usually grows on a solid nutrient surface in the lab. Cells in the center of a colony are older and usually in the stationary or death phase. Cells on the edges of the colony have been formed more recently. Therefore, they are younger and usually in the lag phase.

What Microorganisms Need to Grow

8. Nutrients are chemicals from the environment that cells use to build new cells. Carbon forms the structural basis for many biochemicals. Oxygen is a chemical component and is necessary for aerobic respiration. Nitrogen is an element needed to make proteins and nucleic acids as well as certain metabolites. Sulfur is a minor component of cells, found in tRNA, two amino acids, and some metabolites. Trace elements are inorganic chemicals needed in very small amounts. Organic growth factors are building blocks that cells cannot make and must therefore be supplied from the environment.

9. Oxygen is a structural component of molecules and is the final H acceptor in aerobic respiration. Free radicals are oxygen-containing compounds. Each has an unpaired electron. These radicals are highly reactive and can cause cell death if not inactivated.

10. Nutritional diversity refers to the different requirements among microbes for organic growth factors. Some microbes have no requirements while others have long lists.

11. A rich growth environment has an abundant array of building blocks. In this environment, microorganisms direct more energy toward rapid growth.

12. The significant physical factors in a microorganism's nonnutritive environment are temperature and pH. The significant chemical factors are hydrostatic pressure and osmotic strength.

13. The minimum temperature of growth is the lowest value that will support growth. The maximum temperature is the highest value that will support growth. Most bacteria grow over a range of 40 degrees Celsius. Within this range there is an optimum temperature at which a microorganism grows best. The temperatures for a microorganism depend on the identity of the enzyme-catalyzed reactions and the structures that protect a cell.

14. Thermophiles grow best at high temperatures. Mesophiles grow best at moderate temperatures. Psychrophiles grow best at low temperatures.

15. Hydrostatic pressure is the pressure applied to a liquid. The free movement of water through the cell membrane allows microorganisms to withstand high hydrostatic pressures. High pressures not withstood by a cell can stop the activities in the cell.

16. Most bacteria prefer a slightly alkaline pH. Fungi grow best at a slightly acidic pH. Acidophiles thrive in environments that are highly acidic. Alkaliphiles thrive in highly alkaline environments. Cells can control the intracellular pH by pumping hydrogen ions out of the cell by various amounts.

17. Halophiles are bacteria that can withstand high salt concentrations. Most bacteria maintain turgor pressure by maintaining it at a level greater than the osmotic strength in the extracellular environment. Plasmolysis is the shrinking of the cell due to the loss of water by osmosis.

Measuring Numbers of Microorganisms

18. A total count encompasses all cells. A viable count tallies only living cells that can reproduce.

19. a. Turbidity is an indirect method and gives a total count. The spectrophotometer detects the cloudiness of a culture. A more turbid culture contains more microorganisms. Its measurement is rapid and reproducible, but it only works on dense cultures.

    b. Dry weight is indirect and gives a total count. Cells are removed by filtration, dried, and weighed. It is useful for relating cell mass to measurement by the spectrophotometer. It is, however, tedious and time-consuming.

    c. Metabolic activity is indirect and gives more of a viable count. The rate of forming a product or using a substrate is related to cell mass. It is practical for soil and milk counts, but can be inaccurate.

    d. The direct microscopic count is direct and gives a total count. The cells are counted in a grid through a microscope. This sample is related to large units of volume for a cell density. It is accurate but slow and tedious.

    e. The direct electronic count is direct and gives a total count. It is accurate but expensive.

    f. The plate count is direct and gives a viable count. Cells from a small-volume sample are plated on a growth surface. The colonies that develop on the surface represent the number of cells in the sample. By ratio, this is related to the number of cells in a larger volume. It is accurate but tedious and time-consuming.

    g. The most probable number is indirect and totals viable cells. A sample from a population is diluted serially until culture tubes in this sequence are found that have only one cell or no cells. By determining the probability that tubes do not receive cells, this can be related to statistical tables that give a probable count of the original population.

    h. Filtration is indirect and accounts for viable cells. Samples of microorganisms are concentrated and plated for colony growth. Each colony represents a cell. This cell count can be related back to the original volume filtered. This method can be time consuming and possibly inaccurate.

Answers: Correlation Questions

1. Obtain a total cell count and viable cell count. Subtract the viable cell count from the total cell count to estimate the number of dead cells.

2. Increase the concentration of the limiting nutrient that was stabilizing population size.

3. A cell count, either indirect or direct, is difficult to do from a soil sample. However, an estimate of cell concentration through metabolic activity is more practical. Measuring the rate of removal of nitrogen as a substrate by these bacteria can be related to cell concentration.

4. The slowly growing culture would start to increase its growth rate. The culture already in the exponential phase would maintain its rapid growth rate.

5. By previous rapid growth, they are metabolically ready to multiply rapidly at that point. For example, their cells already have enough ribosomes to grow immediately. This is a normal trend when cells are transferred from a poor to a rich medium.

6. By proportion, the concentration is 4300 per ml. This number multiplied by 1000 equals 4,300,000 per ml for the original culture.

Answers: Essay Questions

1. A continuous culture can produce a dense culture, which in turn can produce a high concentration of antibiotics. However, this culture will produce less antibiotics if it eventually reaches a death phase.

2. The richness of a medium determines which microorganisms can grow. A rich medium supports a greater variety of species. As the concentration of nutrients increases, these is less chance for development of a limiting nutrient. Therefore, exponential growth can occur over a longer duration and the size of the population should increase.

Answers: Discussion Topics

1. Some of the cells produced early may die and not continue to reproduce. Short supplies of nutrients and other limiting factors may start to affect the population.

2. Start with the example of monetary increase through compound interest.

Answers: Correlation Questions in the Instructor's Manual

1. In a new environment, colonizing populations of many species carry out these phases of population growth: lag-log-stationary-death. The size of the population is limited by the availability of nutrients, space and many other factors that affect bacterial population growth in its finite space in a test tube of nutrient broth.

2. Principles include the concentration and identity of molecules, pH, temperature, cell division, cell structure, cell metabolism, and osmosis.

3. The term *growth* in multicellular organisms refers to changes in the individual organism. A plant or animal grows by increasing the number and size of its cells. The term *growth* for microbes refers to a change in the size of a group of microbial cells. Growth is a population phenomenon for microbes and does not refer to the change in the size of one organism.

4. A mineral such as phosphate can limit the size of microbes such as algae in the waterway. If the phosphate concentration in the stream increases, it will probably not continue to limit the size of the microbial population. The size of the microbial population (e.g., algae) can increase. As other organisms (e.g., fish) depend on the activity of these microbes, they are also affected. For example, if algal blooms occur, their activity can deplete the waterway of its dissolved oxygen. Fishing requiring oxygen (e.g., trout) will not be able to survive in this oxygen-depleted water.

Chapter 9
Controlling Microorganisms

Learning Goals

To understand:

The rate of microbial death and D-value

The physical treatments used to control microorganisms

The chemical treatments used to control microorganisms

How we keep food from spoiling

Chapter Outline

The Way Microorganisms Die
    Some Useful Terms
    Death Rate
    Sterilization
Physical Controls of Microorganisms
    Heat
    Cold
    Radiation
    Filtration
    Drying
    Osmotic Strength
Chemical Controls of Microorganisms
    Selecting a Germicide
    Testing Germicides
    Classes of Germicides
Preserving Food
    Temperature
    pH
    Water
    Chemicals
Summary

Teaching Tips

1. Many of the questions at the end of this chapter emphasize vocabulary. Suggest this format to help your students organize this information.

             Term   Definition

Show your students several examples with the terms at the beginning of the chapter: sterilization, antisepsis, etc. Your students should define these terms in their own words and not simply copy definitions out of the textbook.

2. Do your students finally understand the steps of a serial dilution? Assign this practice problem at the end of a class period. Collect the problem and analyze each student's technique and answer.

    A culture from a test tube of nutrient broth is taken through three successive, one-tenth dilutions in sterile nutrient broth. After the third dilution, a 1 ml suspension of cells is plated on an agar surface. 48 hours later, 50 colonies are produced. What was the original concentration of cells per ml in the nutrient broth tube?

3. There are other important mathematical concepts in this chapter. Here are a few examples you can assign to your class. After they have answered them, discuss the results with them.

    A bacterial population has a D-value of 90 minutes. By thermal killing, what percentage of the original cells remain alive after three hours?

    Phenol's end point as a germicide is at a dilution of 1:100. If the end point of another germicide is at a dilution of 1:100,000 what is its phenol coefficient?

4. Continue to emphasize the applications of the text's information to the students' lab experiences. For example, why are many cultures for study in lab grown over 48 hours? What phase of growth are they in at this point? As another example, demonstrate the use of the autoclave.

Discussion Topics

1. Bacteria cannot normally grow in honey and various kinds of canned fruit preserves. Why? Relate this to physical control methods.

2. Botulism is food poisoning that develops from eating canned vegetables that are not cooked properly. Why is the thorough cooking necessary?

Correlation Questions

1. A bacterial population consists of 100,000 cells. It is treated with a sterilizing agent. The environment with this population is sterile in two hours. What is its D-value?

2. How does a background in mathematics support the concept of microbial population growth and control?

3. A group of hunters decides to preserve fresh deer meat by salting it and drying it in sunlight. What strategies of microbial control are used in this example?

4. How is hand washing an effective approach to help prevent the common cold?

Answers: Review Questions

1. a. It has thick-walled oocysts that are resistant to chlorine.

The Way Microorganisms Die

1. Sterilization is a treatment that destroys all microbial life. Disinfection or sanitation is the reduction of the number of pathogens to a level where they cannot cause disease. Decontamination causes an instrument or surface to be safe to handle if it was exposed to microorganisms. Antisepsis is to kill microorganisms on the skin or living tissues.

2. A microbial cell is dead if it cannot produce a colony on a solid medium or produce a turbid culture in a liquid medium.

3. The rate of microbial death is the time interval it takes to kill 90 percent of the cells in a population. This time is the D-value.

4. A microbiostatic treatment inhibits a microbial population but does not kill it. A microbiocidal treatment kills the population. Sterilization is the treatment that kills all of the cells. The thermal death point is the lowest temperature required to kill all microorganisms in a particular suspension in 10 minutes. The thermal death time is the minimal time required to kill all microorganisms in a particular liquid suspension at a given temperature.

Physical Controls of Microorganisms

5. Moist heat kills cells by denaturing their proteins. Dry heat interferes with the cells' oxidation. Heat is quick, inexpensive, and efficient as a sterilization technique.

6. Cold temperature inhibits microbial growth by slowing down the metabolism of cells. It does not kill cells.

7. Bacterial cells are too small for the development of ice crystals. Thus freezing does not physically destroy these cells as it does to eukaryotic cells. Cold shock is the killing of many microorganisms by suddenly chilling the culture.

8. Ultraviolet radiation kills cells by damaging their DNA. Ionizing radiation strips electrons from atoms in cells.

9. Filtration controls microorganisms by trapping them from solutions based on their size. It does not sterilize because it does not remove all cells.

10. Osmotic strength controls cells by killing them through plasmolysis.

11. Heat through an autoclave sterilizes instruments in the medical field. Cold temperatures can be used to refrigerate food. UV light can sterilize clothing. Filtration sterilizes draft beer. Drying sterilizes food. Osmotic strength preserves food when it is salted or sugar is added.

Chemical Controls of Microorganisms

12. When choosing a germicide it should not destroy or damage the tissue or object being treated. It should target specific microorganisms. It should be classified for strength. Its price should be evaluated.

13. The phenol coefficient compares the effectiveness of a germicide to the effectiveness of phenol. Therefore phenol serves as a standard for comparison.

14. By the paper disc method, a filter paper disc is saturated with a dilution of a germicide being tested. It is placed on an agar surface previously seeded with a test organism. After incubation a bacteria-free zone develops around the disc. The size of this zone is an indicator of the effectiveness of the germicide. The larger the disc, the greater the effectiveness.

    By the use-dilution test, a test organism is added to dilutions of a germicide. After incubation the highest dilution that remains clear is an indicator of effectiveness.

15. Germicides are classified by structure and activity.

16. a. Phenol inactivates cellular proteins. It is found at low concentrations in throat sprays.

    b. Phenolics act on lipids and are used in hospital disinfectants.

    c. Alcohols disrupt the lipids in cell membranes and are used on injection sites on the surface of the skin.

    d. Halogens inactivate enzymes and are used as skin disinfectants.

    e. Hydrogen peroxide is an oxidizing agent. A three percent solution is a weak antiseptic.

    f. Heavy metals react against the sulfhydryl groups on proteins and have been used as antiseptics on the skin.

    g. Surfactants break apart oily droplets. They are used in soaps and detergents.

    h. Alkylating agents attach short carbon chains to enzymes, killing them. They are used to preserve tissues.

Preserving Food

17. Foods sometime spoil when refrigerated because psychrophilic bacteria can still carry out their metabolism on the food. Other kinds of bacteria can carry out metabolism at a low rate. Refrigeration is not a steilization procedure.

18. Pasteurization kills most pathogens and causes minimal damage to the product.

19. Safe heat treatments for canning include heat for long enough durations, and at high enough temperatures to kill bacterial endospores.

20. Drying food removes the water bacteria need for their metabolism. Salting causes plasmolysis of cells by inducing osmosis and water loss from the bacterial cells.

Answers to Correlation Questions

1. Write the number 1,000,000,000. Cancel one zero on the right for every 20 minutes. After six cancellations the number will be 1000. 6 X 20 = 120 minutes

2. Gram-negative bacteria have a complete three-layered cytoplasmic membrane. However, as they do not form endospores, they are not heat-resistant.

3. Very low temperatures arrest metabolism. However, at a deep freeze this temperature is too harsh and microorganisms cannot survive. Psychrophiles can grow at very low temperatures.

4. The high acidity is an effective physical control against bacteria. Also, salting the pickles creates a high osmotic strength (hypertonic environment) outside bacterial cells, leading to their loss of water and plasmolysis.

5. UV light from the sun can also kill microbes exposed to it.

6. Washing with soap and water removes microorganisms by abrasion. The chemical control of hydrogen peroxide kills a higher percentage of cells.

Answers to Essay Questions

1. Start with the idea that pasteurization makes milk safe for consumption.

2. There are other safer, more reliable means. Use of any kind of high-energy radiation can have mutagenic effects on humans.

Answers to Discussion Topics

1. The honey or preserves produces an extracellular environment that produces a high osmotic strength (hypertonic environment) outside the microbial cells. They lose water by osmosis, experiencing plasmolysis. This is an effective physical control method.

2. *Clostridium botulinum* is an obligate anaerobe that lives in the soil. It is found on vegetables pulled from the soil before canning. If this microbe remains in the canned vegetables, it can survive and cause botulism if consumed. Cooking is needed, as species of *Clostridium* can form heat-resistant endospores.

Correlation Questions from the Instructor's Manual

1. The population is reduced in size to 10 percent through six cycles. At the end of the sixth cycle, it is eradicated. The numerical pattern of reduction is: 100,000 - 10,000 - 1000 - 100 - 10 - 1 - 0.

2. The subject of calculus presents the pattern of exponential growth. This is the pattern of increase for a bacterial population during the log phase. Statistical analysis is relevant for understanding the density and size of population.

3. The salt creates a high osmotic strength outside microbial cells. Heat and sunlight are effective physical control methods.

4. Hand washing can remove many infectious microbes that can be transferred from the hands to portals of entry in the body, such as the oral cavity or nose.

Chapter 10
Classification

Learning Goals

To understand:

The principles by which organisms are classified

The difference between artificial and natural systems of classification

The concept of species and how it applies to microorganisms

How microbial species are named

The evolutionary relationship among microorganisms, plants, and animals

The methods used to classify microorganisms

The methods used to identify microorganisms

Chapter Outline

Principles of Biological Classification
    Scientific Nomenclature
    Artificial and Natural Systems of Classification
    The Fossil Record
    The Concept of Species
Microorganisms and Higher Levels of Classification
Methods of Microbial Classification
    Numerical Taxonomy
    Traditional Characters Used to Classify Bacteria
    Comparing Genomes
Characters Used to Classify Viruses
Dichotomous Keys
Summary

Teaching Tips

1. Assign the several kinds of questions at the end of the chapter. Use them as a basis for review and discussion as part of one of your class periods.

2. Does your biology or science department have a faculty member doing research in taxonomy? Invite this person as a guest speaker to one of your class meetings. The information that this teacher provides will give your students another perspective on the science of classification.

3. One of the best ways to understand the process of using a dichotomous key is to make one. Ask your students to do this as an activity in one of your class periods. The approach can be simple to illustrate the concept. For example, you can ask the students to make a key for a variety of geometric shapes: circle, square, rectangle, triangle, hexagon. Here is one possible first step for the key.

1. a. It lacks sides - circle

   b. It has three or more sides—go to step 2.

4. Will your students be given an unknown to identify in the lab part of your course?

   This chapter offers an excellent opportunity to prepare them through lecture for that process. The students should first streak a Petri dish for isolation. Why? Explain this to them. A good first step for identification is the Gram stain. Your students could use this as the first step of a dichotomous key, separating bacteria into two specific groups. What other tests could narrow down the identity of the bacterium in question? Are there metabolic tests?

5. Search the Internet for other examples of dichotomous keys.

Discussion Topics

1. Why has it been difficult to establish a phylogenetic classification for bacteria? Will recent technology make this type of classification more likely?

2. The chapter mentions the different strains of *E. coli*. One strain is a normal biota inhabitant of the human colon. However, a strain foreign to the human body can produce a dangerous toxin. If consumed from undercooked, contaminated beef, it can be pathogenic. How can one strain of this bacterium be harmless and another one be a threat to human health?

Correlation Questions

1. From a biologist's viewpoint, how are the various subspecies of humans the result of evolution?

2. A marine biologist discovers new kinds of bacteria on the ocean floor. These bacteria have several different kinds of pigment systems. Is this characteristic a valid way to classify these new bacteria?

3. A biology department chairman plans a meeting of all regional microbiologists. He sorts out their addresses from state to local address as he mails flyers about this event. How can the addresses of these microbiologists be viewed as a hierarchy?

4. A field biologist discovers fossil imprints of microbes in a geological layer of South America. How can carbon dating be used to estimate the age of these fossils?

Answers: Review Questions

Principles of Biological Classification

1. Classification is a system of grouping similar things together. A hierarchical scheme of classification places individuals into groups that range from the broader and more inclusive (e.g., kingdom) to the more exact and specific (e.g., species). Taxonomy is the science of classifying organisms.

2. The arrangement of taxa, from smallest to largest, is species (smallest) - genus - family - order - class - phylum - kingdom - domain.

3. The species name is part of an organism's binomial name. As in *Escherichia coli*, the species name is the second part. It is underlined, or italicized, but not capitalized. Usually the species name represents something about the organism. For example, *E. coli* lives in the colon of a human.

4. An artificial scheme of classification groups organisms on the basis of visible similarities. A natural scheme of classification is based on phylogeny or evolutionary relatedness. The fossil record is a reconstruction of the mineralized remains, or fossils, of an organism from various geologic periods. It is useful for a phylogenetic scheme of classification. Stromatolites are finely layered rocks where fossilized photosynthetic prokaryotes have been discovered.

5. A eukaryotic group of species is a group of organisms that shares and exchanges in a common gene pool. For eukaryotes, members of the same species can interbreed. Members of a bacterial species have similarities and do not conform to the definition of eukaryotic species. As many bacteria reproduce asexually, the potential for interbreeding by sexual reproduction cannot be observed or tested.

6. Strains are two clones of a bacterial species that are genetically different.

7. Viral species are not defined phylogenetically. They are grouped on the basis of the kinds of diseases they cause and organized up through families, but not into any broader taxon.

Microorganisms and Higher Levels of Classification

8. Hackel classified organisms into either the plant or animal kingdom. Chatton separated bacteria into a different subgroup, noting the difference between prokaryotic and eukaryotic cells. Whittaker, noting the unique life cycle of fungi, recognized a five-kingdom scheme: plants, animals, fungi, protists, and monera. Woese, Kandler, and Wheelis more recently supported the idea of many kingdoms spread over three domains: the Eucarya, Bacteria, and Archaea. As knowledge of cell structure and genetic characteristics of organisms has increased, taxonomic schemes have been revised.

9. Viruses, needing hosts to survive and reproduce, are not classified into any currently recognized kingdom.

The Methods of Microbial Classification

10. By numerical taxonomy, organisms are classified based on the number of similar characters they have. Equal weight is given to each character.

11. a. By morphology, bacteria are classified based on their cellular shape and structures.

    b. By biochemistry and physiology, bacteria are classified on conditions that support their growth. These include temperature, pH, osmotic strength, and the end products of metabolism.

    c. By serology, bacteria are classified based on their specificity of reaction to antibodies found in sera.

    d. By phage typing bacteria are classified on their degree of susceptibility to specific bacteriophages.

12. a. Highly related bacteria have greater agreement on the percentage of G+C than bacteria that are less related.

    b. DNA hybridization compares two organisms. The extent of the annealing of two DNA strands is greater among closely related bacteria than among more distantly related bacteria.

    c. The greater the similarity in DNA base sequences among two organisms, the more closely they are related.

13. The characteristics used to identify viruses include the presence or absence of a membrane, host range, and reactions to serology tests.

14. A dichotomous key is a series of questions about important characters that offer two alternatives. The question pairs are ordered from more general characters to more specific pairs. Through a process of elimination, an organism is compared through the question pairs until a species is identified. This process can be accurate if the characters of organisms are very specific and easy to compare. It can lead to incorrect conclusions because a single character is rarely the same in all members of a species.

Answers: Correlation Questions

1. Races or subspecies among humans have genetic differences. They are all members of the same species. However, they are not different enough to be different species. There is a similar pattern for the strains of a bacterial species.

2. A dichotomous key can lead to incorrect conclusions because a single character is rarely the same in all members of a species.

3. Eukaryotes evolved after prokaryotes. Prokaryotes evolved at least 3.5 billion years ago. Eukaryote evolution can be documented through a more extensive fossil record. However, the fossil record only documents the last 600,000 years.

4. Fossil imprints of prokaryotes will occur with more sensitive methods of detection. One example has been the microbial mats found with the electron microscope.

5. The application of the species concept is not the same for prokaryotes as with eukaryotes. The basis for determining species of bacteria has used criteria such as morphology and has not used sexual reproduction (genetic recombination). Also, in some cases, bacteria that belong to different species (based on morphological traits) can exchange genes.

6. Plants have left a more extensive fossil record. Bacterial classification needs to rely on other means.

Answers: Essay Questions

1. A character must be clearly measured and defined. Its similarity must be tied in to closely related members and contrasted from organisms lacking it or where it is different. For example, a vertebral column meets these criteria. Its presence or absence offers a clear distinction among the vertebrates and invertebrate phyla among animals.

2. Start with the idea that the genetic code is universal. There is also great similarity in the patterns of metabolism. Life has many common characteristics such as growth and reproduction.

Answers: Discussion Topics

1. Phylogenetic classifications have relied on accurate, historical fossil records. These are rare for bacteria. Advances in DNA sequencing and related RNA structure offer another possible avenue. The closer the identity of the genomes of two bacteria, the more likely they have a recent, common ancestor.

2. The strains of *E. coli* have somewhat different sequences of DNA. The pathogen has a mutant gene that makes a harmful protein to the human body. The normal biota strain has evolved with the human and are, through their different genetic plan, are biochemically compatible.

Answers: Correlation Questions in the Instructor's Manual

1. Biologists believe that geographical barriers separated the original, ancestral human populations. Each group experienced its own mutations and environmental selection pressures. The resulting geographical variations of humans established the subspecies of Homo sapiens. With the changes in human communication and transportation, these geographical barriers are currently disappearing.

2. The classification of microbes based on superficial characteristics may not be phylogenetically sound. However, if biochemical characteristics (e.g., pigment systems) can be correlated with genetic similarities and differences, then the classification is more meaningful and logical.

3. The addresses of the faculty members range from the very broad categories to the very specific categories: state - county - township - town - street - number.

4. Carbon 14 is a radioactive isotope of carbon. It decays to N-14. Originally all of the carbon in an organism, or its surrounding layer of rock, is C-14. Its half-life is the time required for one half of the carbon in an organism to change to N-14. If, for example, the half life is 100,000 years, the fossilized organism is 100,000 years old if there are equal amounts of C-14 and N-14. If 75% is N-14, the organism is 200,000 years old as another 100,000 years was required for this change to occur.

Chapter 11
The Prokaryotes

Learning Goals

To understand:

Natural schemes of classifying prokaryotes

The Bergey's Manual scheme of classifying prokaryotes

To become familiar with:

The better-known prokaryotic genera and species in Bergey's Manual

The properties and activities of these organisms

The impact of these organisms on our lives and our environment

Chapter Outline

Prokaryotic Taxonomy
The Bergeys' Manual Scheme of Prokaryotic Taxonomy
Domain Archaea
    A1 Crenarchaeota
    A2 Euryarchaeota
Domain Bacteria
    B4 Deinococcus-Thermus
    B5 Chrysiogenetes
    B10 Cyanobacteria
    B11 Chlorobi
    B12 Proteobacteria
    B13 Firmicutes
    B14 Actinobacteria
    B16 Chlamydiae
    B17 Spirochaetes
    B20 Bacteriodetes
    B21 Fusobacteria
Summary

Teaching Tips

1. Assign the several kinds of questions at the end of the chapter. After the students have answered them, use them as a basis for review and discussion of the chapter in your class period.

2. Encourage your students to organize the information in the chapter in several ways. They can make lists of Gram-positive and Gram-negative bacteria. They can classify the bacteria into several groups by means of motility. Metabolic capability is another criterion. This will challenge the students to view the information in the chapter in several different ways. By this active practice they will learn the content of the chapter.

3. Present your students with a list of bacteria discussed in this chapter. Ask the students to make up a dichotomous key to classify them.

   Start with a simple example, listing one bacterium from each of the following: Gram-positive rod, Gram-negative rod, Gram-positive coccus, etc. List a genus-species member from each. Ask the students to look up the characteristics of each in the chapter (e.g., *Staphylococcus aureus* is a Gram-positive coccus). Using this information the students can make up a key.

   After this simple start, make a longer list of organisms with more characteristics (e.g., motility, metabolic capabilities, etc). Ask students to make a key for this longer list.

4. In lab ask the students to draw the basic morphology of some of the bacteria you are describing in lecture. *Sarcina* is in cubical packets. *Staphylococcus* is a cluster of spherical cells. *Streptococcus* is a chain of spherical cells.

5. Encourage your students to visit the Internet to learn the latest trends in the classification of prokaryotes

Discussion Topics

1. This chapter consolidates information from several branches of microbiology you have taught to date. What are they and how do they apply to prokaryote classification? Pose this question to your students as they take stock of their knowledge at this point in the course.

2. In any microbiology course, the concepts of lecture and lab become inseparable. How does the content of this chapter lend support to this statement?

Correlation Questions

1. In lab an instructor presents a student with twelve prepared slides of bacteria. Six are Gram-positive and six are Gram-negative. The instructor asks the student to construct a dichotomous of these twelve bacteria. What is the most logical way to proceed in constructing this key?

2. On a biochemical level, how are thermoacidophiles best adapted to survive in their environment?

3. How do luminescent bacteria produce light without producing large amounts of heat?

4. How does the dry heating system in a building affect the mucous membranes of the human upper respiratory tract? How does this affect the health of a person subjected to these conditions?

Answers: Review Questions

1. a. All belong to the bacterial phylum Proteobacteria and the class Gammaproteobacteria.

Prokaryotic Taxonomy

2. The natural scheme uses DNA sequencing to measure the degree of phylogenetic relatedness between microorganisms. Much information has been gained studying sequences of 16S RNA.

3. In the branching pattern, the prokaryotes that are in lines closer together are more related. The ones in lines further apart are less related.

4. *Bergey's Manual* has used a scheme that matches the criteria used in lab to identify microorganisms such as morphology, metabolism, and ecological preferences. However, in the year 2001 a genealogical tree using a more natural scheme, with phylogenetic information, was also incorporated.

5. The information in the manual includes cell morphology, staining properties, motility, metabolism, means of cultivation, ecological capabilities, and information with a phylogenetic basis.

The Bergey's Manual Scheme of Prokaryotic Taxonomy

6. There are two domains, the Archaea and Bacteria. The Archaea is divided into two phyla and the Bacteria is divided into 23 phyla.

7. The Crenarchaeota (A1) consist of a single class. They are morphologically diverse. All species are thermophilic and most metabolize sulfur. The Euryarchaeota (A2) have three metabolic types. The methanogens are strict anaerobes that make methane. The extreme halophiles are aerobes that require at least 10 percent salt in their outside environment. The thermophiles find optimal environments in hot environments such as geothermal springs.

8. Criteria include cell shape and arrangement plus metabolic abilities. This is the basis for arrangement of bacteria into different phyla, based on similarities and differences on these criteria. In some cases, bacteria with similar abilities (e.g., means of fermentation or photosynthesis) are placed in separate phyla.

9. The phylum Thermus contains two well-known species: *Deinococcus radiodurans*, which is resistant to radiation, and *Thermus aquaticus*, the source of *Taq* polymerase.

10. They have the same size and shape as some blue-green algae. Also, they produce oxygen through photosynthesis as algae do. They fix nitrogen in specialized cells called heterocysts. They carry out photosynthesis in all other cells.

11. The are phototrophic bacteria that trap light. They are found in deep, clear water. The depth offers an anaerobic environment. The clear water allows water to reach them for photosynthesis. They produce sulfur as a by-product of their photosynthesis.

12. This bacterium (*Agrobacterium*) enters the plant through a wound at the crown. Some of the bacterial DNA is a plasmid that is incorporated into the plant cells' chromosomes. These genes transform the plant cells into tumor cells.

    Acetic acid is a component of vinegar. Xanthan gum is a thickener for foods and paints.

    These bacteria, *Rhizobium* and *Bradyrhizobium*, supply the plant with usable nitrogen.

13. Gonorrhea is caused by *Neisseria gonorrhea*.

14. Human diseases caused by this group include typhoid fever and shigellosis.

    E. coli carries out mixed-acid fermentation. It can ferment lactose and convert tryptophan into indole, but it cannot use citric acid as a carbon source,.

15. They live in mud flats, bordering salt water or brackish water. They reduce sulfate and elementary sulfur to hydrogen sulfide. They can corrode iron pipes in soil by the products they make.

16. They are the major cause of diarrheal illness in the U.S.

17. It preys on other bacteria.

18. They lack a cell wall and are closely related to Gram-positive bacteria. As obligate fermenters, they ferment in the presence of oxygen. As with mycoplasmas, they lack a cell wall.

19. *Sarcina* has cells arranged in packets of four cells each. *Streptococcus* is a chain of spherical cells. *Staphylococcus* is a cluster of spherical cells.

20. Vegetative bacterial cells convert into endospores under harsh environmental conditions. Species of *Clostridium* and *Bacillus* form endospores. Thorough sterilization procedures, such as those used in an autoclave, also destroys endospores. If the sterilization procedure is thorough, it will destroy these endospores as well as vegetative cells.

    Species of *Clostridium* cause botulism, tetanus, and gas gangrene. One species of *Bacillus* causes anthrax.

21. Irregular shapes include V-shaped pairs of cells and cells that are swollen and branched.

22. Acid-fast bacteria have an envelope with a peptidoglycan wall attached to a polysaccharide layer which in turn is attached to mycolic acid. Species of *Mycobacterium* cause leprosy and tuberculosis.

23. These were once thought to be viruses because they are very small. They can only survive by carrying out a parasitic existence inside host cells. Diseases they cause include epidemic typhus and Rocky Mountain spotted fever.

    The reproduction of chlamydiae alternates between two cell types: a reticulate body (vegetative cell) and an elementary body (chlamydiospore). Reticulate bodies multiply and elementary bodies spread the infection.

24. Spirochetes move rapidly through dense media by the action of flagella. Their flagella are bundled into two axial filaments. As their endoflagella turn, they cause the helical ridge they form on the outer membrane to move down the cell and propel the cell through its medium. Their cell shape is long and helical, resembling a corkscrew. Diseases they cause include syphilis (*Treponema pallidum*), leptospirosis (*Leptospira interrogans*), relapsing fever (*Borrelia species*), and Lyme disease (*Borrelia burgdoferi*).

25. They are nonoxygenic photosynthetic bacteria that use organic compounds as a source of electrons. Often they are highly colored. Species of Bacteroides are the most abundant bacteria in the mouth and intestinal tract of animals. Most species are harmless, but a few species cause disease.

Answers: Correlation Questions

1. The two domains of bacteria in *Bergey's Manual* are not closely related.

2. The axial filament is an extension of a complete, three-layered cytoplasmic membrane. This kind of membrane is present is Gram-negative bacteria only.

3. Members of the mycoplasmas ferment even when oxygen is present.

4. Certain sulfur-reducing bacteria corrode iron pipes in damp soil. The pipe will not last as long in the mud flat.

5. Most antibiotics are produced by species of *Bacillus* and *Streptococcus*. They are found in aerated environments.

6. Boiling would not kill the endospores from *Bacillus anthracis* and would not make the drinking water safe.

Answers: Essay Questions

1. *Bergey's Manual* emphasizes, in part, the morphological, physiological, and ecological criteria used in tests in the lab. This is an artificial scheme and is not natural, based on phylogenetic lines that emphasize genetic relatedness. Recently, in the year 2001, information with a phylogenetic basis was incorporated.

2. In the dark environment of marine life mutations for luminescence were adaptive in several ways. These adaptations include a confusing series of signals by luminescent species to potential predators.

Answers: Discussion Topics

1. Start by reviewing the information on methods of study (Chapter 3), cells (Chapter 4), metabolism (Chapter 5), and genetics (Chapter 6). Elaborate from that point. In Chapter 3, what are the different kinds of stains (simple, Gram, flagella, acid-fast, etc.)?

2. The information on cell morphology, staining properties, metabolic capabilities, and genetics are the criteria used to classify bacteria. Share examples of this from the chapter with your students. For example, *E. coli* is Gram-negative rod that ferments lactose.

Answers: Correlation Questions in the Instructor's Manual

1. Composing a key based on Gram reactions or cell morphology is one approach. However, this could have a weak phylogentic basis, depending on the bacterial species studied. Relating bacterial traits to similarities and differences with an evolutionary basis is more sound. Relating morphological traits to evolution is acceptable.

2. Harsh conditions, such as high temperature, can disrupt the secondary and tertiary structure of proteins. Bonds that can stabilize protein structure at these levels, such as disulfide bonds, can make an organism more resistant to these harsh environmental conditions.

3. These bacteria have an enzyme (e.g., luciferase) that can catalyze a light-producing reaction without liberating large amounts of heat.

4. Dry heat affects the mucous membranes. As this is a major line of defense to protect the body, changing the makeup of these membranes makes the person more vulnerable to attack through the upper respiratory tract.

Chapter 12
Eukaryotic Microorganisms, Helminths, and Arthropod Vectors

Learning Goals

To understand:

The characteristics, ecological roles, and classification of the major groups of eukaryotic microorganisms: the fungi, algae, and protozoa

The nature of lichens

The properties of slime molds, a small distinct group of eukaryotic microorganisms

The phylogenetic relationships among various groups of eukaryotic microorganisms

The major groups of helminths: their appearance, their life cycles, and the diseases they cause

The characteristics of certain arthropods, including insects, ticks, and mites that cause disease or act as vectors or reservoirs

Chapter Outline

Eukaryotic Microorganisms
    Fungi
    Algae
    Lichens
    Protozoa
    The Slime Molds
    Relatedness of Eukaryotic Microbes
    Helminths
    Arthropod Vectors
    The Organisms
    Arthropods and Human Health

Teaching Tips

1. Invite a representative from a local health department to address your class about the difficulties of controlling the human infections caused by fungi, algae, protozoans, and helminths.

2. If your course has a lab component, you have an excellent opportunity to study the organisms of this chapter firsthand. Various biological supply houses sell prepared slides of fungi, algae, and protozoans for microscopic study.

3. If your course does not have a lab, project the microslides or prepared 35 mm slides of the fungi, algae, and other organisms discussed in this chapter to augment your description of them in lecture.

4. At the end of your lecture on helminth life cycles, ask the students to diagram one of these cycles on a blank sheet of paper. List ten key terms of one of these cycles on the blackboard for guidance.

5. Study several kinds of arthropods in lab, either through models or dissections.

Discussion Topics

1. How do the pathogenic microorganisms discussed in this chapter overcome the mechanisms of the human immune system to cause their effects in the human body?

2. Which type of protozoan do you think fungi show the closest resemblance?

Correlation Questions

1. Slime molds have unique characteristics. Does this warrant their classification into a separate kingdom?

2. Although resembling plants superficially, fungi are more closely related to animals. How?

3. A biology student is handed a protozoan culture in lab. What first step can he carry out to identify it?

4. A new, plantlike organism is discovered by a researcher. How can a researcher uncover the highest level of organization of this organism?

Answers: Review Questions

1. a The infection developed slowly and gradually. Neither bacteria nor viruses cause chronic meningitis.

Eukaryotic Microorganisms

1. All fungi are eukaryotic, heterotrophic, nonphototrophic, and absorptive. Yeasts are single-celled and reproduce by budding. Mushrooms are one kind of fleshy fungi that consist of tightly intertwined hyphae. They produce sexual spores.

2. Typically a fungus consists of a vegetative structure called a mycelium. This is a multinucleate mass of cytoplasm with a system of rigid, branched tubelike filaments called hyphae. In the lower fungi the mycelium is coenocytic. In the higher fungi septa divide the mycelium into incomplete compartments.

3. Yeasts reproduce by budding. In this process, a bubble forms on the cell surface. Usually, it grows and pinches off from the cell.

4. Among the lower fungi, the Chytridiomycetes produce motile sporangiospores and motile gametes that have single posterior flagella. The Oomycetes produce biflagellate sporangiospores

and nonmotile sexual spores, formed after the fusion of nonmotile female gametes with motile and nonmotile male gametes. The Zygomycetes produce sporangiospores that are unflagellated. They are released into the air and fuse to form a zygote. It undergoes meiosis to produce a resistant zygospore.

5. a. The Ascomycetes reproduce from the fusion of tips of the same or different thalli. The nucleus from the resulting zygote undergoes meiosis. Sometimes the four nuclear products divide again, forming sexual spores called ascospores.

    b. The Basidiomycetes form basidiocarps. Asexual reproduction occurs by conidia. During sexual reproduction the mycelium contains nuclei from two different mating types whose hyphae have fused.

    c. The Deuteromycetes make conidia but do not produce sexual spores. They grow as molds or yeast.

6. In a dimorphic fungus, there is a switch in their life cycle between a single-celled yeast phase and mycelial phase.

7. Fungi are harmful because of the many plant diseases they cause. These include wheat rust and Dutch elm disease. They are beneficial by the variety of medicines they produce. These include a family of antibiotics call cephalosporins.

Algae

8. The algae resemble higher plants because they generate ATP by oxygenic photosynthesis through chlorophyll a. Their chloroplasts are the same as plant chloroplasts. They make precursor metabolites from carbon dioxide by the Calvin-Benson cycle. Structurally they differ from the higher plants. Some algae are unicellular. All lack a distinct tissue structure and they do not produce embryos. They are eukaryotic as are the fungi.

9. As photosynthetic organisms, algae cannot live in the human body and therefore do not cause human disease.

10. Among algae the euglenoids are unicellular without a cell wall. They contain chlorophylls a and b.

    The dinoflagellates are unicellular, have cellulose in their cell wall, and contain chlorophylls a and c.

    The diatoms are unicellular, coenocytic, and filamentous. Their cell wall has silica.

    The green algae are unicellular, coenocytic, filamentous, and plantlike. Their cell wall has cellulose.

    The brown algae are plantlike. Their cell wall has cellulose and algin. They have chlorophylls a and_c.

    The red algae are plantlike. Their cell wall has cellulose. They have chlorophyll a.

Lichens

11. Lichens are symbiotic associations between a fungus and a phototroph. They are found in a wide variety of environments, including the surfaces of rocks and tree trunks.

12. A thallus of a lichen can be separated from the phototroph. It changes shape from that in the lichen. The separated alga continues to grow as single cells.

Protozoa

13. Protozoa are nonphotosynthetic, unicellular eukaryotes. They reproduce asexually by fission and budding. Some undergo multiple fission. Sexual reproduction occurs by conjugation.

14. Protozoans are classified into four groups on the basis of locomotion. The four groups are the Mastigophora (flagellates), sarcodinans, sporozoans, and Ciliophora (ciliates).

15. Diseases caused by protozoans include amoebic dysentery, malaria, and African sleeping sickness.

The Slime Molds

16. The true slime molds are a multinucleate mass of cytoplasm at one stage of their life cycle. They form a slimy mass called the plasmodium. The cellular slime molds produce cells that are similar to amoeboid protozoa.

17. The plasmodium is a slimy mass formed by the true slime molds. It forms fruiting bodies and raised structures that form spores.

Relatedness of Eukaryotic Microbes

18. The fungi, algae, and protozoa are not closely related to one another. The protozoans are a diverse group. The groups within this category are often not closely related.

Helminths

19. The helminths are the flatworms and roundworms. They are studied because some are human parasites.

20. a. The Platyhelminthes are the flatworms. Their body has a head and bilateral symmetry.

   b. The Cestoda are the tapeworms. Their flat, segmented body appears as a piece of tape.

   c. The Trematoda are flukes. They have a flattened body but are not segmented.

   d. The Nemathelminthes are roundworms with cylinder-shaped bodies.

21. Humans acquire a tapeworm infection by eating uncooked, infected meat and being infected by their larvae. They may also ingest infective eggs. Symptoms include damage to the skeletal muscles, liver, and lungs.

22. Adult fluke worms develop in the human lung. Tapeworms produce eggs that are coughed up, swallowed, and passed into the feces. If the eggs reach the water in raw sewage, they hatch into miracidia, free-swimming larvae. These larvae penetrate the body of a snail and multiply asexually to produce redia. The redia form free-swimming cercariae. The cercariae leave the snail body and form cysts called metacercariae in the muscles or internal organs of crayfish and crabs. Humans are infected if they eat the crayfish or crabs.

23. a. Whipworms infect the human body if humans consume their material contaminated by feces.

    b. Trichinosis is acquired by ingesting the larvae of the worms in meat not cooked thoroughly.

    c. Hookworms are acquired by filariaform larvae entering the skin of the human.

Arthropod Vectors

24. Arthropods are invertebrate animals with jointed appendages. They are vectors for some diseases caused by microbes.

25. The medically important arthropods include the arachnids, ticks, and mites. They pass on infectious microbes through their eggs.

26. A mechanical vector picks up a pathogen on its body and transports it from one place to another. A biological vector is a stage in the life cycle of the microorganism.

Answers: Correlation Questions

1. The members of the Oomycetes live in water. The members of the Zygomycetes are terrestrial.

2. Deuteromycetes cannot produce sexual spores as the mushrooms do. They produce conidia. They are not unicellular. The yeasts are.

3. An alga still has unique properties, including the potential to produce nutrient molecules. This is a property absent in fungi, as they are not phototrophic. Also, microscopic observation of the fungi would reveal a different cellular makeup.

4. As a fungus, it is heterotrophic, nonphotosynthetic, and absorbs nutrients from another organism. In this case it can live off a human host.

5. A slime mold as a human pathogen would need the human body to complete part of its life cycle.

6. A tick is larger than a mite and has less hair.

Answers: Essay Questions

1. Through heteromorphism the different forms of an organism allow it to pass through several different environments. It can take advantage of each one to promote survival, leading to the next stage of its life cycle.

2. The difficulty in controlling some helminth infections involves following it through several possible hosts and controlling each host. However, learning about its life cycle and controlling all hosts represent the key for controlling the helminth.

Answers: Discussion Topics

1. Begin by learning more about the mechanisms of cellular and humoral immunity in the human body.

2. Consider that the fungi are heterotrophic. Also examine their means of reproduction.

Answers: Correlation Questions in the Instructor's Manual

1. All characteristics must be considered. Some are plantlike, resembling algae. Some traits resemble protozoa. Other traits are unique, such as the grex and their pigment systems.

2. Fungi have a mode of nutrition that is distinctly heterotrophic.

3. Start by observing the means of motility under the microscope: flagellate, ciliate, pseudopod or no motility (sporozoan).

4. Study the responses of the groups of cells of the organism. Do the cells work separately or do they maintain function only when working as an integrated group (tissue)? Do tissues work together, reflecting an organ level of development?

Chapter 13
The Viruses

Learning Goals

To understand:

The nature of viruses—their host range, size, structure, and life cycle—and how they are classified and named

The life cycles of virulent and temperate bacteriophages

The general properties of animal viruses and, in more detail, the properties of retroviruses, influenza viruses, and tumor viruses

The general properties of plant viruses

The nature of viroids and prions

Chapter Outline

The Ultimate Parasites
    The Discovery of Viruses
    Are Viruses Alive?
Classification of Viruses
    Host Range
    Size
    Structure
    Life Cycle
    Taxonomy
Bacteriophages
    Phage Counts and Phage Growth
    Replication Pathways
Animal Viruses
    Cell Cultures
    Replication
    Latency
    Animal Viruses of Special Interest
Plant Viruses
    Growth, Replication, and Control
    Tobacco Mosaic Virus
Viruses of Eukaryotic Microorganisms
Infections Agents That Are Simpler Than Viruses
    Viroids
    Prions
The Origin of Viruses
Summary

Teaching Tips

1. Assign the review, correlation, and essay questions at the end of each chapter. After the students have answered them, use the questions as a basis for class review and discussion.

2. At the end of your lecture, ask each student to sketch the general makeup of a virus. Visit each student and check on their progress. Are they representing the capsid and nucleic acid core correctly?

3. Also at the end of one class period ask each student to outline the life cycle of a virulent phage and temperate phage. Check their outlines.

4. Viruses are constantly in the news. Ask each student to bring in one recent article published on viruses. At the end of one class period, ask the students to break into small groups and compare their findings.

5. Encourage your students to use the Internet to expand their information beyond the chapter content. Use the key terms in the chapter as search terms.

Discussion Topics

1. Viruses have posed a wide range of health hazards and disease to humans. What are some of the examples?

2. Compare the size of viruses to the size of bacteria.

Correlation Questions

1. Why is the use of an antibiotic ineffective against viral infections in the human body?

2. How can viruses be used as vectors to treat human diseases?

3. How are taxonomy and nomenclature different? How are they related?

4. If viruses were classified into a seventh kingdom, what criteria could be used to establish this new scheme?

Answers: Review Questions

1. a The age, clinical presentation, and time of the year of the infection offered clues to the type of microorganism causing the infection. Antibiotics were not prescribed to treat the recurring infection, as it was viral. Knowledge of the characteristics of the virus aided in treating the infection. For example, the viruses causing both infections were minus-strand RNA viruses.

The Ultimate Parasites

1. A virus is a package of nucleic acid within a protein coat. In a host cell, it directs its metabolism to make more viruses. A virion is a circular molecule of ssRNA without a capsid. Acellular means lacking a cellular structure.

2. Iwanowski reported infectious agents from tobacco plant extracts in 1892. He claimed that they were smaller than bacteria. Beijerinck suggested that these agents might be microorganisms. In 1935, Stanley purified and crystallized the tobacco mosaic virus, the first identifiable virus.

Classification of Viruses

3. Viruses are classified on the basis of host range, size, structure, and life cycle.

4. Host range is the spectrum of organisms that a virus attacks. Host specificity is determined mainly by the presence of the appropriate receptors on the host cell surface.

5. A virus is a nucleic acid surrounded by a protein coat and sometimes a membrane. The nucleic acid may be DNA or RNA. Plus-stranded RNA is translated directly by the host ribosome. Minus-strand RNA is converted into mRNA after it enters the host cell.

6. The capsid is the protein that surrounds the nucleic acid core of a virus. Capsomeres are its constituent protein molecules. The head is the polyhedral portion of the capsid. The tail is attached to the head. The tail sheath or plate helps the virion attach to the host cell.

7. An enveloped virus is surrounded by a membrane from pieces of the host cell membrane. Naked viruses lack this envelope. Spikes are glycoproteins that stick out from the membrane.

8. By adsorption the virus attaches to the host cell during the beginning of the life cycle. By penetration the viral genome enters the host cell. During uncoating, the viral capsid and membrane are removed. The next step is viral synthesis as the viral components take over the metabolism of the host cell. After maturation the viral particles are released from the host cell.

9. The family is the broadest viral taxonomic category.

Bacteriophages

10. Plaque count tallies the number of circular regions on a bacterial-covered film. This is on the surface of a growth medium in a petri dish. Each plaque represents one virion from an original diluted sample. A one-step growth curve shows the growth pattern of virions. A mixture of bacterial cells with attached viruses is diluted. At intervals the number of PFU's is determined by conducting plaque counts on samples. This number is plotted against time to produce the growth curve.

The latent period is when there is no increase in viral population size. The eclipse period is when no intact virions are being assembled just before the burst period.

11. By the lytic pathway, bacteriophages are virulent. They overtake the bacterial cell and produce new, released virions. By the lysogenic pathway, the phage is temperate. It enters the host cell and becomes incorporated into the host cell. It is replicated as part of the host genome and does not cause bursting of the cell with new viruses.

12. A virulent phage causes lysis of the cell. A temperate phage takes a bacterial cell through the lysogenic cycle. A prophage is the specific location on the bacterial chromosome where the viral genetic material becomes integrated.

Animal Viruses

13. Animal viruses were originally studied by infecting animals and counting them by dilution end points. Since the 1950s they have been cultivated in animal cells and tissues. A continuous cell line has cells growing infinitely from the original source of cells.

14. Animal virus replication resembles phage replication by having stages of adsorption, penetration, uncoating, maturation, and release. Sometimes uncoating precedes penetration. However, usually the entire animal virus enters the host cell rather than just the nucleic acid.

15. By a latent viral infection, the replication of the viruses is arrested and the infected animal cell can function normally for years. One example of this is the infection of HSV-1 viruses in nerve cells.

16. A retrovirus is a large group of RNA viruses that have a reverse transcriptase. Through this enzyme RNA makes DNA.

17. An antigenic shift is a sudden change in the properties that identify the virus as a foreign invader to defenses of the immune system in the human body. It results from genetic changes. An antigenic drift is a small mutational change. It occurs gradually and incrementally.

18. Some viruses are associated with human cancers. Changes in about 40 human genes can lead to cancer. A gene that causes a tumor is called an oncogene.

Plant Viruses

19. Plant viruses are studied with cell cultures in the same way phages are studied. They are named by the diseases they cause.

20. The absence of an envelope in plant viruses makes it easier for them to enter plant host cells. They are naked viruses.

21. The tobacco mosaic virus is the most extensively studied virus.

Viruses of Eukaryotic Microorganisms

22. The study of viruses that infect eukaryotic cells has lagged behind the study of the viruses that infect plant cells and animal viruses.

23. A mycovirus infects fungi.

Infection Agents That Are Simpler Than Viruses

24. A viroid is a circular molecule of ssRNA without a capsid. Viroids cause plant diseases such as the potato spindle tuber disease.

25. A prion is an infectious agent consisting only of protein. It is not known how their proteins can be self-replicating. They cause mad cow disease and diseases of the human central nervous system.

The Origin of Viruses

26. Viruses are examples of retrograde evolution because they are simpler things that evolved from more complex things.

27. Viruses may have evolved from genes in the same cells that they infect. They could have left one cell and entered another cell, causing that cell to reproduce the excised gene.

28. New viruses arise from gene mutations and cross-species transfer.

Answers: Correlation Questions

1. The eclipse period is when no intact virions are present. If bacteriophages are present and enveloped, this period cannot be found with the viruses in the intact state.

2. Mutations would probably be greatest during the periods of greatest metabolic activity. One possibility is when RNA makes DNA by a reverse transcriptase.

3. The plus-stranded RNA must first be a template to make a complementary copy of DNA, which then makes mRNA. This must occur before the steps of translation directed through mRNA, leading to the synthesis of new virions.

4. The enzymes are necessary to dissolve the contents of the cell wall and/or cell membrane of the host cell before the viral nucleic acid can enter the host cell.

5. Its capsid must have the new, correct specificity for recognition and attachment to a new host cell.

6. Viroids are small circular molecules of ssRNA without a capsid.

Answers: Essay Questions

1. Viruses, viroids, and prions display the properties of life only when inside a living host cell. Outside the host cell they crystallize into chemicals and do not display the properties associated with life.

2. It is more advantageous for a plant virus to keep its host alive and continue to draw on its nutrients instead of killing it.

3. The HIV virus could be inserted into a host chromosome. Its expression could become altered and it could be converted into an oncogene.

Answers: Discussion Topics

1. Start with examples ranging from forms of human cancer and the common cold to the AIDS virus.

2. Viruses are measured in nanometers. Bacteria are measured in micrometers.

Answer: Correlation Questions in the Instructor's Manual

1. Antibiotics usually attack a bacterial cell wall or bacterial ribosome. These are not found in viruses.

2. A virus can be used as a vector to carry desirable DNA into a human host cell, replacing DNA that programs disease development (e.g., cystic fibrosis) with the desirable DNA that can induce health.

3. Taxonomy classifies an organism in a hierarchical scheme. Nomenclature is naming the organism for proper placement into that scheme. *Escherichia coli* is the scientific name for a bacterium for its unique placement into a genus and species, taxonomic categories.

4. Start with the biochemical makeup of a virus: its nucleic acid core and protein capsid.

Chapter 14
Microorganisms and Human Health

Learning Goals

To understand:

The nature of the normal human microbiota and how it can change

The three types of human-microbe symbioses: commensalism, mutualism, and parasitism

The human factors that determine the normal microbiota: structural defenses, mechanical defenses, biochemical defenses

The microbial factors that determine the normal microbiota: physical, nutritional, and special adaptations to life on living tissue

The nature of the microbiota on the skin and conjunctivae; in the nasal cavity and nasopharynx, mouth, intestinal tract, vagina, and urethra

The impact of the normal microbial biota on its human host

The disease-carrying ability of microorganisms as it exists along a continuum, from highly virulent to almost harmless

Chapter Outline

Normal Biota
    Resident Biota
    Transient Biota
    Opportunists
    Changing Biota
Symbiosis
    Commensalism
    Mutualism
    Parasitism
Factors That Determine the Normal Biota
    Living Tissues as an Environment for Microorganisms
    Microbial Adaptations to Life on Body Surfaces
Sites of Normal Biota
    The Skin
    The Conjunctiva
    The Nasal Cavity and Nasopharynx
    The Mouth
    The Intestinal Tract
    The Vagina
    The Urethra
Is Normal Biota Helpful or Harmful?
    Conflicting Theories

Harmful Effects
Beneficial Effects
Loss of Normal Biota
A Spectrum of Disease-causing Abilities
Summary

Teaching Tips

1. Use the human torso model in class to indicate the body regions inhabited by the different groups of normal biota discussed in the chapter.

2. Continue to use the lab component of your course to study the normal biota described in the chapter. For example, you can study species of *Staphylococcus* and *Escherichia* for their morphological, physiological, biochemical, and nutritional characteristics.

3. Invite a local health professional to your class to describe the various opportunists discussed in this chapter. Ask your guest lecturer to emphasize conditions promoting the conversion of an opportunist to a pathogen (e.g., antibiotic therapy).

4. Continue to assign the review, correlation, and essay questions listed at the end of the text chapters. Use some class time for students to discuss and share their answers. This activity can serve as a review session for the chapter content.

Discussion Topics

1. How do concepts learned earlier in the text support the understanding of the major points in this chapter? For example, how does lysozyme activity vary among different bacteria? How does the concept of a pH optimum determine where different normal biota inhabit the human body?

2. There are some species of normal biota that are the same in a given body region for all humans. However, are there also some differences in normal biota, region by region, among humans? What factors could account for these differences, body region by body region?

Correlation Questions

1. Why are space travelers checked for the makeup of their normal biota upon return to earth from a space flight?

2. How, considering the idea of levels-of-organization, is the skin an organ?

3. How is the term *microbiota* more appropriate than the term *microflora* for describing the microbes that inhabit the human body?

4. A microbe attacks the human body, interfering with the ciliary action from the epithelial cells lining the inside surface of the respiratory tract. How does this weaken a line of defense in the body?

Answers: Review Questions

Case History

1. Penicillin G eliminated the streptococci that could have been the source of infection for Baby Girl A.

Normal Biota

2. Normal biota are microorganisms that coexist with humans as hosts, forming stable relationships. They are adapted to the conditions of the human body and usually do not cause disease.

3. Humans acquire normal biota when these microorganisms originally establish themselves on the body from the external environment. This starts to become significant at birth.

4. Resident biota are present on the human body throughout life. Transient biota live on body surfaces but are not there persistently. Neither resident flora nor the transient flora cause disease. Opportunists are present in human hosts and usually do not cause disease. However, they may cause human disease under certain conditions.

5. The normal biota of the mouth and intestine change roles during infancy due to alternations in the diet, medical treatment, and the environment. For example, *Candida albicans* can become an opportunist as a result of antibiotic therapy.

6. Estrogen stimulates vaginal cells to produce glycogen during puberty. The glycogen is a nutrient source for lactobacilli, which establish an acid environment in the vagina. This acidity is effective against potential pathogens.

Normal Biota and Symbiosis

7. Symbiosis refers to two different kinds of organisms living together. The larger organism is a host, providing an environment for the other one, which is often a microbe. Symbiotic relationships are classified by whether they cause harm or benefit to the host.

8. In commensalism the host neither benefits nor is harmed through the symbiotic relationship. The microorganism benefits. In mutualism both the host and microbe benefit. In parasitism the host is harmed and the microbe benefits. Parasitism is unstable whereby commensalism is most stable. The evolutionary trend for human hosts has been toward stable symbiotic relationships.

9. Mutualism does not exist in human symbiotic relationships, for no microbe is essential for human benefit and survival.

10. Microbial antagonism occurs when one microbe interferes with the growth of another in the human host.

11. Commensals can prevent establishment of harmful microbes in the human body. This is beneficial. Commensals can become harmful over time if they become opportunists.

12. A parasite in symbiosis harms its human host. The term "parasite" is used for eukaryotic organisms. A pathogen is a microbial parasite.

Factors that Determine the Normal Biota

13. In addition to physical and nutritional factors, environmental and adaptational factors influence microbial growth.

14. Nonspecific surface defenses prevent the growth of many different kinds of microorganisms. One example is the skin.

15. Epithelial surfaces are our main structural defense against microbial invasion. The two types of epithelia are the skin and mucous membranes. The skin defends by serving as a physical barrier that prevents microbes from entering the body. It also presents a dry, acidic environment that wards off many microbes.

16. Mechanical defenses involve movements along surfaces that rid the body of microbes. Examples include the peristaltic action of smooth muscle in the wall of the digestive tract and the mucociliary system in the respiratory tract.

17. Biochemical defenses involve substances produced by the body that inhibit microbial growth. Examples include keratin in the skin, the pH and fatty acids of the skin, bile secretion, and lysozyme secretion.

18. Microbes adapt on the surface of the skin by locating moist areas that promote growth and by entering breaks in the skin from injury. Adhesions are appendages of the bacterial cell that allow the cell to stick to a surface. This promotes establishment on the skin surface.

19. Bacteriocins are substances that can kill bacteria, thus preventing their establishment in the body.

Sites of Normal Biota

20. a. The skin is acidic and fairly dry. The normal biota inhabitants of the skin are the staphylococci, diphtheroids, and fungi.

    b. The conjunctiva is a moist mucous membrane. It is washed with tear fluid. Normal floral members are the staphylococci and diphtheroids.

    c. The nasal cavity and nasopharynx are lined by a moist mucous membrane. *Staphylococcus epidermidis* is one normal biota member. Species of *Lactobacilli* are found there, as are Gram-negative bacteria.

    d. The mouth is lined with a moist, mucous membrane and usually has a neutral pH. This environment is also warm. Species of *Streptococci* live here. Staphylococci are present, as are lactobacilli and diphtheroids.

e. The intestinal tract is lined with a moist mucous membrane and has a basic pH. Normal biota include species of the genera *Bacteroides, Bifidobacterium, Fusobacterium*, and *Clostridium*. Facultative anaerobes, such as *E. coli*, are present in smaller numbers.

f. The vagina is a warm, moist environment. An acidic pH promotes the growth of lactobacilli. Species include anaerobic and aerobic streptococci, staphylococci species, and anaerobes of *Bacteroides, Clostridium*, and *Fusobacterium*.

g. The urethra is lined with a moist mucous membrane. There are few normal biota members. Members can include enterococci and *Staphylococcus epidermidis*.

21. *Demodex folliculorum* is the only arachnid that normally inhabits the human skin.

22. A newborn lacks microorganisms until it passes through the terminal region of the female reproductive tract and contacts the new environment. Various lines of defense prevent growth of microbes until after birth.

23. The intestinal tract contains hundreds of different species of bacteria. This environment is more complex than in other body regions.

24. Some microbes in the intestinal tract produce bacteriocins that kill other microbes. Others control the growth of neighbors by producing acids. Others change oxidation states.

Is the Normal Biota Helpful or Harmful?

25. Microbiota are not essential to human life but can enhance it by providing some beneficial effects. Normal biota that become pathogens can be harmful. Therefore, they carry out harmful and helpful roles. Most microbiologists would say that the exact role of a microbe depends on the species being described.

26. Beneficial effects include microbial antagonism, stimulation of the immune system, and vitamin production.

27. The loss of normal biota can be dangerous because harmful opportunists can move into the sites vacated by normal biota. The loss of normal biota from antibiotic treatment can promote the growth of *Candida albicans* in their place.

28. The classification of normal biota into commensals, opportunists, and pathogens is not clear-cut because there is a spectrum of abilities among microbes. Depending on changing conditions, a commensal may change into an opportunit, thus the categories merge.

29. Microorganisms exist along a continuous spectrum from highly virulent species to harmless species. There is a continuous range of outcomes.

Answers: Correlation Questions

1. Lysozyme cleaves specific chemical bonds found in peptidoglycan, a molecule found in the cell wall of Gram-positive bacteria. *S. aureus* is Gram-positive and will be destroyed by the action of lysozyme. *E. coli*, which is Gram-negative, will not be affected by lysozyme because of a difference in its cell wall structure.

2. The oil allows transient microbiota to adhere to the skin. However, the acid pH of the oil and fatty acids of the skin create an inhospitable environment for long-term establishment of the microbiota.

3. The term "flora" refers to plant life. In ancient classification schemes, bacteria were classified as plants. In modern classification schemes, bacteria are recognized as unique biota with their own kingdom.

4. The infant establishes a normal biota of *Bifidobacterium* in the intestine through breast-feeding. This bacterium ferments sugars to acids that create an environment that is inhospitable to the pathogens that cause diarrhea.

5. If the environment is germ-free, normal biota are not needed to ward off harmful microbes through microbial antagonism.

6. The animal must be relocated in a sealed-off, germ-free environment.

Answers: Essay Questions

1. The continuing relationships among microbes and humans involve the evolution of the human immune system, which is met by the evolution of microbial mechanisms to overcome these defenses. New mechanisms arise in microbes by genetic mutations. If these mutations and mechanisms are adaptive, they can be preserved through natural selection.

2. Studies describing germ-free humans have proven that humans can live without the presence of normal biota.

Answers: Discussion Questions

1. There are countless lessons from earlier chapters that can be tied into this chapter. Cell wall (Gram-positive vs. Gram-negative) makeup accounts for the differences in lysozyme activity. The pH preference by *E. coli* in the small intestine, which is alkaline, is different that the optimal environment for normal biota in the oral cavity, which has a neutral pH. The pH of the stomach is far too acidic to support most microbial populations.

2. Different diets can cause the normal biota to vary in the oral cavity and intestine. Humans, with genetic differences and somewhat different immune systems, will respond differently to some species of bacteria. This could also account for some variation. Also, physical conditions may vary. Some people have drier skin or a moister, upper respiratory tract.

Answers: Correlation Question in the Instructor's Manual

1. From another planet, a new kind of microbe could infect the space travelers. Humans on planet earth may not have evolved immunity to this microbe. If infected by the returning space travelers, an unprotected human population would be highly vulnerable to an infection that could spread rapidly.

2. An organ is two or more tissues working together. The epidermis of the skin is stratified squamous epithelium. The dermis of the skin is mainly dense connective tissue. Smooth muscle and nerve tissue is also present in the dermis.

3. *Microflora* is a term more pertinent to plants. *Microbiota* is more appropriate for the widespread variety of microbes inhabiting the human body.

4. The cilia are a major line of defense, trapping and removing debris entering the human respiratory tract. Working with the mucous membranes lining the tract, interference with this line of defense makes the invasion of inhaled microbes more likely.

Chapter 15
Microorganisms and Human Disease

Learning Goals

To understand how microbial pathogens that cause human infection:

    survive between hosts

    come in contact with the body

    adhere to body surfaces

    penetrate into deeper tissues

    avoid host defenses and multiply

    cause disease

    leave the host

Chapter Outline

The Seven Capabilities of a Pathogen
One: Maintaining a Reservoir
    Human Reservoirs
    Animal Reservoirs
    Environmental Reservoirs
Two: Getting To and Entering a Host
    Portals of Entry
    Modes of Transmission
Three: Adhering to a Body Surface
Four: Invading the Body
Five: Evading the Body's Defenses
    Evading Phagocytosis
    Evading the Immune System
    Obtaining Iron
Six: Multiplying in the Host
    Toxins
    Other Toxic Proteins
    Damage Caused by a Host
    Responses
    Viral Pathogenesis
Seven: Leaving the Body
Emerging and Reemerging Infections Diseases

Summary

Teaching Tips

1. Does your biology department have an ecologist or environmental biologist on staff? Invite this person to your class to describe the various kinds of wildlife, animal reservoirs.

2. Visit the microbiology lab in your department. Demonstrate some of the measures taken to prevent the transmission of diseases through fomites and other sources.

3. Use a human torso model to locate and describe the various kinds of portals for entrance and exit of different pathogens.

4. Ask the students to compose a vocabulary list of the important terms in this chapter. The terms should be defined in the students' own words and not simply copied from the text.

Discussion Topics

1. Ask your students to preview the several upcoming chapters in the text. How does the information in these chapters tie in with the concepts presented in Chapter 15?

2. How does the information in earlier chapters support the concepts presented in Chapter 15?

Correlation Questions

1. A mosquito is a vector to spread an infectious microbe to humans. How is a biological control more effective than a chemical control for this disease over a long time period?

2. Diseases with wild animal reservoirs can be difficult to eradicate. Why?

3. Why must an injection with a hypodermic needle penetrate the hypodermis of the skin to be effective?

4. Why is the ability of the blood to coagulate necessary, considering a situation when the human body is not wounded ? Therefore, how can the production of a coagulase by a bacterium be a threat to human health?

Answers: Review Questions

Seven Capabilities of a Pathogen

1. The seven capabilities are maintaining a reservoir outside the host, leaving the reservoir and entering a host, adhering to the surface of a host, invading the body of the host, evading the body's defenses, multiplying within the body, and leaving the body to return to the reservoir or new host.

2. Pathogenesis is the ability of a microorganism to cause disease. Infection is the growth of microorganisms in the body apart from the normal biota.

One: Maintaining a Reservoir

3. A disease reservoir is a place in which a pathogenic microorganism is maintained between infections. One disease reservoir is the human body that harbors the AIDS virus. Another example is animal reservoirs that hold the microbes for influenza and Lyme disease. The third example is environmental reservoirs such as soil that holds species of *Clostridium*.

4. A carrier is a human reservoir for infection. An incubatory carrier is in early stages without symptoms. A chronic carrier harbors the pathogen for a long period of time and becomes ill.

5. Zoonosis is a human disease caused by a pathogen that is maintained in an animal reservoir. The microbe for Lyme disease is found in wild mammals such as mice and deer.

6. If an animal reservoir is removed, it can eradicate the human disease.

Two: Getting to and Entering a Host

7. Disease transmission occurs when a pathogen leaves a reservoir and enters the body of a host. There are many modes of transmission listed in Table 15.3 of the text. They include respiratory droplets, fomites, direct contact, fecal-oral, vectors, airborne means, and parenteral.

8. A portal of entry is the anatomical site through which a pathogen enters the body. The most common are the skin, nose, conjunctiva, mouth, urethra, vagina, and placenta.

9. ID50 is the number of microorganisms that must enter the body to establish infection in 50 percent of test animals. LD50 is the number of microorganisms that must enter the body to cause death in 50 percent of test animals.

10. a. Pathogens are transmitted in respiratory droplets by coughing, sneezing, laughing, and talking.

    b. Pathogens are transmitted by fomites, which are inanimate objects such as unsterilized syringes.

    c. Pathogens are transmitted by direct body contact such as touching, kissing, and sexual intercourse.

    d. Pathogens are transmitted by the fecal-oral route from sources of infected feces that pass into the mouth.

    e. Pathogens are transmitted by arthropod vectors, mechanical vectors, or biological vectors. Mechanical vectors pick up the pathogens. Biological vectors are essential links in transmission.

    f. Pathogens can be transmitted from the air if they are inhaled.

g. Pathogens are transmitted by parenteral means if the microbes are deposited directly into blood vessels or tissues below the skin or mucous membranes.

11. More diseases are transmitted by respiratory droplets than any other mode because of the frequent communication among people.

12. There are many examples. Whooping cough is transmitted by respiratory droplets. Fomites transmit blood-borne pathogens. Sexually transmitted diseases are communicated by direct contact. Tuberculosis is one example of an airborne disease.

13. STD is a sexually transmitted disease. Sexually transmitted diseases are transmitted by sexual contact. They are communicable diseases because they are person-to-person diseases.

14. The fecal-oral route can overlap with direct hand-to-hand or mouth-to-mouth vehicles.

15. Vertical transmission can be prenatal and perinatal.

16. A mechanical vector picks up a pathogen for transmission. A biological vector is an essential link, as it plays a role in the life cycle of the microorganism.

17. Deep wounds in the skin introduce microbes into the blood stream, increasing the probability for infection.

Three: Adhering to a Body Surface

18. Pathogens must attach to specific types of target cells by means of adhesins. This is necessary for pathogens and normal body flora.

19. For *Bordetella pertussis* a filamentous hemagglutinin is an adhesin for attachment of the cells to the lining of the respiratory tract. It is not a true adhesin. It does not consist of pili but consists of thin, wavy filaments.

Four: Invading the Body

20. An invasive pathogen penetrates the body's surfaces and enters cells or deeper tissues. A noninvasive pathogen does not do this.

21. An intracellular pathogen enters a host cell and multiplies there. It gains an abundant supply of nutrients from the cell.

22. Some bacteria attach to receptors on the human host cell surface and enter the cell by endocytosis. They can be trapped by vacuoles in the cell. Viruses with envelopes fuse with the human cell's plasma membrane and enter by endocytosis. Eukaryotic modes include the ringworm destroying keratin with enzymes and the malarial protozoan entering human erythrocytes. The helminth that causes hookworm attacks the intestinal lining.

23. Etiology is the study of the cause of human diseases.

24. Koch's postulates are four steps used to provide absolute proof that a particular microorganism causes a disease.

25. Koch's postulates cannot be applied to bacteria that cannot be grown in culture in the lab. One example is the causative agent of syphilis.

26. River's postulates are a series of steps to prove that a virus is the causative agent of a disease.

Five: Evading the Body's Defenses

27. Phagocytosis, cellular eating, is a process by which a cell flows around a microorganism or particle and ingests it. After being pinched off inside the cell, it is often digested intracellularly.

28. Pathogens evade phagocytosis by extracellular capsules and by producing surface proteins.

29. After being phagocytized, *Mycobacterium tuberculosis* wards off digestion by protection through its waxy cell wall.

30. By antigenic variation, a pathogen changes its antigens before they can be recognized by host cells. IgA proteases are enzymes that destroy the antibodies of host cells. By serum resistance, features on the surface of the bacterial cell defeat the complement proteins of the host.

31. Pathogens compete for iron in the human body because very little of it is available in a free form. Pathogens acquire it by iron-binding proteins or by producing iron receptors on their cell surface.

Six: Multiplying in the Host

32. Producing toxic products and damaging the defenses of the body are the two most common ways pathogens cause disease.

33. Exotoxins are very destructive proteins produced by pathogens. Most consist of a B binding component and an A active component. A cell produces exotoxins in response to certain receptors on host cells.

34. Exotoxins affect only tissues where matching receptors exist. A neurotoxin, such as the one causing botulism, exerts its effect only on nervous system cells. An enterotoxin, such as the one causing shigella, affects the epithelial cells lining the intestinal tract.

35. The botulism toxin specifically disrupts nerve cells. The pertussin toxin disrupts the adenylate cyclase system after entering the bloodstream and spreading through the body. It affects many cellular systems.

36. An endotoxin is released only by Gram-negative bacteria. Exotoxins are produced by Gram-negative and Gram-positive bacteria. Endotoxins are not proteins and are not very potent. Endotoxins are also not specific.

37. An endotoxin stimulates host cells to produce messenger proteins. The resulting reactions produce toxic effects in the body. Interleukin-1 is a protein produced by white blood cells to an endotoxin. Tumor necrotizing factor is a protein produced by phagocytes to an endotoxin.

38. An extracellular enzyme is produced by a bacterium and produced outside the cell. Three types are ones that lyse cells (cytolysins), ones that break down materials holding cells together (hyaluronidase), and ones that affect the balance between the formation (coagulases) and destruction of blood clots.

39. The response pathogens can disrupt normal body functions, producing pathogenesis.

40. Cytocidal viral pathogenesis kills the host cells. Cytopathic viral pathogenesis damages the cells but does not kill them.

41. A lytic infection is cytocidal because the host cell is killed after the virus overtakes its metabolism and causes autolysis. A persistent infection is cytopathic as viruses are released from the host cell by budding over many years. A latent infection is cytopathic, as the virus is dormant in the host cell, not producing new viral particles. A cancer-causing infection causes fatal damage to the cell and is cytocidal. The metabolism is taken over by viral nucleic acid and destroyed.

42. Autolysis is destruction in the cell by the production of enzymes. An oncogenic virus causes cancer. Inclusion bodies are viral components accumulated in the cell. Viral genes can cause a cell to be transformed, as it escapes the controls of normal cell division and becomes the seed for a tumor.

Seven: Leaving the Body

43. A portal or exit is an anatomical route through which a pathogen leaves the body. Typical portals are the nose (respiratory), anus (gastrointestinal), mucous membranes of the genital tract for STDs, and by a drop of blood for arthropod-transmitted pathogens.

Answers: Correlation Questions

1. An incubatory carrier is healthy but has not yet developed symptoms for a particular disease. The correct test, however, can establish evidence of a causative microbe in this person's body. Chronic carriers harbor the microbe for years and a history must be worked out over a longer time interval to document this.

2. The widespread distribution of human populations makes human diseases difficult to eradicate.

3. Very small concentrations of exotoxins are highly potent.

4. They probably have different structures for adherence to the different tissue types. They are probably different antigenically, depending on the exact part of the body's immune system they must overcome.

5. *S. pneumoniae* is normally contained locally by a phagocytic attack by white blood cells. *B. pertussis* stops the mucociliary action of the respiratory tract when it adheres to the epithelial lining of the tract. With the loss of this body defense, this bacterium can spread further throughout the tract.

6. Phagocytosis allows a microbe to enter the cell of the host. If the host cannot defeat the microbe intracellularly, the microbe has gained an entry to damage the host cell.

Answers: Essay Questions

1. *Bordetella pertussis* enters the body through the respiratory tract after leaving another human reservoir. It adheres to epithelial cells of the upper respiratory tract and can invade the blood stream. It forms capsules for protection against the immune system responses in the body. The pertussis toxin disrupts the adenylate cyclase system in the body. It exits through the nose of the host.

2. By Koch's postulates the causative microorganism must be isolated, identified, and grown in all cases. Inoculating this pathogen and reisolating it, however, would be difficult steps.

Answers: Discussion Topics

1. The upcoming chapters describe the mechanisms of immunity to fight off the diseases caused by microbes. Begin by studying some of the mechanisms of cellular and humoral immunity.

2. There are many examples. Topics include viral structure, bacterial morphology (e.g., pilus), and Gram-staining. At the midpoint of the text, Chapter 15 allies many topics presented earlier in microbiology.

Answers: Correlation Questions in the Instructor's Manual

1. A chemical control has only as short-lived effectiveness, as the insect population will evolve a resistance to it. Therefore, an insecticide such as DDT is eventually ineffective. On the other hand, a biological control could involve releasing sterile insects into the population. This would serve as a reproductive block to the population and could have longer-lasting results.

2. A wild animal often has a wide ecological range that is difficult to identify completely. The prospect of eliminating every member of the population is difficult.

3. The hypodermis of the skin has the blood flow necessary to circulate the drug to sites in the body where it can function.

4. Blood vessels are always rupturing in the body on a microscopic level. To coagulate escaping blood from these vessels is a normal, ongoing repair process in the body.

Chapter 16

The Immune System: Innate Immunity

Learning Goals

To understand:

The three lines of defense against microbial infection

The steps in the inflammatory response and how inflammation activates and coordinates the body's nonspecific defenses

The different types of leukocytes (white blood cells) and how they contribute to the body's defenses

The steps in phagocytosis and its central role in the body's nonspecific internal defenses

The complement system, including the complement cascade and the classical, alternate, and terminal pathways

Interferon, particularly its role in defending against viral infection

Chapter Outline

The Body's Three Lines of Defense Against Infection
    Fever
The Innate Immune System
    Activation of Complement
    Phagocytes and Phagocytosis
    Inflammation
    Effects of Inflammatory Mediators
    Acute Inflammation
    Inflammatory Repair
Defense Against Viral Infections
    Interferons
    Natural Killer Cells
Summary

Teaching Tips

1. As you teach your students, use the adult human skeleton to locate the sites of hemopoiesis in the human body. Be specific in your references. Show the limited areas where red bone marrow is found in the adult. Point out the specific regions of the axial skeleton and the ends of long bones in the appendicular skeleton.

2. Use prepared slides in lab to study the different kinds of leukocytes. You will need to use the oil-immersion, objective lens to see the differences in cytoplasmic granules and nuclear morphology among the different kinds of white blood cells.

3. Conduct a red blood cell count and total white blood cell count in the lab. Also, consider a differential white blood cell count. Spread out a drop of blood with proper staining on a slide. Tabulate the number of cells for each leukocyte while observing the first 100 cells viewed under the microscope.

4. Students can carry out some calculations on cell counts. For example, if the total white cell count from a subject is 6000 per cubic mm, what is the number of each kind of leukocyte in this sample? Multiply the total number with the percentage of each leukocyte. State the percentages in the classroom for reference. In the case of neutrophils it could be 0.65 x 6000 = _____.

Discussion Topics

1. Often the extracellular fluid of the human body is labeled the internal environment of the body. Explain this reference.

2. The term "homeostasis" refers to maintaining relatively constant conditions in the body's internal environment. How do the three lines of defense against infection contribute to body homeostasis?

Correlation Questions

1. What is the relationship between erythema and phagocytosis?

2. How is the skin a first line of defense compared to second lines of defense?.

3. Are the different kinds of white blood cells different in their genetic makeup? Explain the origin of the variation among them.

4. Prostaglandins are substances produced by the body they function during inflammatory responses. Aspirin targets and inhibits their activity. What result does this have on human body response?

Answers: Review Questions

The Body's Three Lines of Defense Against Infection

1. The first line of defense is surface defenses: structural, mechanical, and biochemical. The second line of defense is the immune system, with the innate immune system part of it. The adaptive immune system is the third line of defense.

2. Most animals have an innate immune system. Animals other than vertebrates lack an adaptive immune system.

3. If a pathogen evades the third line of defense, it causes disease in the body.

The Innate Immune System

4. Leukocytes are white blood cells. The plasma is the liquid, noncellular part of the blood.

5. Complement is a set of microbe-attacking proteins in the blood, lymph, and extracellular fluids.

6. A phagocyte is a type of leukocyte that destroys pathogens by phagocytosis.

Activation of Complement

7. It proceeds through the alternate pathway.

8. They are quickly destroyed by hydrolysis.

9. It enters the terminal complement pathway, which leads to the formation of the membrane-attack complex. It acts as an opsonin. It participates in forming C5a, which attracts phagocytes.

10. It leads to the formation of the membrane-attack complex.

11. It facilitates phagocytosis.

12. It is formed from C3. It attracts phagocytes.

Phagocytes and Phagocytosis

13. Phagocytic cells recognize, engulf, and destroy pathogenic invaders. They expel the resulting bacterial debris.

14. They are macrophages or neutrophils.

15. They are derived from monocytes.

16. Neutrophils circulate in the blood.

17. They recognize molecules on microbial cells that are not present on host cells.

18. Phagocytes are able to recognize specific groups of microorganisms.

19. One receptor recognizes Gram-negative pathogens. Another recognizes the peptidoglycans on the outer surface of Gram-positive bacteria.

20. It is an armlike extension of a phagocyte.

21. The tips of pseudopods fuse and form the membrane of phagosomes.

22. It is a lysosome inside a phagocytic cells that attacks a bacterium. Granules within neutrophils play a similar role.

23. They kill most bacteria in 30 minutes or less.

24. The phagolysosome fuses with the cell membrane and expels debris.

Inflammation

25. They are substances released from macrophages that signal other components of the immune system to attack invaders.

26. Macrophages are the first cells to release cytokines.

27. Interleukin-1 increases access for other leukocytes. Interleukin-6 stimulates the adaptive immune response. Interleukin-8 is a chemotactic factor, attracting leukocytes.

28. The alert the adaptive immune system. Others coordinate and expand the antipathogen activities of the innate immune system. Others cause inflammation.

29. There is swelling, redness, pain, and increased temperature in the inflamed area.

30. Mast cells are attracted to a site of inflammation where they degranulate, releasing more inflammatory mediators.

31. Inflammatory mediators are substances released into damaged tissues by the inflammatory stimulus. They include histamine and kinins. Each causes vasodilation and increased blood vessel permeability.

32. Chronic inflammation is less dramatic that acute inflammation, but it is much more destructive.

Effects of Inflammatory Mediators

33. Inflammatory mediators stimulate the production of other inflammatory mediators, stimulate nerve endings that causes pain, alter capillaries, and attract and stimulate phagocytes.

34. It is redness in a body area by increased blood flow to that area.

35. They dilate blood vessels, bringing more blood to the affected area.

36. The inflamed area is often warm to a person's touch.

37. This minimized swelling to the affected area.

38. It is the adherence of phagocytes to the wall of a capillary.

39. Diapedesis is the migration of white blood cells out of the circulation into the intercellular spaces. Inflammation brings more blood flow to an area, making more white blood cells available for diapedesis to serve an area.

40. Pus consists of dead white blood cells and dead body cells.

Inflammatory Repair

41. Macrophages consume and destroy microbes, dead and dying cells, and foreign participants that have entered a wound. Debris is cleared away from an area so it can regenerate and heal.

Defense Against Viral Infection

42. It produces interferons and natural killer cells.

Interferons

43. Interferon is a group of small proteins that interfere with viral replication. The infection of body cells by a virus stimulates their production.

44. They are useful in treating some rare leukemias.

45. Interferons are antiviral proteins.

Natural Killer Cells

46. They kill infected host cells, stopping the multiplication of the pathogen infecting them.

47. It depends on how viruses change the cells they infect. Viruses that infect cells cause these cells to stop making surface proteins.

48. Repeated viral infections occur in a person lacking NK cells.

Answers: Correlation Questions

1. It is a back-up to the first lines of defense in the body if they fail.

2. It can if the infection leads to conditions stimulating inflammatory mediators.

3. Erythema brings more blood to a body area, offering more phagocytes to protect an area.

4. The complement response is rapid in protecting the body.

5. Cells infected by viruses are stimulated to produce interferon molecules. These molecules are taken up by neighboring cells. These cells produce antiviral proteins that prevent the protein synthesis by viruses. This prevents the spreading of an infection.

6. All of the different kinds of blood cells are derived from a common stem cell. A stem cell population is the starter cell population for all lines of blood cell production. These stem cells are found in the hemopoietic/hematopoietic (blood-forming) tissues in the red bone marrow.

Answers: Essay Questions

1. Treatment may be necessary for a wound on the skin if the symptoms of inflammation develop: swelling, redness, pain, and high temperature. Initial treatment must reduce the severity of these symptoms without suppressing the immune response necessary for fighting infection and promoting healing.

2. If blood cannot reach an area of the body, it cannot bring the variety of leukocytes and phagocytic cells necessary for fighting infection. Therefore, these areas are vulnerable to infection.

Answers: Discussion Topics

1. Although outside the cells, the extracellular fluid (ECF) is within the body. About two-thirds of human body fluid is intracellular. The other one-third, the ECF, consists of the blood plasma and tissue fluid.

2. The body's three lines of defense keep the blood plasma and tissue fluid free of pathogens. Therefore, these lines contribute to maintenance of a normal biota throughout the human body while ridding the body of abnormal, unwanted microbes.

Answers: Correlation Questions in the Instructor's Manual

1. Erythema in a body region indicates increased blood flow to that body region. Blood vessels supplying these body regions dilate. By increasing blood flow to a body region, more phagocytes are available to exit from capillaries and enter the interstitial spaces of that body region, helping to defend it.

2. The skin is a first barrier of protection against invading microbes. However, if it fails in this function, innate lines of defense are the next or second line of defense that these invading microbes must encounter.

3. All body cells have the same genome through mitosis, barring the rare mutation of a somatic cell. Cell specialization, including the development of different white blood cell types, is due to differential gene activation.

4. Prostaglandins are inflammatory mediators. By suppressing their action, aspirin suppresses the inflammatory response. This can be advantageous if the inflammatory response is too powerful, causing pain and harming the body.

Chapter 17
The Immune System: Adaptive Immunity

Learning Goals

To understand:

The components and function of the adaptive immune system

The humoral immune response: how a diversity of antibodies are made by B cells and how they defend us against pathogens

The cell-mediated immune response: how T cells protect us against intracellular pathogens and how they regulate our immune system

Immune tolerance: why our immune system does not attack our own cells and tissues

The types of adaptive immunity: naturally and artificially acquired

How T.L.'s adaptive immune system saved him

Chapter Outline

The Adaptive Immune System: An Overview
    Lymphocytes
    Humoral Immunity
    Cell-mediated Immunity
    Lymphoid Tissues
    Antigens
The Humoral Immune Response
    Generating Antibody Diversity
    Structure of Antibodies
    B-Cell Activation
    Reactivation: Immunological Memory
    Action of Antibodies
The Cell-Mediated Response
    Antigen Recognition
    T-Cell Activation
    T-Cell Response
Natural Killer Cells
Immune Tolerance
Types of Adaptive Immunity
The Role of the Adaptive Immune System in T.L.'s Recovery
Summary

Teaching Tips

1. Continue to answer the review questions, correlation questions, and essay questions at the end of the chapters. Use some class time to discuss the answers with the students.

2. Use a human torso model to locate and explain the functions of the primary and secondary lymphoid organs.

3. A fresh long bone can be acquired at the local meat market. Bring it to class and section it, revealing the location of bone marrow and stem cells.

4. After your lecture, ask your students to outline the mechanisms of cellular and humoral immunity. For review, list three similarities and three differences between the two processes.

5. Encourage your students to carry out an Internet search with the key term: *stem cells*.

Discussion Topics

1. How does autoimmunity against a structure (e.g., nephrons of the kidney or cornea of the eye) develop in the human body?

2. How is the concept of cell specialization presented in this chapter?

Correlation Questions

1. What is the advantage of a pentamer structure in an antibody?

2. How does a knowledge of cell structure help in recognizing the different kinds of immune cells?

3. Does the term *stem cells* have a meaning beyond the meaning used when studying the immune system?

4. Can the administration of a vaccine be dangerous to a person's health? How?

Answers: Review Questions

The Adaptive Immune System: An Overview

1. The adaptive immune system is a network of cells, particularly lymphocytes. and lymphoid tissues throughout the body. It functions as the last line of defense against infection. It is slow to act initially. However, its response is quicker and more powerful upon a subsequent exposure to the same microorganims. The three kinds are B lymphocytes, T lymphocytes, and natural killer cells.

2. Humoral immunity is also called antibody-mediated immunity. B cells respond to antigens by producing defensive proteins called antibodies.

3. T cells carry out cell-mediated immunity. They respond to antigens that appear on the surface of pathogen-infected cells. They differentiate into a wide variety of types, such as helper T cells, to defend against various foreign agents that attack the body.

4. The primary lymphoid organs are the bone marrow and thymus. All blood cells, including B and T lymphocytes, are formed from stem cells of the bone marrow. B cells differentiate in the bone marrow. T cells differentiate in the thymus gland.

    The secondary lymphoid organs include the lymph nodes and spleen. They are storage sites for fully differentiated lymphocytes. They are also the sites where B and T cells interact and become activated to attack invading pathogens.

5. The lymphatic circulation begins with lymph capillaries that collect lymph at the tissue spaces. These capillaries combine into larger lymphatic vessels that form larger vessels including the thoracic duct. The lymph nodes are found with lymphatic vessels along the pathway of lymph circulation. The vessels combine the lymph with the blood near the heart. The lymph nodes produce lymphocytes and filter out debris. The phagocytic cells in the nodes help to fight infection.

6. An antigen is a foreign molecule to the body. An antibody is a molecule that can react with the antigen and destroy it.

The Humoral Immune Response

7. B cells cut and rejoin gene fragments into different combinations. They have their own genes through genetic differentiation.

8. Antigenic binding sites on antibodies bind with antigen molecules, producing clumps that inactivate the antigens.

9. The fit between antigens and antibodies is somewhat variable.

10. Resting B cells can bind to an antigen, leading to many changes. B cells multiply and undergo additional differentiation. They produce quantities of soluble antibody. The result is a clone of cells that make an effective form of the same antibody. Some members of this clone differentiate to become effector cells. They are plasma cells that produce huge quantities of antibodies to fight a current infection.

11. They are dedicated to producing lymphocytes that stimulate and regulate differentiation and antibody-production by B cells.

12. Lymphokines are small signal proteins produced by lymphocytes. They are necessary for the continued proliferation of B lymphocytes during B cell activation.

13. By immunological memory, memory B cells continue to circulate within the body and retain their ability to recognize the same antigen if they encounter it again. This greatly accelerates a secondary immune response.

14. As clonal selection produces a group of identical B cells to fight an infection, plasma cells are effector cells that produce large quantities of antibody to fight a current infection.

15. The linking activity of antigens forms large clumps of molecules when they react and bind with antibodies. This inactivates the antigens.

16. An antibody has a Y shape called an antibody monomer. The monomer consists of two heavy glycoprotein chains and two light glycoprotein chains. There are two antigen-binding sites on the ends of the arms of the Y. These sites are variable. The rest of the arms and the stem of the Y are constant. As the monomers have two antigen binding sites, they are divalent. An antibody must have a valence of two to be immunogenic.

17. IgG (75%) act as opsonin and activate complement. IgA (15 - 20 %) protect mucosal surfaces. IgM (5 - 10%) are the early antibodies produced during the primary immune response. IgD (less than 1%) have an unknown function. IgE (less than 0.01 %) stimulate cells to degranulate.

The Cell-mediated Immune Response

18. T cells control infections within cells. This is a capability that B cells do not have.

19. T-cell recognition occurs when T cells produce antigen-receptor molecules that bind foreign antigens and therefore cause recognition to occur.

20. T cells divide to produce lymphokines. Each lymphokine has a particular role. Interleukin-1, for example, is an inflammatory mediator.

21. An infected cell is marked as a target for TC cells. A TC cell with a complementary antigenic receptor encounters and binds to the displayed viral antigen.

22. Human cells, usually macrophages, can signal that they have been infected by a bacterium.

23. Receptors on TH cells bind to antigen-class II MHC. The bound TH cell releases lymphokines that stimulate the infected cell to kill the bacteria it contains.

24. TH cells stimulate the cell to kill invader bacteria through phagocytosis.

25. MHC proteins are on the surface of all nucleated cells of the human body. They are antigenic when introduced into the body of another person. MHC class I proteins play a role in T cell response to virus-infected cells. MHC class II proteins hold antigen fragments on antigen presenting cells.

Natural Killer Cells

26. These cells function without recognizing antigens. They lack the markers that recognize B and T cells.

27. They lyse human target cells.

28. They destroy cells that have been coated with antibody. Their antibody-direct attack is nonspecific. They cannot distinguish amongst antibodies.

Immune Tolerance

29. The immune system in a person's body does not normally treat its own molecules as antigenic. If it did, it would destroy its own makeup.

30. Differentiating B and T cells are killed by the body's own proteins early in development. This prevents them from establishing an immune line against the body's own biochemical makeup.

31. Apoptosis is programmed cell death. Immune cells that could destroy the body's own chemical makeup are killed early in development by this process.

Types of Adaptive Immunity

32. By active immunity, the body produces its own defense cells and molecules. By passive immunity a person acquires antibodies.

33. Naturally acquired active immunity develops from infections encountered in daily life. Artificially acquired active immunity develops from vaccination. Naturally acquired passive immunity refers to antibodies transferred from mother to fetus. Artificially acquired passive immunity refers to antibodies formed by an animal or human, administered to prevent or treat infection.

Answers: Correlation Questions

1. B cells cannot be distinguished from T cells by structure. Different kinds of T cells can be distinguished by different functions.

2. Upon a subsequent exposure to an antigen, the immune response is quicker with higher antibody concentrations.

3. B cells change into plasma cells that make antibodies. These molecules defeat viruses by humoral immunity. T cells incorporate viruses and defeat them intracellularly.

4. TC cells fight virus-infected cells. TH cells fight bacteria-infected cells.

5. A soluble antigen would not be affixed to a cell. Congregated cells form clumps.

6. Passive immunity would not establish an immunologic memory to defeat the virus.

Answers: Essay Questions

1. The nonspecific defenses, such as the skin, are the body's first line of defense to fight infection. If defeated, the body's immune system is the last line of defense for infection.

2. Each antibody has a unique capability. One type is specific to fight allergies. Another is specific for the primary immune response.

Answers: Discussion Topics

1. The particular line of immune cells is not eliminated through clonal deletion early in development. If this line of cells survives, it can carry out an immune response against a unique protein in the cornea or kidney. This is an autoimmune response.

2. Refer to the wide variety of T cells as one example. Although they are derived from a source with identical genetic makeup, they develop unique abilities based on differential gene expression. The wide production of antibodies by B lymphocytes is another example through genetic recombination.

Answers: Correlation Questions in the Instructor's Manual

1. A pentamer has numerous binding sites, allowing it to combine and inactivate more antigen molecules.

2. Each immune cell has a distinct morphology, ranging from the shape of the nucleus to the appearance of the cytoplasm. Staining properties of the nucleus and cytoplasm can be distinctive.

3. Stem cell research, currently in the new, refers to immature, undifferentiated cells in the fetus.

4. Rarely, an attenuated form of a virus can be potent enough to be virulent to a person's immune system.

Chapter 18
Immunological Disorders

Learning Goals

To understand:

How abnormal or misdirected immune responses, called hypersensitivity, can harm the body

The basis of type I hypersensitivity and its relationship to allergy

The basis of type II hypersensitivity and its relationship to blood transfusion and certain autoimmune diseases

The basis of type III hypersensitivity and its relationship to certain autoimmune diseases

The basis of type IV hypersensitivity and its relationship to tissue transplantation, contact dermatitis, and granulomatous infections

Congenital and acquired immunodeficiency disorders

How failure of immune surveillance might lead to cancer

Chapter Outline

Immune System Malfunctions
Hypersensitivity
    Type I: Anaphylactic Hypersensitivity (Allergy)
    Type II: Cytotoxic Hypersensitivity
    Type III: Immune-Complex Hypersensitivity
    Type IV: Cell-Mediated (Delayed) Hypersensitivity
Organ Transplantation
    Immunosuppression
    Immunodeficiencies
    Congenital Immunodeficiencies
    Acquired Immunodeficiencies
Cancer and the Immune System
Summary

Teaching Tips

1. Continue to assign the several kinds of questions listed at the end of each chapter.

2. Invite a local health professional to your class to discuss the treatment of the various kinds of hypersensitivities discussed in this chapter.

3. Students can study the transverse sections of blood vessels and bronchioles in lab. Knowledge of this histology will help the students understand how these structures dilate and constrict.

4. Use artificial blood kits in lab to demonstrate the agglutination reactions of the ABO and Rh antigen-antibody systems.

5. Continue to use the human torso model in class. Point out such structures as the thymus gland, spleen, and lymph nodes.

Discussion Topics

1. The thymus gland tends to atrophy in the human adult. Can you explain this pattern of development? How do you think this affects the functioning of the immune system in the adult?

2. Does the cross-matching of human blood, to prevent the agglutination of recipient blood during blood transfusion, only involve the ABO and Rh antigen-antibody systems? What are the others?

Correlation Questions

1. How can research in the field of endocrinology advance the treatment for Grave's disease?

2. Blood types O and AB are often referred to as the universal donor and recipient respectively for blood transfusions. How are these descriptions inaccurate?

3. How is the Rh blood typing system simpler to understand compared to the ABO blood typing system?

4. How can research in the field of angiogenesis reveal possible treatments for cancer?

Answers: Review Questions

Immune System Malfunctions

1. An immunologic disorder is caused by a malfunction of the immune system. An inadequate or inappropriate immune response results. An immunodeficiency results from the failure to mount an adequate immune response, leading to recurrent infection.

Hypersensitivity

2. Hypersensitivity is an exaggerated and/or damaging immune response carried out by the body. The four types are anaphylactic (Type I), cytotoxic (Type II), immune-complex (Type III), and cell-mediated (Type IV).

3. Anaphylactic hypersensitivity is immediate because its symptoms develop rapidly. Its more common name is allergy.

4. In anaphylactic hypersensitivity the immune system produces antibodies against a foreign antigen. This sets the stage for a harmful reaction the next time the antigen is encountered by the immune system. B cells and T cells produce IgE. As the antibody attaches to mast cells, histamine and other powerful inflammatory mediators are released. The basophils and mast cells degranulate.

5. The signs and symptoms of anaphylactic hypersensitivity are dilating blood vessels and constricting bronchiole passages. There are also the local signs of inflammation. SRS-A constricts the smooth muscle of the bronchioles. Exposure of a sensitizing agent, such as phospholipase a, starts the stimulation of B and T cells and causes anaphylactic shock. The treatment for this component of insect venom is the administration of epinephrine to constrict blood vessels and relax the smooth muscle in the bronchioles.

6. Penicillin is an injected allergen. Pollen and mold spores contain inhaled allergens. Ingested allergens include medications and foods such as shellfish and peanuts.

7. Hay fever develops when an inhaled allergen triggers mast cells in the mucous membranes of the nasal cavity. Inflammatory mediators are released that cause tissue swelling and excess mucous production. Antihistamines are used to reverse the effects of histamine.

   Asthma develops when inhaled allergens affect the lower respiratory tract, leading to edema and swelling of the respiratory passages. The bronchioles constrict. Inflammatory mediators other than histamine are involved. Inhalation of epinephrine drugs is used to prevent these symptoms.

8. Penicillin can become an inhaled allergen. Repeated exposure can enhance the anaphylactic reaction each time it occurs.

   The drug is a hapten that combines with human albumin. IgE antibodies can react against this combination and bind to mast cells or basophils, leading to adverse reactions.

9. By cytotoxic hypersensitivity IgM and IgG antibodies bind abnormally to antigens on the surface of human cells. This can activate complement and lyse target cells through the terminal complement pathway. In other cases antibodies and activated complement attract and activate human leukocytes that attack and damage marked human cells. Usually the binding of antibodies to human cells alters functions of human cells but does not kill them.

10. The ABO antigen system has two antigens, A and B. The antigen content on the surface of erythrocytes names the blood type: O with neither antigen, A with the A antigen, B with the B antigen, and AB with both antigens present. AB is the universal recipient because both antibodies are lacking to react against an A or B antigen. O is the universal donor because no antigen is present to react against an antibody.

11. Immunologic incompatibility occurs when the antigen of the donor and antibody of the recipient match by letter. The result is an agglutination reaction. This leads to a transfusion reaction with symptoms of fever, vomiting, and shock. Cross matching of blood is done to assure that an agglutination reaction does not occur in a recipient receiving blood.

12. By the Rh system of blood typing, a person is Rh positive if the Rh factor is on the surface of erythrocytes. If absent, the person is Rh negative. It is important to check to be certain that Rh blood types are compatible for transfusion. A hemolytic disease occurs if a sensitized Rh negative mother reacts against the blood of an Rh positive newborn. An exchange transfusion removes the blood from a newborn in this case to prevent damaging agglutination reactions.

13. In an autoimmune disorder a person's antibodies react against substances of the same body as antigens. In Goodpasture's syndrome the body produces antibodies against antigens of the kidney. This fixes complement and attracts activated leukocytes, yielding a destructive inflammatory reaction. In Grave's disease autoantibodies bind to the cells that produce the thyroid hormone. The antibodies stimulate hormone production.

14. In type III hypersensitivity the antigens are free in circulation. In type II the antigens are bound to cells or tissues. In type III, antibodies bind to circulating antigens and form soluble complexes. Hugh numbers of complexes can overwhelm the macrophages. This activates complement and provokes an inflammatory response.

15. SLE is an autoimmune disease because autoantibodies are produced against antigens in the cell nucleus. Antigen-antibody complexes are lodged in the body, stimulating complement and leukocytes. This stimulates a chronic destructive inflammatory response.

16. The threat of SLE can short-circuit the essential immune response.

17. In addition to self antigens, type III hypersensitivity can be provoked by microbial antigens and antigens from plants and animals. Rheumatoid arthritis and serum sickness are other examples of type III hypersensitivity.

18. Type IV hypersensitivity is unique because it does not involve antibodies. It is called delayed hypersensitivity because a reaction occurs 12 hours to several weeks after exposure.

19. In type IV reactions an antigen is presented to TD cells that have a matching antibody receptor. The TD cell proliferates to form an activated clone. The person is sensitized. If exposed to the antigen again, the TD cells release lymphokines that stimulate macrophages and provoke inflammation.

20. During organ transplants, the T cells react against antigenic substances in the transplanted organ. In a graft-versus-host disease a recipient's immune system is destroyed by radiation. T cells from the donor's marrow attack the recipient's cells.

21. An autograft is a graft from one part of a person's body to another part. An isograft is between genetically identical individuals. An allograft is between genetically different members of the same species. A xenograft is from a nonhuman primate to a human.

22. Histocompatibility is the antigenic compatibility between tissues. The antigens are encoded by a group of genes. A person's tissue type is a constellation of HLA antigens. It is determined by mixing antigen-bearing lymphocytes with complement and antisera that contain monoclonal antibodies. A match for antigens and antibodies is examined.

23. Organ rejection is blocked by the use of immunosuppressive drugs or the use of cyclosporine to suppress the immune response.

24. Contact hypersensitivity is when dermatitis develops from exposure to certain compounds. Exposure to urushiol in poison ivy is one example.

25. Exposure to poison ivy may not yield an immediate reaction because the haptens from the substance may require time to combine with proteins that sensitize TD cells. Subsequent reexposure to the same agent can cause more combinations and a potent reaction.

26. The tuberculin skin test requires TD cells initiating an inflammatory response. This causes lymphocytes and macrophages to accumulate but this requires two to three days.

27. A granulomatous reaction is a delayed hypersensitivity reaction. Microbial antigens persist in a macrophage. Lymphokines are released and stimulate the production of granuloma. A continuing inflammation develops.

Immunodeficiency Disorders

28. Immunodeficiency disorders are categorized as defects in T-cell function, B-cell function, both T-cell and B-cell function, phagocyte function, and complement.

29. a. In SCID the B-cell and T-cell immunities are disabled due to deficiencies of these cells.

    b. In X-linked agammaglobulinemia patients cannot produce antibodies due to an absence of B cells.

    c. In DiGeorge's syndrome T cells do not differentiate.

    d. In chronic granulomatous disease there is a deficiency in phagocyte function.

    e. In C5 dysfunction there is abnormal function of the C5 complement protein.

30. Patients with long-term therapy of systemic steroids and patients with leukemias and lymphomas are at high risk for acquired immunodeficiencies. In AIDS a retrovirus affects the function and survival of TH cells.

Cancer and the Immune System

31. In transformation cancer cells experience uncontrolled multiplication. A tumor is a large growth of cancer cells. Tumor-specific antigens mark cancer cells for destruction.

32. By the immune surveillance theory the immune system eliminates malignant cells before they cause cancer. People with defective immune systems are at high risk for cancer. By immunologic escape tumors with cancer antigens cause disease in healthy people. Small numbers of cancer cells may not stimulate an effective immune response.

33. Cancer immunotherapy uses the products of the immune system to treat cancer. Interferons are used, for example, to treat certain kinds of blood cancer.

Answers: Correlation Questions

1. Asthma is an inhaled allergy that affects the lower respiratory tract. There are other kinds of classical type I hypersensitivity reactions. Irritants and viral infections can cause asthma.

2. The autoantibodies from the mother would be transferred from the mother to the baby. Therefore, this is not advisable.

3. A person with type O blood has both the A and the B antibodies. Therefore, this person would react against the antigens of an AB blood type.

4. The agent causing contact dermatitis leads can be washed away with the proper detergent within fifteen minutes of contact. An allergy cannot be prevented this way.

5. The viral flu vaccine could stimulate some of the same memory cells that oppose bacteria.

6. The immunotoxin may have a unique chemical identity to kill the tumor cells. Also, the tumor cells may have mutated compared to their original line and respond differently.

Answers: Essay Questions

1. Examples you could pick include someone who had hay fever or asthma. Read the information on Type I hypersensitivity at the beginning of the chapter for background.

2. Start with Internet sources. Desensitization allows a person to resist substantial substances of a foreign substance without experiencing anaphylaxis. If substantial concentrations of IgE antibodies do not develop, however, it may not be effective.

Answers: Discussion Topics

1. The thymus gland, located in the mediastinum of the human body, atrophies during human development. However, by the teenage years, other body sites have developed to process T cells.

2. There are dozens of human antigen-antibody systems in the human body that must be checked for cross-matching. Refer to hematology texts to discuss such systems as the MN antigen-antibody system.

Answers: Correlation Questions in the Instructor's Manual

1. Grave's disease develops from hyperactivity of the thyroid gland. Treatment depends on slowing down the activity of the gland and/or diminishing the concentration of the thyroid hormone secreted by this gland.

2. There are other blood typing systems that must be cross matched between donor and recipient in addition to the ABO blood typing systems.

3. The Rh system has only one antigen and one antibody compared to two of each for the ABO blood typing system. A person is either Rh positive (Rh factor present) or Rh negative (Rh factor absent).

4. Cancer cells will not divide as rapidly if deprived of the blood supply needed to nourish these new cells. Inhibiting angiogenesis, the development of new blood vessels, is a strategy to stop cancerous growth.

Chapter 19
Diagnostic Immunology

Learning Goals

To understand:

How antigen-antibody reactions can be used to diagnose diseases

The methods for detecting antigen-antibody reactions—precipitation, agglutination, and complement fixation

The procedures for performing various immunoassays including radioimmunoassays, immunofluorescence assays, and enzyme-linked immunosorbent assays (ELISA)

The uses of fluorescent antibodies

Chapter Outline

Diagnostic Immunology
Detecting Antigen-Antibody Reactions
    Precipitation Reactions
    Agglutination Reactions
    Complement Fixation Reactions
Immunoassays
Fluorescent Antibodies
Summary

Teaching Tips

1. Do you know a faculty member who conducts research with antigen-antibody reactions or who conducts immunoassays? Invite this person as a guest speaker.

2. The human pregnancy test uses monoclonal antibodies. Use this as a demonstration in the lab component of your course.

3. Use molecular models to demonstrate the various bonding patterns between antigens and antibodies.

4. Visit the Internet to find animations on antigen-antibody reactions.

Discussion Topics

1. What are some of the practical uses of diagnostic immunology?

2. What is the difference between the serum and plasma of the blood?

Correlation Questions

1. Autoimmunity has often been explained as the inability of the human body to distinguish between self and nonself. Explain.

2. Is an agglutination test performed on a slide (e.g., ABO blood typing) qualitative or quantitative?

3. Can a precipitation reaction occur if the antigen and antibody involved each have only one binding site?

4. When is a qualitative diagnostic test preferable to a quantitative diagnostic test?

Answers: Review Questions

Diagnostic Immunology

1. Serology is the diagnostic testing of antibodies of the serum, which is the cell-free part of the blood.

2. Monoclonal antibodies are identical antibodies against one specific epitope. Their use gives highly specific, reliable results for detecting antigens.

Detecting Antigen-Antibody Reactions

3. A precipitation reaction occurs when free antigen and antibody molecules combine to form lattices, an interlocking web in solution.

4. The zone of equivalence is the range of proportions, between antigen and antibody, at which a lattice can form in a precipitation reaction. If either the antigen or antibody is in excess amount, a lattice will not form.

5. Antigens and antibodies diffuse in a gel, forming concentration gradients. Where gradients overlap, there is a zone of equivalence. A precipitate forms here as a visible sharp line.

6. A double diffusion reaction determines whether two antigens are similar, identical, or different.

7. A spur develops where two antigens have the same epitopes, indicated in a double diffusion reaction.

8. A radial diffusion reaction estimates the relative concentration of an antigen.

9. In an immunoelectrophoresis test, antigens are separated by the identity and size of the charges of the antigen molecules.

10. Antigens separated by immunoelectrophoresis are transferred onto a sheet of nitrocellulose. If the antigen is present, a labeled antibody will combine with it, forming a blot.

11. In an agglutination reaction the antigens and antibodies involved are attached to large particles, such as cells. Antigens and antibodies are not attached this way in a precipitation reaction.

12. An agglutination reaction that uses red blood cells is called hemagglutination.

13. The term "titer" refers to the concentration of an antibody, which may rise with the development of an infection. With this increasing antibody concentration, the agglutination reaction to detect the antibody will also become more prominent.

14. When antigen-antibody reactions occur, complement binds to them. By binding, the complement is fixed. This indicates the reaction.

Immunoassays

15. Tags for immunoassays include radioactive compounds, enzymes, and fluorescent compounds.

16. Various plastics bind a layer of protein to their surface. By binding one of the reactants to their surface, the antigen-antibody product will also be bound. The unused reactant will be washed away.

17. ELISA stands for enzyme-linked immunosorbent assays.

18. ELISA can detect very small quantities of antibodies against test antigens.

19. ELISA is used effectively for a wide variety of tests, ranging from viral hepatitis to rotavirus infections.

Fluorescent Antibodies

20. Fluorescent antibodies are used to visualize specific antigens in tissues or on the surface of microorganisms. They also separate different antigens on different cells in mixture.

21. A fluorescent antibody is irradiated with invisible ultra violet light. Depending on its makeup, it shows a distinct color.

Correlation Questions

1. If the antigen diffuses more slowly than the antibody, the precipitation line will lie closer to the antigen well.

2. In a radial diffusion test, antibody is incorporated uniformly throughout the gel. The antigen from a well diffuses into this gel, forming a ring when precipitation occurs.

3. If too much complement were added in a complement fixation reaction, the excess complement would not be fixed, as it would not react with the antigen-antibody.

4. Without gelatin in the ELISA, the uncoated surface in the well would not be blocked. Without this, the complementary antibody could not bind to the antigen.

5. If the bacterial cells stain differently by this technique, they can be distinguished in a mixture of cells.

6. The albumin and IgM molecule probably have opposite charges and, therefore, migrate to opposite poles of an electrical field.

Answers: Essay Questions

1. DNA probes are remarkably accurate. Immunological-based tests have wide applicability.

2. Immunological-based tests are used to detect the specific antibodies for many different kinds of microorganisms. Because of their specificity, they have diagnostic value.

Answers: Discussion Topics

1. There is diagnostic value to this branch of science. As one example, start with diagnosing hepatitis A by identifying the antibodies that the human body makes against the virus causing the disease.

2. Plasma is the complete liquid part of the blood. Serum is similar to plasma, except that it does not have the components used by the blood for blood coagulation.

Answers: Correlation Questions in the Instructor's Manual

1. In autoimmunity, part of a person's own biochemical makeup is sensed as foreign. Therefore there is a lack of ability to detect self, one's own makeup, from nonself or foreign bodies.

2. It is qualitative, as it is based on detecting the presence of a product and not its exact quantity.

3. Each kind of molecule needs at least two binding sites to form a molecular lattice.

4. A qualitative test is needed to detect the presence or absence of a substance without measuring the exact amount of the substance present.

Chapter 20
Preventing Disease

Learning Goals

To understand:

How epidemiology contributes to our understanding of disease

How epidemiologists collect information and why statistics are central to epidemiology

The types and uses of epidemiology—descriptive epidemiology, surveillance epidemiology, field epidemiology, and hospital epidemiology

How public health organizations help prevent disease

How controlling reservoirs and disease transmission helps prevent disease

The types and uses of vaccines

Chapter Outline

Preventing Disease
Epidemiology
    The Methods of Epidemiology
    Types of Epidemiological Studies
Public Health
    Public Health Organizations
    Limiting Exposure to Pathogenic Microorganisms
Immunization
    Active Immunization
    Passive Immunization
Summary

Teaching Tips

1. Arrange a field trip to a local hospital. A health professional there can explain the safeguards taken to prevent the development of nosocomial infections.

2. Invite a professional from the local health department to visit your class and explain the current procedures used to prevent diseases.

3. Assign some practice problems to calculate incidence rates and prevalence rates. For example, if 6 people per 100,000 develop a disease, what is the incidence rate when expressed as a percentage?

4. Place some recently published articles on reserve from the CDC and MMWR. Encourage each student in your class to read several of these articles and submit a synopsis on the content of the articles.

Discussion Topics

1. Why are some diseases specific for humans while not developing in other animal species?

2. Visit the Web site quoted in the chapter on DNA vaccines. What potential does this breakthrough hold for improving the prevention of diseases?

Correlation Questions

1. Prevalence rates are particularly high for long-lasting diseases. Explain.

2. What branches of epidemiology are relevant to the subject of ecology?

3. What is the advantage of active immunization compared to passive immunization?

4. What is the advantage of passive immunization compared to active immunization?

Answers: Review Questions

Preventing Disease

1. In epidemiology, the focus is on populations. Epidemiology is the study of when and where diseases occur and how they are transmitted in human populations. The field of public health uses information from epidemiology to carry out effective programs.

2. An epidemic is a pattern of disease transmission that affects many members of a population in a short time period. An epidemic is pandemic if it spreads worldwide. An endemic disease is always present in a population at the same level. A sporadic disease occurs only occasionally in a population.

Epidemiology

3. Reliable sources of information determine the accuracy and success of epidemiology studies. Vital statistics give information on births, deaths, and other human events. A census offers age distributions and other useful facts. Other sources of information include physician records, public health records, and journal records.

4. Notifiable diseases are reportable diseases. The CDC is the Centers for Disease Control and Prevention. It receives reports of local public health statistics. The MMWR is the *Morbidity and Mortality Weekly Report*. It offers weekly and cumulative annual statistics on reportable diseases in the United States.

5. Statistics offers quantifiable verification to epidemiology studies.

6. A rate is the ratio of the number of people in a particular category to the total number of people in the population being studied. Incidence rate is the number of people who develop a disease or condition during a certain period of time. Prevalence rate is the incidence rate times the average

duration of an illness. The age-adjusted rate is the death rate for a particular age group. A rate, such as an age-adjusted rate, offers a basis for comparison.

7. A retrospective study analyzes events that have already occurred. A prospective study records events as they happen and then analyzes them. An experimental study has events deliberately influenced by the investigator.

8. Descriptive epidemiology provides general information about a disease. Overcrowding, poor nutrition and health, alcoholism, and AIDS are conditions for the survival and spread of the bacterium causing tuberculosis.

9. Surveillance epidemiology used information to track epidemic diseases. It directed the organization needed to vaccinate people against smallpox worldwide.

10. Field epidemiologists track down the spread of a disease and devise means to eradicate it.

11. The most common kinds of nosocomial infections are urinary tract infections from enteric microorganisms, surgical wound infections from *Staphylococcus aureus*, and pneumonias from *Streptococcus* and *Staphylococcus* species.

12. A hospital epidemiologist recognizes a possible hospital infection, isolates infected patients, and prevents the spread of the infection. Universal precautions include confining and treating infected patients while eradicating the source of the hospital disease.

Public Health

13. Local health departments, state health departments with news letters, the United States Public Health Service, and the World Health Organization all contribute to the work of scientists and clinicians of public health.

14. Prophylaxis is the prevention of disease, a main goal of public health. The principal methods of prophylaxis are limiting exposure to pathogens, eliminating the pathogen's reservoir, and by interrupting disease transmission.

15. Water can have sewage removed to prevent bacterial and viral disease. Canning and cooking make food safer for consumption. Milk is pasteurized. Personal cleanliness removes microbes from the skin and other body surfaces. Insect control has removed the vectors for malaria and yellow fever. STDs can be controlled by blocking the chain of transmission of the microbe causing the disease. Respiratory diseases such as diphtheria can be controlled by isolating infected individuals.

Immunization

16. Immunization is the stimulation of a person's immune system by active or passive methods. A vaccine is a preparation that stimulates active immunity without causing the disease. A vaccine is immunogenic if it stimulates the immune response to confer protection against natural infection. Herd immunity is the prevention of epidemics due to the scarcity of new susceptible hosts.

17. Active immunization stimulates immunity in a person's body through, for example, introduction of an attenuated vaccine. Passive immunization introduces the antibodies into the human body.

18. Good vaccines do not cause disease, but they do stimulate immunity in a high percentage of cases.

19. An attenuated vaccine is a weakened strain of a microorganism that stimulates active immunity. However, it might also cause the disease. An inactivated vaccine has killed microorganisms. However, it may also have destroyed antigens needed to stimulate the immune response.

20. Genetic engineering has provided a whole cell vaccine for pertussis. It provides only the antigens that stimulate the needed immunity without including antigens that are harmful. Genetic engineering has produced a safer vaccine for hepatitis B. Genetic engineering has cloned the bacteria that produce different diseases. Often these bacteria cannot be cultured in the lab.

21. DNA in a vaccine can encode for antigens that stimulate the immune system. Therefore, the injected person makes the vaccine naturally.

22. Toxoid vaccines have toxins modified so they are immunogenic but harmless. Examples are ones for tetanus and diphtheria.

23. More immunization is needed to completely eradicate some diseases in the United States. This is particularly true among adults.

24. By passive immunization antibodies are not made but are transferred into a person. It can be immediately effective but the effect is not long-lasting. It is used in treating diseases that cannot currently be treated by an effective vaccine or when immediate treatment is necessary. Building up one's own active immunity takes time.

25. Gamma globulin is a collection of antibodies pooled from many different donors. Tetanus immune globulin has a high concentration of antibodies against tetanus toxin.

Answers: Correlation Questions

1. The prevalence rate is the incidence rate times the average duration of an illness. The duration is longer for AIDS compared to cholera. Therefore, the prevalence rate for cholera is also greater.

2. An increased incidence rate means that the rate of acquiring a disease is increasing. If it continues to increase, the disease could reach epidemic proportions.

3. An incidence rate is based on a per 100,000 individual basis. This statistic can be expressed as a percentage. Therefore, it uses the same basis of comparison for populations of varying sizes.

4. The number of affected members must be related to a time interval to differentiate between endemic and epidemic diseases. Endemic diseases are always present in a population. Epidemic diseases affect many population members over a short time interval.

5.   Prevalence rate and incidence rates allow one to determine the duration of a disease. If, for example, the prevalence rate is significantly greater than the incidence rate for a disease, the disease has a long duration.

6.   Passive immunization offers only a short-term treatment for a disease and does not represent a long-term solution.

Answers: Essay Questions

1.   The Snow study found the source of cholera and eliminated it.

2.   People of different age groups may have different susceptibilities to a disease. They may also need to be treated differently.

Answers: Discussion Topics

1.   The key must reside in the different genetic blueprints in different species. This programs different immune systems with different capabilities.

2.   Visit the Internet site. Try to compose a list of diseases that potentially will be treated through this technology. Use it as a basis for class discussion.

Answers: Correlation Questions in the Instructor's Manual

1.   A long-lasting disease occurs over a long time span. The probability of a disease occurring during a long time frame is greater than in a short time frame.

2.   Field and surveillance epidemiology depend on investigation of ecosystems.

3.   Active immunization can confer long-lasting immunity but it requires time to develop.

4.   Passive immunization can confer quick immunity but its effect is usually not long-lasting.

Chapter 21
Pharmacology

Learning Goals

To understand:

How antimicrobial drugs are selected and administered

How drugs become distributed throughout the body and eliminated from it

How antimicrobial drugs act and how microorganisms become resistant to them

How microbial sensitivity to drugs is tested

The properties of the drugs commonly used to treat bacterial, mycobacterial, fungal, parasitic, and viral infections

Chapter Outline

Principles of Pharmacology
    Drug Administration
    Drug Distribution
    Eliminating Drugs from the Body
    Side Effects and Allergies
    Drug Resistance
    Drug Dosage
Targets of Antimicrobial Drugs
    The Cell Wall
    Cell Membranes
    Protein Synthesis
    Nucleic Acids
    Folic Acid Synthesis
Antimicrobial Drugs
    Antibacterial Drugs
    Antimycobacterial Drugs
    Antifungal Drugs
    Antiparasitic Drugs
    Antimalarial Drugs
    Antiviral Drugs
    Interferons
Summary

Teaching Tips

1. Use a human torso model in class to show the most common sites for IV and IM administration of drugs.

2. Most of your students should have taken courses in human anatomy and physiology. Review the processes of blood circulation and GI tract absorption to emphasize the physiological processes that transport drugs and account for their assimilation in the human body.

3. Use the lab component of your course to study the disc-diffusion and broth-dilution methods explained in this chapter.

4. Apart from the information in Table 21-3, assign a project whereby the students study the antimicrobial drugs in the chapter and compose their own table for drug comparison.

5. Continue to assign the review, correlation, and essay questions at the end of each chapter. Make the answers the focus of a chapter review in class when you complete teaching the unit.

6. Encourage your students to type in the search term *pharmacology* on the Internet and begin a search on this topic.

Discussion Topics

1. How do the previously studied units of cell structure and biochemistry contribute to the concepts of pharmacology?

2. Protease inhibitors are advertised frequently to treat human GI tract problems. What is their mode of action?

Correlation Questions

1. A protein drug will be ineffective if administered orally. Why?

2. For the most rapid results in the body, what is the best method for administrating a drug into the human body?

3. Under what conditions is a narrow-spectrum drug a good choice to treat a microbial infection?

4. Under what conditions is a broad-spectrum drug a good choice to treat a microbial infection?

Answers: Review Questions

Principles of Pharmacology

1. Pharmacology is the study of drugs. Chemotherapeutic agents are drugs used to treat any disease. Antimicrobial agents are specific chemotherapeutic agents used to treat infectious diseases. An antibiotic is a metabolic product of one microorganism that kills or inhibits the growth of another microbe. A synthetic drug is a chemical produced in the laboratory. A semisynthetic drug is an antibiotic that has been chemically modified in the laboratory.

2. Local or topical therapy is the application of an antimicrobial drug directly on an infected area.

    Systemic therapy involves allowing a drug to enter a patient's bloodstream. By intravenous therapy a drug is injected into a patient's vein. It is the most rapid way to produce high levels of a drug in the bloodstream. However, it is technically difficult and painful. By intramuscular administration a drug is injected into a muscle. Maximum levels of the drug result in the bloodstream about 15 minutes after the injection. However, the injection is painful.

    By oral administration the drug is swallowed and absorbed into the bloodstream. This technique is simple and painless. The absorption, however, can be slow and possibly ineffective.

3. The membranes surrounding cells and organs are one barrier to the distribution of drugs in the body. Many drugs cannot pass through the blood-brain-barrier. Lipid-soluble drugs can pass through the cell membranes. If they are not lipid-soluble, they must pass through the protein part of the membrane. If drugs bind to the plasma proteins of the blood, they cannot cross the cell membranes.

4. Drugs are eliminated from the body at different rates. If a drug is lost from the body rapidly, it must be administered more frequently to maintain the proper concentration in the blood for effectiveness.

5. A drug side effect is the undesirable toxicity of the antimicrobial agent. These side effects must be weighed against the potential benefit of the drug before choosing to use it.

6. Whether a microorganism is drug resistant depends on many factors related to specific cell structures. For example, resistance to penicillin depends on whether a bacterial cell wall is present. Eukaryotic microorganisms, lacking a cell wall, are not affected by penicillin. Gram-negative bacteria are resistant to many drugs because their outer cell membrane is impermeable to many of these substances. Most penicillins kill only Gram-positive bacteria.

    Natural drug resistance results from unique structures in different kinds of microorganisms. One example, is the differences in the cell wall/cell membrane composition of microbes. Acquired drug resistance results from mutations and genetic exchange. Some species are naturally resistant by their inherited genetic makeup. Others acquire it through several mechanisms. Some acquire enzymes that work against drugs. Others change the cellular target on which a drug acts. Others exclude or remove the drug from the microbial cell.

7. A narrow-spectrum drug affects only a single microbial group. A broad-spectrum drug is effective against two or more groups.

8. Chromosomally mediated resistance results from genetic mutations altering structures and metabolism in the bacterial cell. These changes can confer drug resistance. Plasmid-borne genes, called R factors, are incorporated into the microbe's chromosome. These factors can change the resistance to antibiotics by changing gene expression once they are incorporated into the microbial cell.

9. Drug resistance can be slowed by limiting the use of antibiotics. High use favors the survival of antibiotic-resistant bacterial strains. If careful thought is not given to the rate and dosages of administration of antibiotics, a resistant population of bacteria can evolve.

10. Drug dosage is the quantity of drug to be administered. Antimicrobial susceptibility is a measure of how much drug is required to kill or stop the growth of a pathogen. Drug synergism is the enhanced effect of two drugs administered together.

11. By a disc-diffusion susceptibility test, filter paper discs absorb known quantities of an antimicrobial agent. The discs are placed on a nutrient agar surface in a petri dish that has been inoculated with bacteria. After incubation the size of the halos around the different discs shows the effectiveness of the different concentrations of the drug. The halos indicate where the bacteria have been killed. A comparison of the size of the halos indicates the most effective drug concentration. The larger the halo, the more effective the drug.

   By a broth-susceptibility test, bacteria are cultivated in nutrient broths having varying concentrations of a drug. The varying degrees of turbidity in the broth tubes indicate the effectiveness of the drug at varying concentrations. The tube with the least turbidity indicates the concentration that is most effective.

   A bacteriostatic drug inhibits the growth of a bacterial population. A bactericidal drug kills all organisms.

12. The MIC is the lowest concentration of drug in the broth-dilution that inhibits bacterial growth. The MBC is the lowest concentration that is bactericidal. The serum-killing power test offers information to choose between using the same drug or changing to one that is possibly more effective.

Modes of Action of Antimicrobial Drugs

13. a. Drugs that block peptidoglycan synthesis can inhibit the cell wall synthesis of the bacterium. Penicillin is one example

   b. Drugs that disrupt the cell membrane, damage its permeability. Polymixin is one example.

   c. Many drugs that interfere with the activity at the ribosome inhibit protein synthesis. Chloramphenicol inhibits peptide bond formation.

   d. Drugs that work on nucleic acid synthesis change the activity of DNA or RNA. Rifampin selectively inhibits bacterial RNA polymerase.

   e. Drugs that inhibit folic acid synthesis interfere with the synthesis of this cofactor. The sulfonamides do this through competitive inhibition.

Antimicrobial Drugs

Refer to Table 21.3 for more information.

14. a. The penicillins are broad-spectrum and break the peptidoglycans in the bacterial cell wall. There are few side effects but there is some chance for allergy.

   b. The cephalosporins are broad-spectrum and inhibit the synthesis of peptidoglycan. There are few side effects but allergy is common.

   c. The sulfonamides are no longer used frequently. They interfere with folic acid synthesis. They can cause allergies and are used currently to treat infections of the urinary tract.

   d. The aminoglycosides are used only to treat serious infections. They inhibit protein synthesis by binding to the 30S ribosomal subunit. They are limited by their toxicity and are accompanied by the rapid appearance of drug-resistant strains.

   e. Chloramphenicol is broad-spectrum and interferes with peptide bond formation. It can cause aplastic anemia and gray baby syndrome.

   f. The tetracyclines are broad-spectrum and block protein synthesis by inhibiting the recognition of aminoacyl-tRNA. They can cause gastrointestinal pain and vomiting.

   g. Erythromycin is narrow-spectrum and blocks protein synthesis by binding to the 50S ribosome. It is effective only against Gram-negative bacteria. It can cause nausea and abdominal pain.

   h. The quinolones are broad-spectrum and block DNA synthesis. Side effects are uncommon.

   i. Nalidixic acid and nitrofurantoin are narrow-spectrum and inhibit DNA synthesis. They are used only to treat urinary tract infections.

   j. Vancomycin acts on Gram-positive bacteria and interferes with peptidoglycan synthesis. It has a fairly high incidence of side effects.

   k. Bacitracin and polymyxin B are narrow-spectrum and destroy lipid membranes. They are toxic if used systemically.

15. Tuberculosis is difficult to treat because it is resistant to most antimicrobial drugs. The bacterium grows slowly and some antibiotic-resistant strains exist. Only drugs that enter human cells are effective against the causative bacterium. Isoniazid inhibits the synthesis of mycolic acid. Rifampin inhibits the synthesis of RNA. Ethambutol inhibits the incorporation of mycolic acids into the cell wall. Treatment is usually more effective when these drugs are used in combination.

16. Antifungal agents are difficult to develop because they can harm eukaryotic human and fungal cells.

    a. Nystatin combines with a unique sterol, ergosterol, in fungal cell membranes. It damages the cell membranes of fungi.

    b. Amphotericin B disrupts fungal cell membranes. It treats infections such as cryptococcosis and mucomycosis. It can damage human cells and produce chills, vomiting, and fever.

    c. The imidazoles and triazoles stop the synthesis of sterols in the fungal cell membranes. They treat local and systemic infections.

    d. Flucytosine interferes with RNA synthesis.

    e. Griseofulvin interferes with fungal cell division. It can treat ringworm infections and does not have side effects.

17. Mebendazole is effective against many kinds of roundworms. It interferes with the ability of helminths to take up glucose. Metronidazole treats protozoan infections, including amebic dysentery and diarrhea caused by *G. lamblia*. It blocks metabolic pathways. It is absorbed orally. Chloroquine is selectively toxic for protozoa and used against those attacking the blood, especially malaria.

18. The intimate association of a virus with the host cell makes it tough to treat by any agent.

    a. Amantadine is used against influenza and interferes with viral replication during uncoating. It can cause anxiety, headaches, and insomnia.

    b. Acyclovir inhibits the synthesis of viral DNA. It is used against herpes simplex viruses.

    c. Ribavirin inhibits the synthesis of viral RNA. It can cause lung infections in infants.

    d. Interferons are antiviral but can be toxic.

    e. AZT interferes with reverse transcriptase. It is used to slow the pace of immune failure.

    f. ddI inhibits the action of reverse transcriptase. It is used to slow the pace of immune failure.

    g. Indinavir is a protease inhibitor.

Answers: Correlation Questions

1. Penicillin cannot harm human cells, as it works against the peptidoglycan molecules in bacterial cell walls. The cell wall is a structure that is absent in human cells. AZT works against reverse transcription. This is a process that does not occur in human cells.

2. The main consideration is how effectively the drug is absorbed into the bloodstream by each method of administration. The more effective means of administration and adsorption should determine the method of administration used.

3. If the causative bacterium is known, select the narrow-spectrum antibiotic for treatment. It will target the exact bacterium that needs to be eradicated. It is not as likely to harm normal biota during the treatment.

4. Mutant strains to any antibiotic usually arise randomly, often independently of any time factor. However, the longer the time interval, the more likely that a resistant, mutant strain will finally appear. Increased use of an antibiotic over time can also increase the likelihood that resistant, mutant strains will appear.

5. Flucytosine is an antifungal agent. Fungal cells are eukaryotic and are more vulnerable to a chromosomal mutation than the effects from a plasmid.

6. A broad-spectrum penicillin would affect more kinds of microbes. Although it could eradicate the bacterium causing an infection, it would affect other species. This possibly includes normal biota in the subject being treated.

Answers: Essay Questions

1. Over time, a microorganism becomes more resistant to a drug if mutant strains selectively arise during the treatment with that drug. The surviving microbes, which are genetically superior, are more likely to reproduce. In the next generation, they will produce genetic variations with drug resistance. Scientists must continually find new drugs effective against the surviving, resistant microorganisms.

2. Advantages include increased survival for the livestock. However, what effects do the antibiotics have on the quality of the meat produced by the livestock?

Answers: Discussion Topics

1. Most of the antimicrobial drugs target the cell wall, cell membrane, genetic structure, and ribosomes of microbial cells. In order to understand drug action, a student must understand cell structures and functions. Each kind of drug has a unique chemical structure that accounts for its mode of action.

2. Start by reviewing enzyme structure. Most of an enzyme's makeup is protein.

Answers: Correlation Questions in the Instructor's Manual

1. Proteases in the stomach and small intestine will chemically digest a protein drug before it can be absorbed across the mucosa of the small intestine and enter the blood.

2. IV administration of a drug introduces into the circulation immediately, taking it to body cells. It does not need to clear barriers from other lines of administration.

3. If the causative microbe is known, a narrow-spectrum drug targets the destruction of that microbe specifically.

4. If the causative microbe is not known, a broad-spectrum offers more alternatives to defeat a wide array of microbes.

Chapter 22
Infections of the Respiratory System

Learning Goals

To understand:

The anatomy and function of the respiratory system and its defenses against microorganisms

The clinical syndromes that characterize respiratory infections

The bacterial and viral causes of upper respiratory infections; their diagnosis, prevention, and treatment

The bacterial, viral, and fungal causes of lower respiratory infections; their diagnosis, prevention, and treatment

Chapter Outline

Clinical Science
    Diagnosis
    Prognosis and Treatment
    Types of Infection
    Progress of an Infection
Organization of Part IV
The Respiratory System
    Structure and Function
    Defenses and Normal Biota: A Brief Review
    Clinical Syndromes
Upper Respiratory Infections
    Bacterial Infections
    Viral Infections
Lower Respiratory Infections
    Bacterial Infections
    Viral Infections
    Fungal Infections
Summary

Teaching Tips

1. Invite a representative from a local health department to address your class about the difficulties of controlling and treating the microbial diseases of the upper respiratory tract.

2. Use a human torso model in class to teach the anatomy of the respiratory tract. Emphasize the lines of defense in the tract. Show where each microbe, discussed in this chapter, attacks the system to cause its particular disease.

3. If your course has a lab component, study the microorganisms of this chapter firsthand with prepared slides under the microscope.

4. If your course does not have a lab, project the microslides or prepared 35 mm slides of the microorganisms described in this chapter.

5. Information about microorganisms can also be retrieved from the Internet and shown to your class through a Smart Board

6. Also, in the lab or through projection, teach the histology of the respiratory tract. For example, what type of epithelial tissue composes the mucous membranes of the upper respiratory tract?

Discussion Topics

1. How do the lessons you taught in earlier chapters from this text assist in the understanding of the concepts in this chapter?

2. How does the information from other branches of science relate to the key concepts of this chapter?

Correlation Questions

1. What adaptations would you expect to see in the upper respiratory tract of a nonsmoker, protecting that person against the development of pneumonia?

2. Surgical removal of a person's tonsils can be harmful to that person's health. Explain.

3. Upper respiratory infections can possibly spread to a person's middle ear. How?

4. A person suffers from a sore throat, experiencing difficulty swallowing as a result. Is this person suffering from laryngitis or pharyngitis?

Answers: Review Questions

The Respiratory System

1. Use Figure 22.2 as a guide to sketch the anatomy of the respiratory system.

2. Many different species of microorganisms are inhaled into the body through the respiratory system. The upper respiratory tract provides a warm, moist, nutrient-rich environment for the dense colonization of commensal microorganisms.

3. The respiratory system exchanges oxygen from the air for carbon dioxide that is produced by metabolism in the tissues.

4. The mucous coverings and ciliary action of the epithelial cells of the respiratory tract are major defenses of the respiratory system. Other defenses include phagocytic alveolar macrophages and

the secretion of IgA antibodies. Normal biota of the upper respiratory system include the different species of streptococci, lactobacilli, and some Gram-negative species of *Moraxella catarrhalis*.

5. A clinical syndrome is the combination of symptoms that characterize a disease.

    a. Pharyngitis is the infection of the throat. There is a sore throat and sometimes fever.

    b. Bronchitis is the infection of the bronchi, with swelling of the bronchial membranes.

    c. Epiglottitis is the infection of the epiglottis. The structure can swell to many times its normal size.

    d. Bronchiolitis is the infection of the bronchioles with swelling of the membranes of these passageways.

    e. Laryngitis is the infection of the larynx, often involving swelling.

    f. Pneumonia is infection of the lungs with fluid and microorganisms replacing the air normally present in the alveoli.

6. Rhinitis, for example, can result from infection of a wide variety of microorganisms. All of them can cause swelling of this region.

Upper Respiratory Infections

7. The new vaccine for *Haemophilus influenzae* type b is successful against the most important causative microbe for epiglottitis. Type b stands for this strain of the bacterium.

8. Strep throat is caused by a highly virulent microorganism that can spread rapidly to other body regions from the respiratory system. It is caused by species of *Streptococcus* that produce alpha hemolysis. The virulence of streptococcal virulence may be changing due to the appearance of three types of erythrogenic toxins from bacterial cells.

9. The diphtheria toxin consists of two protein subunits. One of these binds to receptors on human cells, allowing the toxin to enter the cells. In the cells, it interferes with protein synthesis. Treatment is by an antitoxin. Cutaneous diphtheria is the infection of a wound in the skin by the causative microorganism.

10. The common cold is caused by viruses. Penicillin inactivates the synthesis of bacterial cell walls which are absent in viruses. Transmission of the common cold can be interrupted by prevention of reinfection and reducing the number of carriers of the viruses that serve as their human reservoir. The most common causative agents include the rhinoviruses.

11. The primary causative agent of acute bacterial pneumonia is *Streptococcus pneumoniae*. The clinical manifestations include an intense inflammatory response in the respiratory system. Blood vessels leak and fluid collects in the alveoli. The affected region of the lung becomes consolidated. The microbes can continue to spread. Treatment is through administration of antibiotics.

12. Mycoplasmal pneumonia is atypical pneumonia because it is mild and develops slowly. The microorganism causing this disease is not sensitive to penicillin.

13. *Chlamydia psittaci* is the causative agent of ornithosis. It invades various organs and is excreted in bird droppings. A human inhales these droppings which can sometimes be transferred to other humans.

    Coxiella burnetii causes Q fever. It is transmitted to a domestic animal by an insect bite, usually a tick. Humans can become infected by inhaling the microbe. If humans work in environments with insects and domestic animals, they can be exposed to the microorganism.

14. *Legionella pneumophila* was only discovered recently because a definitive diagnosis is seldom made for pneumonia and this bacterium is difficult to identify in the lab.

15. Pertussis produces an intensive cough and damage to the respiratory system. The pertussis vaccine can produce side effects such as pain and redness at the site of infection plus other complications. An acellular pertussis vaccine has been developed.

16. *Mycobacterium tuberculosis* is caused by a bacterium that flourishes in the environment of the respiratory tract, accounting for its high degree of incidence. Its waxy cell wall resists drying and allows it to survive. It resists lysosomal enzymes, oxidants, and phagocytes. The bacterium produces substances harmful to human cells and is easily spread as an airborne microorganism.

17. Bovine tuberculosis is atypical because it enters the gastrointestinal tract of the human and has a reservoir in the soil. This infection can progress rapidly in AIDS patients.

Lower Respiratory Infections

18. The influenza virus is highly likely to change genetically, leading to antigenic drift and antigenic shift. The flu pandemic of 1918 could occur again if a new genetic strain occurs and there is an absence of human antibodies to protect against it.

19. Parainfluenza viruses are the causative agents of croup. Symptoms include infection of the larynx and trachea. Treatment includes moistening the air with a humidifier.

20. Prevention is important against RSV because it is transmitted by hand contact and respiratory droplets. Immunity against the microbe causing it is not long-lasting.

21. The hantavirus pulmonary syndrome is an emerging disease that apparently has been unrecognized for a long time. On the other hand some scientists think it may be an emerging disease.

22. Histoplasmosis is transmitted by conidia, or asexual spores. Infected people develop a flulike illness. It is treated with amphotericin B or ketoconazole.

    Coccidioidomycosis is transmitted by arthrospores. It usually produces a mild respiratory illness. It is treated with amphotericin B.

    Blastomycosis is transmitted by conidia. It can cause symptoms resembling pulmonary tuberculosis. It is treated by amphotericin B.

23. *Pneumocystis carinii* is closely related to fungi by base sequencing studies. It can flourish in patients using immunosuppressive medications.

Answers: Correlation Questions

24. Each disease is caused by a fungus. Each fungus flourishes in a somewhat similar environment.

25. Smoking removes the cilia of the respiratory tract that are a first line of defense against bacterial invasion. Loss of these cilia makes the person more susceptible to bacterial invasion.

26. Both microorganisms produce antigens to humans and use the respiratory tract as a portal of entry. In *Streptococcus*, the antigen is a polysaccharide that is part of the bacterial cell capsule. In *Corynebacterium*, the antigen is carried by a temperate bacteriophage.

27. A new cephalosporin could possibly be effective against causative agents that have not yet evolved a resistance to it.

28. The majority of untreated patients with this disease survive by their adaptive immune defenses. Those who survive are permanently immune.

29. *Haemophilus influenzae* produces a polysaccharide capsule, making it resistant to phagocytosis and resistant to complement.

Answers: Essay Questions

1. Skin-test screening is an effective program of tuberculosis control. An effective vaccine is also the key to currently controlling TB. With new strains recently appearing, new anti-TB drugs are needed.

2. With the appearance of new strains of *M. tuberculosis*, the incidence of a pandemic outbreak of this disease is beginning to rise. Effective vaccination and decreasing the number of humans acting as a reservoir that carry the bacterium are keys to preventing this outbreak.

Answers: Discussion Topics

1. Start with a review of bacterial cell morphology (e.g., bacterial capsule) and the Gram-staining procedures.

2. The anatomy and physiology of the respiratory tract is one discipline with application to this chapter. Principles of immunology also apply here.

Answers: Correlation Questions in the Instructor's Manual

1. An observer should find healthy mucous membranes and cilia lining the upper respiratory tract. There are major lines of defense protecting the body.

2. The tonsils are lymphoid tissue, an important part of the immune system. Their removal can weaken the immune system.

3. An infecting microbe could migrate from the nasopharynx into the middle ear via the eustachian tube.

4. Pharyngitis is inflammation of the throat. Laryngitis is inflammation of the larynx, a part of the respiratory tract.

Chapter 23
Infections of the Digestive System

Learning Goals

To understand:

The anatomy and function of the digestive system and its defenses against microorganisms

The clinical syndromes caused by infections of the digestive system

The bacterial and viral causes of oral cavity and salivary gland infections; their diagnosis, prevention, and treatment

The bacterial, viral, protozoal, and helminth causes of intestinal infections; their diagnosis, prevention, and treatment

The viral and helminthic causes of liver infections and their clinical syndromes; their diagnosis, prevention, and treatment

Chapter Outline

The Digestive System
    Structure and Function
    Clinical Syndromes
Infections of the Oral Cavity and Salivary Glands
    Bacterial Infections
    Viral Infections
Infections of the Intestinal Tract
    Bacterial Infections
    Viral Infections
    Protozoal Infections
    Helminthic Infections
Infections of the Liver
    Viral Infections
    Helminthic Infections
Summary

Teaching Tips

1. Invite a representative from a local health department to address your class about the difficulties of controlling the infections of the human digestive tract.

2. Another person to invite to your class in a representative from the hospitality or food preparation field. What measures must these people take against microbes to assure quality service and safe food?

3. Use the human torso model in class to teach the anatomy of the digestive tract. Name each compartment of the tract and describe its function. Do the same for each associated structure. Point out where each microbe and helminth discussed in this chapter attack the digestive system.

4. If your class has a lab component, study the microorganisms of this chapter firsthand with prepared slides under the microscope. Also study the histology of the human digestive tract. For example, show a slide with the simple columnar epithelium of the mucosa. The mucosa lines the inside free surface of the small and large intestine. Specify how different infectious microbes or helminths attack this layer.

5. If your course does not have a lab component, project microslides or prepared 35 mm slides of the microbes and human histology that relate to this chapter. These slides can augment your descriptions in lecture.

6. Another option for lecture is to retrieve images of the bacteria discussed in this chapter and project them in class through a Smart Board.

7. Explain your knowledge of the functioning of the respiratory and digestive systems with the following search terms: *respiratory system - animation* and *digestive system - animation*.

Discussion Topics

1. As suggested in the last chapter, look for concepts learned in earlier chapters that tie in the concepts of infections of the human body. In this case, draw a relationship to the human digestive tract.

2. What information from other branches of science relates to the key concepts of this chapter? This is a question that can constantly be applied to the remaining chapters of the text.

Correlation Questions

1. The mucous membrane lining on the inside of the digestive tract has villi. How is this adaptive?

2. How can stress in an individual make a person more vulnerable to stomach ulcers caused by the bacterium, *Helicobacter*?

3. How is the pH of the oral cavity related to dental caries?

4. What conditions in the digestive tract make it a likely place for the development of infections?

Answers: Review Questions

The Digestive System

1. The digestive system consists of a long, tubelike tract and six associated structures: the teeth, tongue, salivary glands, liver, gallbladder, and pancreas.

2. The digestive system breaks down molecules to a size that enables the body to use them as nutrients. Food masses are broken down mechanically, without chemical change of the molecules in the mass. In addition, the molecules are broken down chemically. When macromolecules are broken into smaller subunits, the smaller subunits can be absorbed. One example of this needed chemical change is the hydrolysis of starch into maltose and, eventually, glucose.

3. a. Gastritis is the infection and inflammation of the stomach. There is pain in the upper abdomen and, sometimes, bleeding.

   b. Gastroenteritis is the inflammation of the stomach and small intestine. It produces nausea, vomiting, and abdominal pain.

   c. Colitis is the infection and inflammation of the large intestine. There can be damage to the intestinal wall and bleeding. Sometimes dysentery develops.

   d. Dental caries is tooth decay. The outermost enamel layer of the tooth is broken.

   e. Periodontal disease causes destruction of the gums and bone tissue.

   f. Parotitis is the infection of the parotid gland. There is swelling of the gland.

   g. Hepatitis can produce jaundiced conditions in the body.

4. Intoxication is poisoning of the body. Foods can be one source. However, intoxication can also develop from other sources.

Infections of the Oral Cavity and Salivary Glands

5. *Streptococcus mutans* produces lactic acid, which damages the tooth enamel. Fluoride in drinking water and the development of a vaccine are possibilities for the treatment of dental caries.

6. Periodontal disease is caused by a bacterial infection of the periodontium that surrounds the teeth. It is treated by removing plaque from gum margins and periodontal pockets.

7. Mumps is caused by a virus that spreads from the respiratory system to the salivary glands. It can be serious if it spreads into the bloodstream and infects other body regions.

Infections of the Intestinal Tract

8. Shigellosis is caused by many species of *Shigella*. It binds to colon epithelial cells and produces toxins. It multiplies in the host cells and inhibits protein synthesis. Symptoms include bleeding and inflammation of the intestine. Treatment includes fluid therapy for dehydration and antibiotics. Often it is treated with cephalosporin. A vaccine is under development.

9. Typhoid fever can be prevented by maintaining a clean water supply. Carriers of the microorganism have high fever, loss of appetite, and fatigue. A vaccine has some effectiveness. The formation of new strains can make treatment a challenge.

10. Although its symptoms resemble those of food poisoning, salmonellosis is a food infection. Treatment with antibiotics makes some people chronic carriers of *Salmonella*.

11. An enterotoxigenic strain of *E. coli* causes traveler's and infant diarrhea. An enteroinvasive strain causes a dysentery syndrome similar to the one caused in shigellosis. An enteropathogenic strain causes diarrhea in newborn infants. It produces a toxin that destroys the microvilli of the intestinal lining.

12. The toxin from *Vibrio cholerae* has one peptide that facilitates entry into the host cell. A second peptide increases the intracellular level of cyclic AMP. Cholera can be prevented by maintaining clean water supplies. Treatment includes replacing lost fluid from the body by ORT. The recent epidemiology has revealed epidemics of new genetic strains. The current vaccine is not very effective.

13. *Vibrio parahaemolyticus* produces low-grade fever, diarrhea, nausea, and abdominal cramps. People who eat fish from contaminated waters can be at risk.

14. The enterocolitis caused by *Yersinia enterocolitica* has a distinctive reservoir in animals in addition to humans. It multiplies and causes disease in the gastrointestinal tract. Infection comes from wild or domestic animals, raw milk, oysters, and water.

15. The infection of *Campylobacter jejuni* is not life-threatening. However, all *Campylobacter* species cause over 2 million illnesses per year.

16. *Helicobacter pylori* attaches to the wall of the stomach. It releases enzymes that cause changes in the wall of the stomach.

17. Iatrogenic illness is medically induced diarrhea. *Clostridium difficile* produces toxins to cause this. The illness is resolved by treatment with vancomycin.

18. *Staphylococcus aureus* survives environmental stresses to contaminate food. It produces a heat-stable enterotoxin. The symptoms are vomiting, diarrhea, and abdominal pain. The food poisoning is prevented by keeping food uncontaminated.

19. *Bacillus cereus* causes food poisoning by surviving through endospores and contaminating food. *Clostridium perfringens* also causes food poisoning after forming endospores.

Viral Infections

20. Gastroenteritis is caused by rotaviruses affecting epithelial cells lining the gastrointestinal tract. It can cause diarrhea and dehydration. Good hygiene prevents entry of the virus. Treatment involves rehydration therapy.

21. Norwalk agents are viruses causing gastroenteritis. They cause nausea, vomiting, diarrhea, and abdominal cramps. They mainly, however, infect older children and adults rather than infants.

Protozoal Infections

22. The symptoms of amoebic dysentery include intestinal bleeding, fever, and abdominal pain. Diagnosis is difficult because the trophozoites of the life cycle disintegrate outside the body. Diagnosis must be prompt to prevent liver infection. Amoebic dysentery is caused by *Entamoeba histolytica.*

23. The two forms of *Giardia lamblia* are a trophozoite, which causes the infection, and a cyst, which is the form for transmission from host to host. It has a wilderness life cycle. Symptoms are diarrhea and a bloated abdomen. Clean water prevents the disease. Treatment is by antimicrobial drugs metronidazole or quinacrine.

24. *Balantidium coli* causes colitis. It is usually restricted to tropical countries.

25. Cryptosporidiosis can cause a life-threatening diarrhea in AIDS patients. The increased frequency of AIDS in the human population has led to an increased outbreak of this disease. Prevention includes good hygiene.

Helminthic Infections

26. Pinworm infection is the most common helminth infection in the United States. It is easy to acquire through fomites. It is not a serious disease. Usually there are no symptoms.

27. *Ascaris lumbricoides* eggs can be ingested by a person, causing infection. The larvae from the eggs burrow through the wall of the small intestine and reach the lungs via the bloodstream. They are coughed up from the lungs, swallowed, and reenter the digestive tract. Eggs are shed in the feces. Symptoms include coughing. The helminth causing it is a roundworm.

28. The two species of hookworms are almost identical. Filariform larvae penetrate human skin and enter the bloodstream. They enter the alveoli, are coughed up, and swallowed. Eggs are shed in the feces. Hookworms are diagnosed by finding eggs in the feces. Iron supplements may be required if an anemia results from the infection.

29. *Strongyloides stercoralis* is a roundworm with a larva that can penetrate the skin. It can reproduce without a human host and its eggs hatch within the intestine. Larvae from these eggs can reenter the body, producing an autoinfection that is a continuous reinfection.

30. Whipworm eggs are swallowed and mature in the intestine wall. Adults lay eggs there. Treatment is with thiabendazole, mebendazole, and possibly steroids.

31. *Trichinella spiralis*, a nematode, burrows into skeletal muscles of the human host. Symptoms are fever, muscle pain, and malaise. It could be fatal if microbe populations in the body become high. It is rare if the nematode is eradicated from pork before the pork is eaten. This is usually done in most households.

32. The *Taenia* species are cestodes and tapeworms. The infections result from a parasitic existence in the body. They are diagnosed by finding proglottids in stool samples. Cysticercosis is infection of cysts in tissues from a tapeworm.

33. *Echinococcus granulosus*, a tapeworm, causes hydatid disease by producing cysts that lodge in human tissues. Infection is highest in sheep-raising regions. Treatment is surgical removal of the cysts.

Infections of the Liver

34. Hepatitis A is caused by a small, noneveloped virus with single-stranded RNA. It is transmitted by the fecal-to-oral route. Families with young children are at high risk. Symptoms include jaundice and loss of appetite. Usually there is recovery. Two vaccines are now available.

    Hepatitis B is caused by a DNA-containing hepadnavirus. It enters body fluids. Accidental transfusions of blood cause high risks. Symptoms include liver damage. Steroids and alpha interferon are used for treatment.

    Hepatitis C is caused by a virus with single-stranded RNA. It is promoted by blood transfusion or sexual contact. Alpha interferon may be effective in treating the disease.

    Hepatitis D is caused by an RNA-containing virus. It can cause cirrhosis and liver disease. Effective treatment is not currently known.

    Hepatitis E is caused by an RNA-containing virus. Clean water supplies prevent infection. Little is known about the virus.

35. *Fasciola hepatica* is the sheep liver fluke. *Opisthorchis sinensis* is the Chinese liver fluke. Larvae of each enter the human host. They penetrate the intestine and enter the liver, developing into egg-producing liver flukes. Eggs leave the body through the feces. Symptoms include liver damage. Treatment can be by the drug praziquantel. People at risk are those who visit sheep-raising areas outside of the United States.

Answers: Correlation Questions

1. The person probably lived most of the expected human life span, free of the bacterium causing dental caries and/or practicing good dental hygiene. The person, however, could have developed periodontal disease.

2. How recently did they consume the meal? Symptoms from staph infection are rapid, 2 to 6 hours. It takes one to two days for salmonellosis.

3. The antibiotic may have also destroyed the normal biota population of the lower GI tract, precipitating the diarrhea. The antibiotic could also have damaged the mucosa of the intestine.

4. The unique composition of their cell wall allows them to overcome the lines of defense in the human body.

5. The vaccine is now safe and should be recommended although it is expensive.

6. It is possible with good hygiene, clean water supplies, and a vaccine.

Answers: Essay Questions

1. The lines of defense of the respiratory tract include the action of cilia and mucous membranes. The digestive tract is less fortified and ingested pathogens can quickly spread throughout the remainder of the body by entering the blood through absorption in the small intestine.

2. A mutant gene could have occurred spontaneously in the nonpathogen. This could have been a point mutation, leading to a biochemical change that could overcome the lines of defense in the human body. This mutant, resistant to change, could have increased in population size through natural selection.

Answers: Discussion Topics

1. Start with a review of bacterial cell morphology and the Gram stain. Concentrate on adaptations that make microbes successful at overcoming the lines of defense in the human body.

2. Explore more about the anatomy and physiology of the human body. What are the layers of the tooth? The activity of *S. mutans* breaks through the outermost enamel. What are the four layers of the GI tract? The mucosal layer carries out absorption. The contraction of the smooth muscle layer produces peristalsis.

    Also, continue to apply the principles of immunology. Look for the adaptations that the microbes (e.g., pili) and helminths (e.g., proglottids) have evolved to overcome the immune mechanisms of the human body.

Answers: Correlation Questions in the Instructor's Manual

1. The villi increase the surface area of the mucosal surface, facilitating the absorption of the subunits of digestion: monosaccharides, amino acids, etc.

2. Stress can weaken the immune system, aiding bacterial attack.

3. The metabolism of bacteria can produce acid end products, changing a normally neutral pH to a more acidic one. The acids produced can erode away tooth enamel, causing dental caries.

4. The digestive track is a warm, moist, nutrient-laden environment. It is dark with a favorable pH to support many microbes in addition to its normal biota.

Chapter 24
Infections of the Genitourinary Tract

Learning Goals

To understand:

The anatomy and function of the urinary and reproductive systems and their defenses against microorganisms

The clinical syndromes that characterize genitourinary infections

The bacterial causes of urinary tract infections and their clinical syndromes, prevention, and treatment

The bacterial and viral causes of sexually transmissible (STDs) and their clinical syndromes, prevention, and treatment

The bacterial, fungal, and protozoal causes of female reproductive tract infections and their clinical syndromes, prevention and treatment

The causes of male reproductive tract infections and their clinical syndromes, prevention and treatment

The bacterial and viral causes of infections transmitted from mother to infant and their clinical syndromes, prevention, and treatment

Chapter Outline

Teaching Tips

1. If you decide to invite a representative from a local health department, ask this person to describe the difficulties of controlling all human infections discussed over the last several chapters.

2. If you decide to invite a local health professional, also ask that person to consolidate information on the infections of the human respiratory, digestive, urinary, and reproductive tracts.

3. Use your lab as an opportunity to study firsthand the prepared slides of the pathogens of the respiratory, digestive, and genitourinary tracts. Most biological supply houses sell the equipment that projects mounted slides under the microscope onto a TV monitor. If this technology is available to you, it can add another dimension to your teaching.

4. Project prepared microslides or 35 mm slides of the human pathogens in lecture if your course does not have a lab component.

5. Retrieve images of bacteria, discussed in this chapter, from the Internet and project them in class using a Smart Board.

6. Use the human torso model in lecture to explain the structure and function of the urinary and reproductive systems. Locate each structure and explain its function as you locate it. Relate the structures to the microorganisms discussed in this chapter, showing where each microbe attacks the human body and causes damage.

7. Visit the Internet with the following search terms: *reproductive system - animation* and *urinary system - animation*

Discussion Topics

1. The human urinary and reproductive tracts offer the perfect environment for the growth of numerous microorganisms. What are some of the optimal conditions it offers?

2. How do earlier concepts learned in this text promote the understanding of the information in this text?

Correlation Questions

1. How can infection by HSV lead to the loss of skeletal muscle control?

2. How is the development of hematuria abnormal considering normal kidney function?

3. How can an infection of the urinary tract produce dysuria?

4. Why are blood tests necessary as part of the diagnosis for many of the infections of the urinary and reproductive systems?

Answers: Review Questions

The Genitourinary System

1. The kidneys and ureters belong to the upper urinary tract. The bladder and urethra belong to the lower urinary tract. The urinary system controls the composition of the blood and eliminates liquid wastes from the body.

   The male reproductive system includes the testes, a series of ducts, the prostate gland, and urethra. The female reproductive system includes the ovaries, fallopian tubes, the uterus, and vagina. The reproductive system in either sex produces sex cells. The female reproductive system also provides the environment for fertilization and prenatal development.

2. a. Cystitis is the infection of the bladder. It can cause frequent, painful urination.

   b. Urethritis is the inflammation of the urethra. It can cause frequent, painful urination.

   c. Pyelonephritis is the infection of the kidneys. It can produce fever and flank pain.

   d. UTI is a urinary tract infection.

   e. PID is an infection of the genital organs and also organs of the abdominal cavity. It is associated with fever and abdominal pain.

   f. Vaginitis is inflammation of the vagina. There is vaginal irritation and discharge.

3. Perinatal infections occur around the time of birth. They are usually transmitted from mother to infant.

Urinary Tract Infections

4. The urethra tract is shorter in females and close to the end of the digestive tract, making it a likely region for infections. Recurrent UTIs include cystitis and pyelonephritis. A urine sample for diagnosis must be collected carefully and refrigerated.

5. Patients with UTIs should drink large amounts of water to increase elimination of fluids and disease-causing microorganisms. Lower urinary tract infections include dysuria, the urgency and frequency to urinate. Upper urinary tract infections include fever, vomiting, and flank pain.

6. Many bacteria-caused urinary infections are sensitive to sulfa drugs.

7. Virulence factors in uropathogenic strains of *E. coli* include production of hemolysins and R factors.

8. Many cases of leptospirosis are undiagnosed because the causative bacterium is small and difficult to detect.

9. STDs still occur at high incidence as new pathogens are continually discovered.

10. Safer sex promotes protective techniques to decrease the probability of being infected with microorganisms that invade the urinary and reproductive systems.

11. Women are vulnerable to STDs due to the effective transmission of the causative microorganisms from men to women. The microbes causing STDs can continue to live and cause changes for years in the female reproductive tract. A newborn baby can be infected by them at birth.

Sexually Transmissible Diseases (STDs)

12. The virulence factors of the gonococcus are adhesion-bearing pili and an outer-membrane protein for adherence to epithelium. They also have an outer membrane molecule, lipid A, which can destroy tissues. Symptoms in men include painful urination and a discharge from the urethra. In women symptoms include fever, dysuria, and abdominal pain. There can also be inflammation of the fallopian tubes. Gonorrhea is treatable with antibiotics.

13. Syphilis is diagnosed by serological tests. Primary syphilis begins early with the appearance of a chancre. Secondary syphilis occurs six to eight weeks after the chancre, with enlarged lymph nodes. Latent syphilis is the following prolonged stage without symptoms. Tertiary syphilis leads to destruction of the nervous and cardiovascular systems and perhaps death. Syphilis is treated with penicillin. Congenital syphilis leads to deformities of the bones and teeth as the newborn baby becomes infected.

14. The highest risk group of chlamydia is composed of sexually active adults. Symptoms include a mucoid discharge from the urethra and vagina. Long-range complications include female infertility. Protected sex is a major safeguard. Treatment is with doxycycline, erythromycin, and azithromycin.

15. Clinical symptoms from *Ureaplasma urealyticum* and *Mycoplasma hominis* include urethral discharge.

16. Chancroid is less communicable because it can only enter the body through a break in the skin. Many patients with the disease are cocaine addicts.

17. Granuloma inguinale is diagnosed by identifying Donovan bodies in the cells of the patient. Symptoms are lesions on draining ulcers. Treatment is by several antimicrobial agents.

18. Genital herpes is transmitted at high frequencies. The virus causes active infections by harming cell metabolism of the host. Latent infections do not interfere with cell function. Primary infection symptoms include fever, headaches, and muscle aches. Recurrent infection symptoms include stress, fever, and trauma.

    The causative virus can reach areas of the body not covered by a condom. Use of a condom offers some protection. Neonatal herpes infects newborns. Treatment by acyclovir in adults shortens the duration of the primary infection, but does not cure the infection. Acyclovir treatment reduces the mortality rate in newborns.

19. The treatment for genital warts includes freezing them with liquid nitrogen. It controls them. Another approach is painting them with podophyllin or trichloroacetic acid.

Infections of the Female Reproductive Tract

20. *Gardnerella vaginalis* changes the pH of the vagina. It is diagnosed by the presence of clue cells. It is treated with metronidazole.

21. Toxic shock syndrome results from the production of toxins by infecting bacteria. Vaginal abrasion increases the rate of bacterial multiplication. Changing tampons regularly is a major preventive step.

22. PID can produce fever, abnormal vaginal bleeding, and severe lower abdominal pain. Infection is by various pathogens through sexual transmission. Treatment can be by intramuscular injection or oral administration of antibiotics. Intravenous antibiotics is the course for more serious cases.

23. Uterine infections, such as endometritis, can occur after childbirth. Pelvic examinations can also introduce microorganisms. Abortions can also promote uterine infections. Treatment is usually with the most effective antibiotic.

24. *Candida albicans* normally lives in the vagina but can cause infection as an opportunist in a susceptible host. Symptoms include vaginal discharge and itching. Treatment is by antifungal applications.

25. *Trichomonas vaginalis* is a flagellated protozoan. It is transmitted by unprotected sex. Symptoms include vaginal discharge. Treatment is by oral metronidazole.

Male Reproductive Tract Infections

26. Symptoms of male urethritis are dysuria, or urethral itching and urethral discharge. It is usually caused by a Gram-negative diplococcus through unprotected sex.

Infections Transmitted from Mother to Infant

27. *Listeria monocytogenes* thrives at low temperatures in foods. It is an opportunist but can cause disease in people with weakened immune systems and also in pregnant women. A fetus or newborn can be infected. The disease can produce abscesses, meningitis, and septicemia.

28. Infants acquire group B streptococcus infection from the female reproductive tract. There are risks to new mothers and protection can result by administration of ampicillin.

29. Cytomegalic inclusion disease is extremely common worldwide. It is transmitted by a virus through sexual contact or by close contact with body fluids. It produces a mononucleosis-like infection. Ganciclovir is the only useful agent known to treat the disease.

Answers: Correlation Questions

1. Questions should include information about the pattern of sexual activity. There should also be questions about one's physical well being. A thorough physical exam is essential. Tests should

include microscopic analysis of the cells and microbes from the reproductive tract. Analysis of a urine sample is also necessary.

2. Questions should include information about the pattern of sexual activity and physical symptoms. The two tests are the nontreponemal and treponemal.

3. Questions should include known changes in his life that correspond to the four stages as the disease develops.

4. *Gardnerella vaginalis* causes pH changes and irritation with discharges from the vagina.

5. This includes any bacterium causing a disease that can be isolated and viewed under the light microscope. For example, you can Gram stain the Gram-negative diplococci causing gonococcal urethritis.

6. They are both caused by bacteria through sexual contact. Both adhere to epithelial cells of the reproductive tract and damage those cells.

Answers: Essay Questions

1. A new STD arises if a mutated strain of a bacterium arises that can overcome the human immune system. It will spread with unprotected sex and a failure to control and eradicate the microorganism causing the disease.

2. It is difficult to test all blood supplies and not practical to discard all contaminated blood.

Answers: Discussion Topics

1. Start with the fact that the tracts provide a warm, moist environment in the absence of light. Emphasize the physical conditions of temperature and moisture that maximize the growth of many microbial species.

2. Review the details of cell morphology. Discuss the aspects of anaerobic and aerobic metabolism. Reinforce the principles supporting the Gram reactions.

Answers: Correlation Questions of the Instructor's Manual

1. HSV infectious neurons, the signal-sending cells of the body. Skeletal muscles need this signaling to contract and produce body motion. Without the signaling of malfunction motor neurons, a person's movement will be affected.

2. Normally, the kidney does not filter whole blood. It filters the plasma, except for the plasma proteins. Cells of the blood are not filtered.

3. An infection from a microbe can cause inflammation of the mucous membranes lining the inside surface of the urinary tract. One symptom of this inflammation is pain and swelling from the inflamed area.

4. Part of the immune response to these conditions is a change in the overall number and different kinds of white blood cells. The change of a particular kind of immune cell (e.g., increased numbers of eosinophils during allergies or parasitic infections) can pinpoint the cause of a disease.

Chapter 25
Infections of the Nervous System

Learning Goals

To understand:

The anatomy and function of the nervous system and its defenses against microorganisms

The clinical syndromes caused by nervous system infections

The bacterial, viral, and fungal infections of the meninges—their diagnosis, prevention, and treatment

The bacterial, viral, prion-associated, and protozoal infections of neural tissue—their diagnosis, prevention, and treatment

Chapter Outline

The Nervous System
    Structure and Function
    Clinical Syndromes
Infections of the Meninges
    Bacterial Causes
    Viral Causes: Aseptic Meningitis
    Fungal Causes
Diseases of the Neural Tissue
    Bacterial Causes
    Viral Causes
    Prion Causes
    Protozoal Causes
Summary

Teaching Tips

1. Assign the several kinds of questions at the end of the chapter. Use some time at the end of one of your class periods to discuss the answers with your students.

2. Use a human torso model and articulated human skeleton to demonstrate the locations and anatomy of the structures of the human body (e.g., brain and spinal cord) that are infected by the microorganisms described in this chapter.

3. Project prepared microslides, or 35 mm slides, in class to extend your descriptions of the neuron, neuroglia cells, blood, and various kinds of microorganisms that invade the human nervous system.

4. Retrieve images of the nerve and blood cells from the Internet and project them in class using a Smart Board.

5. Invite a health care professional (e.g., physician, nurse practitioner) to your class to offer firsthand observations of the symptoms and treatments of the infections of the human nervous system.

5. Explain to your students how a knowledge of the structures and functions of the human body can help them to understand the facts and concepts explained in this chapter. To make this connection, ask them to explain the function of each organ system in the human body. You can list the organ systems on the blackboard or an overhead transparency. Start with these examples.

   circulatory system - internal transport

   respiratory system - gas exchange

6. Visit the Internet and start with these search terms: *nervous system - animation*

Correlation Questions

1. The nervous system is divided into the central nervous system and the peripheral nervous system. Explain the meaning of these titles.

2. Brain cells require a constant input of glucose from the blood. What does this indicate about their carbohydrate storage capacity?

3. Some cranial nerves are sensory. Some are motor. Some are mixed. Explain each of these labels.

4. With respect to the meninges, where is the subarachnoid space?

Answers: Review Questions

1. He had meningismus, irritation of the meninges.

2. Lack of contact with the bacterium *Neisseria meningitidis* could have prevented the disease.

The Nervous System

3. The central nervous system (CNS) consists of the brain and spinal cord. The peripheral nervous system (PNS) includes the nerves that send signals to the CNS from receptors and the nerves that send signals from the CNS parts to various regions of the body. The blood-brain barrier is the limited permeability of the walls of capillaries serving the brain. Many microorganisms and toxins cannot cross this barrier. However, certain drugs for treatment also cannot cross this barrier.

4. Meningitis is the inflammation of the meninges. The CSF becomes cloudy and there is increased pressure on the brain. Encephalitis is the inflammation of brain tissue. It affects consciousness and behavior. Myelitis is the inflammation of the spinal cord. This interferes with its message-sending ability. Neurotoxins are substances that are highly destructive to the nervous system.

   A lumbar puncture removes CSF from the space beneath the arachnoid mater below the end of the spinal cord. As the spinal cord ends at L1 or L2, the puncture is performed between L3 - L4 or L4 - L5. Withdrawal of the fluid at this level will not puncture the spinal cord.

Infections of the Meninges

5. a. *Neisseria meningitidis* causes meningococcal meningitis. It is transmitted by respiratory droplets. Symptoms include disruption of the CSF and convulsions. Diagnosis can be the appearance of a skin rash. Meningococcal prophylaxis is a prevention method. Treatment can be administering the antibiotic rifampin. For a systemic meningococcal infection, penicillin is administered.

   b. *Haemophilus influenzae* causes meningitis. Infants and young children are at high risk. Rifampin is prescribed. A vaccine has also been developed.

   c. *Streptococcus pneumoniae* causes pneumococcal meningitis. The microorganism can spread from the respiratory tract. People with a weakened state of health are at high risk. Treatment can be with antibiotics.

   d. *E. coli* causes a form of meningitis in newborn infants and patients of neurosurgery. Treatment is with ampicillin and gentamicin.

6. The properties include the enzyme IgA protease. The microbe can bind to transferrin and lactoferrin.

7. Aseptic meningitis is caused by a virus. The treatment for this type of meningitis is different than that for bacterial meningitis.

8. Cryptococcal meningitis is caused by a fungus. Treatment can be with amphotericin B, sometimes in combination with 5-flucytosine.

Diseases of Neural Tissues

9. *Clostridium tetani* causes tetanus. It produces endospores that can enter deep anaerobic wounds. It multiplies in the blood and produces a toxin that enters the bloodstream. It interferes with neurons that signal skeletal muscles. Prevention involves avoiding environments with the microbe. Treatment is from a tetanus immune globulin.

   Clostridium botulinum causes botulism. It produces a potent toxin that prevents the release of acetylcholine signaling muscle contraction. It is acquired from contaminated food. Proper sterilization of food is a preventive step. An antitoxin is used for treatment.

10. Symptoms of rabies include flulike reactions. There is nervousness, anxiety, and loss of muscle function. Fatality is the usual result. Removing the reservoir of infected animals is a major prevention along with immunization of pets and humans. The Pasteur treatment has been employed. A vaccine is now available.

11. Poliomyelitis can produce flulike symptoms, fever, headache, and gastrointestinal problems. The Sabin vaccine gives long-lasting immunity.

12. Encephalitic arboviruses include the EEE, WEE, CE, and SLE. Infectious encephalitis is characterized by disturbed brain function. It is transmitted by the bite of a mosquito. Only the arboencephalitis, Japanese B, is prevented by a vaccine.

13. Encephalitis can be caused by common viral pathogens. Herpes simplex virus types 1 and 2 can also cause it. It can be deadly, requiring prompt diagnosis.

14. Kuru is caused by a prion. It affects the brain tissue. The Creutzfeldt-Jacob disease begins with dementia and progresses to coma and death. Little is known about this disease.

15. *T. brucei gambiense* and *T. brucei rhodesiense* are transmitted by the bite of a tsetse fly. Both cause encephalitis. *T. rhodesiense* has a large reservoir in game animals and domestic cattle and sheep. It produces a more fatal disease. Prevention of both involves removing the tsetse fly. Treatment is with melarsoprol, suramin, and tryparsamide.

Answers: Correlation Questions

1. Meningitis includes inflammation and swelling of the brain. There is reduced bloodflow to the brain. Encephalitis has inflammation of the brain but also includes symptoms such as drowsiness and fever.

2. Toxins produced by bacterial cells pass through the blood brain barrier, an effective strategy to enter and harm brain cells.

3. They are symptoms of cryptococcal meningitis.

4. Both diseases are caused by prions.

Essay Questions

1. Effective immunization is one key step. Another is eradicating all animal reservoirs harboring the virus.

2. The OPV is not as safe. Now all infants are immunized by the IPV.

Answers: Discussion Questions

1. They offer dark, warm, moist environments with optimal temperatures for many microbes.

2. Concepts include cell morphology, bacterial metabolism, microbial genetics, and immune mechanisms.

Answers: Correlation Questions in the Instructor's Manual

1. The brain and spinal cord compose the CNS and resemble the central trunk of a tree. The PNS consists of the cranial nerves attached to the brain and the spinal nerves attached to the spinal cord. They also resemble branches attached to the trunk of a tree.

2. Brain cells do not convert large amounts of glucose into glycogen. Within a store of glycogen internally, they do not have a source within to make glucose. Therefore, they need a constant external source from the blood.

3. Sensory nerves consist of neurons sending signals toward the CNS to detect a sensation. Motor nerves consist of neurons sending signals away from the CNS to signal muscles for motor function. Mixed nerves contain sensory and motor neurons.

4. It is a space beneath the arachnoid mater. This is the middle meningeal layer between the outermost dura mater and innermost pia mater.

Chapter 26
Infections of the Body's Surfaces

Learning Goals

To understand:

The anatomy and function of the skin and eye and their defenses against microorganisms

The clinical syndromes that characterize infections of the skin and eye

The bacterial, viral, fungal, and arthropod causes of skin infections and their diagnosis, prevention, and treatment

The bacterial, viral, and helminthic causes of eye infections and their diagnosis, prevention, and treatment

Chapter Outline

The Body's Surfaces
    Structure and Function of the Skin
    Structure and Function of the Eye's Surfaces
    Defenses and Normal Microbiota: A Brief Review
    Clinical Syndromes
Skin Infections
    Bacterial Causes
    Viral Causes
    Fungal Causes
    Arthropod Causes
Eye Infections
    Bacterial Infections
    Helminth Causes
Summary

Teaching Tips

1. Invite a representative from local health department to explain the problems controlling the infectious diseases on the body surfaces.

2. Illustrate the structures of the eye using a take-apart model in lecture. Emphasize structures of the eye discussed in the chapter such as the conjunctiva and cornea. Mention the specific microorganisms that attack each structure of the eye.

3. Study the dermis and epidermis of the skin through prepared slides under the microscope in the lab. As students study the skin, remind them of the microorganisms that infect one or both of these layers of the skin.

4. Project slides of the histology of the skin and the microorganisms/arthropods described in this chapter.

5. Retrieve illustrations of the skin from the Internet and project them in class using a Smart Board.

6. Start an Internet search with the term *dermatology*.

Discussion Topics

1. The skin is an important first line of defense for the human body, warding off invading microorganisms and arthropods. How does it fulfill this role? What are some other first lines of defense protecting the human body that the students have learned?

2. As one of the final chapters in the book, the information in Chapter 26 offers the opportunity to apply lessons taught earlier in the text. Continue to emphasize these ideas and use new examples if you have discussed these before.

Correlation Questions

1. The tissue makeup of the skin is stratified squamous epithelium. How is this adaptive?

   Compare this with the simple squamous epithelium composing the wall of an alveolus. How is this adaptive?

2. How is the production of sebum by the skin adaptive?

3. A bacterial infection produces visible red spots on the skin. How deeply has this infection spread into the layers of the skin?

4. An infecting microorganism produces streptokinase in the human body. How does this threaten the health of the body?

Answers: Review Questions

1. Zoster is a reactivation of the VZV that has caused chickenpox earlier in the life of an individual.

The Body's Surfaces

2. The epidermis is the outer layer of the skin. The stratum germinativum is the innermost sublayer that has cells dividing to produce the more external sublayers. The stratum corneum is the outermost layer. It is composed of dead layers with keratin. The dermis is the deeper layer of the skin. It contains blood vessels, nerves, sweat glands, sebaceous glands, and hair follicles.

   The conjunctiva is a mucous membrane that covers the cornea of the eye and the part of the sclera that is exposed to the external environment.

3. Infections of the skin are described by their appearance.

   a. A lesion is a color change of the skin.

   b. Erythema is a reddening of the skin from inflammation.

   c. Petechiae are tiny purple discolorations.

   d. Purpura are large purple discolorations.

   e. Macules are complete flat spots.

   f. Papules are small raised spots.

   g. Nodules are large, firm elevations.

   h. Maculopapular are bumpy regions.

   i. A vesicle is a small, water-filled blister.

   j. A bulla is a large, water-filled blister.

   k. A pustule is a blister that contains pus.

   l. An erosion is a superficial loss of the skin.

   m. An ulcer is a hole in the skin.

   n. A crust is dried blood or serum on the surface of the skin.

   o. Exanthem is a skin rash from systemic disease.

   p. Enanthem is a rash on the mucous membrane surface.

4. Conjunctivitis involves dilated blood vessels of the conjunctiva. Keratitis is an infection of the cornea. Keratoconjunctivitis is the infection of the conjunctiva and cornea.

Skin Infections

5. The virulence factors of group A streptococcus include an antiphagocytic protein, the M protein. An erythrogenic toxin is another factor. Other toxic products are leukocidins, streptolysins, streptokinase, and hyaluronidase. Impetigo is the most common infection. Infections can be deeper in the skin such as with streptococcal gangrene. Diseases are transmitted by *Streptococcus pyrogenes*. Various antibiotics are used in treatment.

6. Phage typing distinguishes among the various strains of *Staphylococcus aureus*. The virulence factors are alpha and delta toxins, leukocidin, and exfoliative toxin. Skin infections include folliculitis, boils, abscesses, and cellulitis. A surgical suture or splinter often facilitates transmission. Treatment is usually with semisynthetic penicillins.

7. Infections by *Pseudomonas* are difficult to control because the species are found in a wide variety of environments. The groups at highest risk are people already injured. Treatment is usually through a combination of antimicrobial compounds.

8. *Clostridium perfringens* enters the body through a break in the skin. It produces numerous toxins in the body. The symptoms of gas gangrene are tissue death and an impaired blood supply. Muscle and skin can be destroyed with a gas byproduct. Treatment is through high doses of penicillin.

9. Acne is an inflammatory disorder. The drug isotretinoin has side effects.

10. *Mycobacterium leprae* infects the skin, producing a rash and loss of sensation in Hansen's disease. It is rare in the United Stated. It is treated with a combination of drugs, including dapsone, rifampin, and clofazimine.

Viral Causes

11. Varicella infection is a mild disease in children. It is more serious in adults, particularly pregnant women. Shingles occurs most often in patients over 40. There is pain in affected nerves. Cell-mediated immunity is needed for recovery. There is passive immunization for chickenpox. Acyclovir is a safe drug for treatment. The Oka strain vaccine is now recommended for children over age 1.

12. Herpes simplex type I causes vesicles on infected skin. This can lead to cold sores and fever blisters. Gingivostomatitis is the most common clinical syndrome. It is often transmitted through human saliva.

13. Rubeola is transmitted by inhaling a paramyxovirus. It multiplies in the respiratory tract and spreads to the lymphoid tissue. It destroys and agglutinates human red blood cells.

    Cell-mediated immunity is needed for recovery. Chemotherapy and poor nutrition can inhibit recovery. An unbroken chain of infection increases the rate of infection in parts of the world. A vaccine with the attenuated measles virus is used for prevention. Successful vaccination leads to eradication.

14. SSPE results from the replication of the measles virus in brain cells. Brain damage occurs five years later, causing seizures and paralysis.

15. Rubella is a rash-producing illness in children. Lymph nodes are enlarged. It can be prevented by effective vaccination. Rubeola is true measles. It follows a typical pattern of transmission and development. A rubella vaccine has been developed to prevent this disease.

16. The HPV causes common warts and plantar warts. There is a link between HPV and cancer.

Fungal Causes

17. Dermatophytes are a group of fungi that infect body surfaces. Infections include various tinea infections. The body's immune system is relatively weak to these infections.

18. *Candida albicans* produces candidiasis of body surfaces. Thrush is white plaques on the mucous membranes. Diaper dermatitis is a fiery red rash. Both are treated with antifungal creams. Chronic mucocutaneous candidiasis affects the skin and mucous membranes. It is most likely in people with weak cell-mediated immunity. Systemic candidiasis is treated with amphotericin B.

Arthropod Causes

19. *Sarcoptes scabiei* causes scabies. It burrows into the epidermis and causes a hypersensitivity reaction. There can be skin breakdown and secondary bacterial infections.

20. Pediculosis is transmitted by blood-sucking lice. Those on the skin are transmitted by direct body contact or fomites. Treatment is by insecticides.

Eye Infections

21. Bacterial conjunctivitis is often caused by *Streptococcus* and *Haemophilus*. Treatment is with antibiotic ointments. *Pseudomonas aeruginosa* can infect the conjunctiva if there is contact with a foreign body.

22. Inclusion conjunctivitis is caused by an intracellular bacterial parasite. It is treated with oral erythromycin. Trachoma develops when *C. trachomatis* contacts and multiplies on the conjunctiva. It causes inflammation and possible scarring. Transmission occurs by direct ocular secretion. Treatment is by many different antibiotics. It occurs in the Middle East, Africa, and Asia.

23. Neonatal gonorrheal ophthalmia is caused by *Neisseria gonorrhoeae*. Good prenatal care prevents it. Systemic antibiotics are used to prevent it.

24. Onchocerciasis is a disease of the skin and eye. It is transmitted by larvae of the genus *Simulium*. They cause inflammatory reactions of the subcutaneous tissues. Treatment is with antihelminthic drugs such as suramin.

25. Loaiasis can be painful lumps in the skin and can cause blindness. It is caused by *Loa loa*. Treatment is by diethylcarbamazine.

Answers: Correlation Questions

1. *S. pyrogenes* is a Gram-positive coccus and grows as whitish colonies. It is protected from phagocytosis by an M protein. It is treated with penicillin. *S. aureus* is a Gram-positive coccus and grows as yellowish colonies. It can succumb to phagocytosis. It is treated with semisynthetic penicillins or with cephalosporins.

2. The exudate from *Pseudomonas* has a blue-green pigment from the bacterium.

3. Sebum causes acne, an unwanted disease. However, the fatty acids lower the pH, controlling any bacterium sensitive to an acid pH.

4. *C. perfringens* produces an escaping gas.

5. *Pediculus* is more likely to spread in the unsanitary, crowded conditions after war.

6. The bacterium first destroys the conjunctiva and later destroys the cornea.

Answers: Essay Questions

1. It must be administered safely and cheaply to children and adults. The vaccine must stimulate active immunity without harming the human recipient.

2. Two immunizations must be administered to children at the critical ages of 15 months and 5 years.

Answers: Discussion Topics

1. The skin presents a physical barrier and the sebaceous glands secrete fatty acids that also establish a protective layer. Other first lines of defense include the acidity of the stomach and the mucous membrane-ciliary action of the respiratory tract.

2. Other than bacterial morphology and metabolism, try to tie in earlier lessons of bacterial nutrition and genetics. Does the genetics of a microbe determine the toxins it produces? Explain this relationship. Also, draw a relationship between nutritional requirements and where bacteria can meet these needs by inhabiting the body.

Answers: Correlation Questions in the Instructor's Manual

1. The stratification of the epithelial cells in the epidermis provides a thick, protective covering. The simple squamous epithelium in an alveolus provides the needed thin surface for gas exchange.

2. Sebum is a waterproofing agent, therefore protecting the surface of the body.

3. The red spots reveal the bursting of blood vessels, most likely in the vascular dermis. The epidermis lacks a blood supply.

4. Streptokinase destroys blood clots. The formation of blood clots is a protective mechanism, either to plug wounds or to repair small blood vessels that are always rupturing as they wear out.

Chapter 27
Systemic Infections

Learning Goals

To understand:

The anatomy and function of the cardiovascular and lymphatic systems and their defenses against microorganisms

The clinical syndromes that characterize cardiovascular and lymphatic infections

The principal microbial infections of the heart: their diagnosis, prevention, and treatment

The bacterial, viral, protozoal, and helminthic causes of systemic cardiovascular and lymphatic infections: their diagnosis, prevention, and treatment

What is known about the human immunodeficiency virus (HIV), the clinical syndromes of AIDS, its transmission, prevention, and treatment; how the epidemiology of AIDS is changing and what future prospect might be

Chapter Outline

The Cardiovascular and Lymphatic Systems
    Structure and Function
    Defenses and Normal Biota: A Brief Review
    Clinical Syndromes
Infections of the Heart
    Endocarditis
    Myocarditis
    Pericarditis
Systemic Infections
    Bacterial Infections
    Viral Infections
    Protozoal Infections
    Helminthic Infections
Summary

Teaching Tips

1. Use a human heart model to teach the important facts of this organ in your class. Emphasize the structure and function of the chambers, valves, and associated blood vessels.

2. Use a human torso model and human articulated skeleton to trace the general circulation of the blood through the circulatory system and the lymph through the lymphatic system.

3. Study a cross-section of an artery and vein, side by side, on a prepared slide through the microscope in lab. Outline the similarities and differences between these two kinds of blood vessels. For example, which kind of vessel has a proportionately thicker layer of smooth muscle (middle layer)? Which vessel has valves?

4. Demonstrate the typing of ABO and Rh blood groups in the lab. Most biological supply houses sell prepared kits with artificial blood samples and reagents for this activity.

5. Invite a local physician assistant or nurse practitioner to your class. Ask this person to address the challenges in treating the variety of diseases discussed in this chapter.

6. Visit the Internet and start with the search terms *heart - animation*.

Discussion Topics

1. Capillaries are exchange vessels. In these vessels, the blood pressure pushes plasma out of the capillaries and into the tissue spaces. Tissue fluid returns to the circulation through a colloidal osmotic pressure developed in the capillaries. Normally a balance is maintained between the volume of plasma and tissue fluid. How is this balance lost in the development of edema?

2. How do the principles of human anatomy and physiology support the understanding of the concepts in this chapter on systemic infection?

Correlation Questions

1. Cystic fibrosis is an autosomal recessive disease. If the chance to produce an offspring with the disease is 25% , what are the genotypes of the parents.

2. The myocardium of the left ventricle is thicker than the muscular layer in the right ventricle. Explain the reason for this difference.

3. The blood pressure in an systemic artery is higher compared to a systemic vein. Explain the basis for this difference.

4. Why are systemic infections difficult to diagnose?

Answers: Review Questions

1. Intravenous drug use can introduce an infectious microbe into a person's blood. This microbe could cause endocarditis.

The Cardiovascular and Lymphatic Systems

2. The heart is a four-chambered pump that forces blood, a complex tissue, through a series of blood vessels. Valves prevent the back flow of blood in the heart. Arteries are vessels that carry blood away from the heart. Veins return blood to the heart. Capillaries are microscopic exchange vessels. The lymphatic system consists of lymphatic vessels and lymph nodes. This system collects and returns lymph to the blood near the heart.

3. Endocarditis is the infection of the inner lining of the heart. Myocarditis is the infection of the heart muscle. Pericarditis is the infection of the membrane surrounding the heart. A systemic infection is a body-wide infection. It can involve many possible body regions.

Infections of the Heart

4. Acute, bacterial endocarditis occurs suddenly and progresses rapidly. It is often caused by *Staphylococcus aureus*. Intravenous drug users often develop the disease. Heart valve damage is a common result of this disease. It is treated with cephalosporins and penicillinase-resistant penicillins.

   Subacute, bacterial endocarditis occurs in people who have an abnormal heart before an infection. It starts more gradually and progresses more slowly. Patients suffer from pain and fatigue. It is caused by *Streptococcus* species. It is treated with penicillin.

5. Myocarditis in the United States is usually caused by a coxsackie virus and other, unidentified viruses. Chest pain and irregular heartbeat can develop. Rest is the only treatment.

6. Chagas' disease is American trypanosomiasis. It is transmitted by a flagellated protozoan. It is endemic to many parts of the Western Hemisphere. A bite from the insect *Triatoma* introduces the protozoan into the bloodstream. It attacks the brain, liver cells, and brain cells. Symptoms are fever, fatigue, swelling at the site of the bite, and swelling of the face and eyelids. The only treatment is medication to sustain a failing heart.

7. Bacterial pericarditis is more serious than viral pericarditis. It can cause death. Fungal pericarditis can be serious and produce scarring.

Systemic Infections of the Cardiovascular and Lymphatic Systems

8. Bacteremia is the harmless invasion of bacteria into the bloodstream. Septicemia occurs when it becomes persistent and serious.

9. The bubonic plague is caused by *Yersinia pestis*. It enters the lymphatic system and lymph nodes. The nodes become swollen. Prevention includes controlling the reservoir of rodents. Treatment is with a variety of antibiotics. The pneumonic plague infects the lungs from bacterial cells. It is more virulent than the bubonic plague.

10. Tularemia is transmitted by a small Gram-negative coccobacillus. Ticks transmit it transovarially. Ulceroglandular tularemia is the most common clinical symptom. It is treated with streptomycin and tetracycline.

11. People who handle diseased animals are at high risk for brucellosis. Fever is a diagnostic sign.

12. Lyme disease was discovered in 1975. The first stage is a circular, red rash on the skin. The next stage is the spread of the bacteria into the lymph nodes. The last stage is chronic arthritis. It is caused by a spirochete bacterium. Transmission is by several arthropod and mammalian hosts. Removing hosts from a region can eradicate the disease. Diagnosis is through the symptoms of the stages. Treatment is by several antibiotics. A vaccine became available in 1998.

13. Epidemic relapsing fever is transmitted by a body louse and occurs in crowded, unsanitary conditions. Endemic relapsing fever occurs in the western United States. Serious problems result when many bloodborne bacteria die at one time, therefore prompting the gradual treatment by antibiotics.

14. Cutaneous anthrax occurs when bacteria pass through the skin and enter the bloodstream, causing septicemia. Endemic anthrax occurs when people inhale bacterial spores. Symptoms are mild.

15. Cat scratch disease will usually resolve on its own.

16. Symptoms of Rocky Mountain spotted fever involve damage to capillaries and a spotty rash. There can be abnormal blood clotting, shock, and death. Rapid identification of the microorganisms does not exist. Treatment is most effective early with antibiotics.

17. Epidemic typhus is caused by *Rickettsia prowazekii* and body louse. The microbe multiplies on a wound on the skin and enters the bloodstream. It multiplies in small blood vessels. Tetracycline and chloramphenicol are used for treatment. Murine typhus is caused by *Rickettsia typhi*. It is less severe. It causes fever, a rash, and headaches. It is treated with the same antibiotics.

18. Yellow fever is transmitted by an RNA virus. It is absorbed into the lymph nodes and transported to nearby lymph nodes. It produces fever, headache, and significant liver damage. The urban form is common in cities. The endemic form exists in jungles of the world with monkeys as a reservoir.

19. Compared to yellow fever, dengue fever is caused by several closely related viruses through the bite of an insect.

20. EBV established a latent infection in B lymphocytes. The virus can proliferate here and spread via the bloodstream, causing fever and fatigue.

21. HIV is a retrovirus. Its RNA makes DNA. T4 cells are damaged. They are important in the immune response. The HIV enters the circulatory-lymphatic system and binds to a target cell by a protein. Its viral RNA directs synthesis of DNA in the host cell. CD4+T cells are killed and their count drops significantly. The crippled immune system leaves an infected person susceptible to other diseases.

    The several modes of transmission involve the mixing of body fluids. Prevention involves inhibiting this mixing. The spread of the disease in the United States now involves all kinds of sexual contacts and interactions.

22. Discovery of the type of immune response against HIV infection is the key to developing a vaccine. Current treatment involves HAART and agents that inhibit reverse transcriptase and HIV protease.

    AIDS has become increasingly common among drug abusers who share needles. It is no longer found exclusively among homosexual males. Men and women with drug-acquired AIDS are heterosexual. Safe sex and the stoppage of using dirty needles during drug use are key steps in curtailing the increase in cases of AIDS.

23. *Plasmodium* develops sporozoites and merozoites in the human bloodstream as part of its life cycle. It causes lysis of red blood cells and fever. Control involves eradicating the arthropod vector. New drugs are being sought and a vaccine is a possibility.

24. Humans acquire toxoplasmosis from a protozoan. They acquire it by eating meat or by eating oocysts accidentally. Prevention is by avoiding these two possibilities. A normal immune system can usually defeat the disease.

25. Babesiosis is caused by a protozoan. It is transmitted by a tick vector. It causes fever, headache, chills, and fatigue. The microbe does have rodents as a reservoir. Lyme disease is also transmitted through the bite of the same kind of tick and has a reservoir in the deer population. It is also a protozoal disease.

26. The schistosome life cycle includes the larval attack of the human host blood vessels. This leads to internal bleeding and loss of blood. The essential snail hosts are not found in North America. The disease is treated with praziquantel or oxiaminiquine.

27. The life cycles of the microbes causing filariasis cause infection of the blood and lymph nodes. There is fluid accumulation and swelling of the lymph nodes and scrotum. Prevention involves avoiding the bite of the mosquito vector. Treatment is by diethylcarbamazine.

Answers: Correlation Questions

1. The black spots of the plague develop from subcutaneous bleeding. Bacteria enter the blood from infected lymph nodes. Mass destruction of red blood cells occurs during malaria. Hemoglobin is released from these cells and turns black. This is the source of the black color in the urine. Therefore, blood is responsible for the symptoms in both diseases. However, the changes the blood undergoes are different.

2. Relapsing fever has an epidemic form, as does epidemic typhus. *Borrelia* species cause relapsing fever and Lyme disease.

3. When the organisms causing anthrax enter the blood and produce substantial quantities of toxin, the toxin cannot be treated with antibiotics.

4. A live, attenuated vaccine exists to stimulate the immune system for the treatment of yellow fever. An HIV infection cripples the immune system to the point it cannot carry out an effective response. Also, AIDS is caused by a unique virus rather than by the well-understood bacterium that causes yellow fever.

5. Schistosomiasis cannot develop in North America because the essential snail hosts are not found there.

6. Both diseases are caused by Gram-negative, rod-shaped bacteria.

Answers: Essay Questions

1. Testing and using an AIDS virus is a long, arduous process. There are many side effects and the treatment is costly. However, an effective cure could save many lives.

2. Eliminate the reservoir of the Ebola virus, an unknown animal living in the African savanna or rain forest.

Answers: Discussion Topics

1. The push of the blood pressure becomes much greater than the pull of the fluid back into the capillaries. This can promote the accumulation of fluid into the tissue spaces, causing edema. Also, the pull of fluid into the capillaries is due to a hypertonic plasma established by plasma proteins. If these proteins are lost due to poor nutrition or a liver malfunction, fluid will not be pulled back into the circulation. Fluid will accumulate in the tissue spaces, causing edema.

   Adding to this problem, infected capillary walls can become overly permeable to fluid, causing more of it to leak into the tissue spaces.

2. There are many examples including the circulation of blood through the body. Drugs are assimilated into the blood after absorption across the mucosal wall on the small intestine. Once absorbed, drugs can flow in the blood and reach target sites to treat infections. Drugs are cleared from the blood and become part of the urine through the action of nephrons in the kidney. Penicillin, for example, is cleared from the blood, in part, by tubular secretion in the distal convoluted tubules and collecting ducts of the nephrons.

Answers: Correlation Questions in the Instructor's Manual

1. This is a monohybrid cross from genetics. Each parent is heterozygous, with a genotype of Cc. The chance to produce an offspring with the genotype cc, producing cystic fibrosis, is 1/4.

2. The left ventricle pumps blood through the systemic circulation, a longer trip for blood flow compared to the route taken by blood from the right ventricle through the pulmonary circuit. The thicker musculature in the left ventricle is an adaption for the greater pumping pressure needed for blood circulating from the left ventricle to distant body sites.

3. Arteries transport blood away from the heart. They are closer to the heart, the source of blood pressure as it pumps blood. Veins, returning blood to the heart, are at the end of the trip for blood flow. The pressure has diminished in these vessels compared to the arteries.

4. The entire body can be infected as the blood serves as a vehicle to transport an infection to many body sites.

Chapter 28
Microorganisms and the Environment

Learning Goals

How the evolution of organisms led to our present environment

Soil and water as habitats for the microorganisms that mediate major biogeochemical transformations

The major cycles of matter—the nitrogen cycle, the carbon cycle, the phosphorus cycle, and the sulfur cycle—and the microorganisms involved

The ecological impact of the major cyclic transformations of matter

How knowledge of cycles of matter is applied to treating waste water and drinking water

How some human-made chemicals escape from the carbon cycle and what can be done about it

Chapter Outline

Life and the Evolution of Our Environment
Microorganisms in the Biosphere
    Soil
    Water
    Air
The Cycles of Matter
    The Nitrogen Cycle
    The Carbon Cycle
    The Phosphorus Cycle
    The Sulfur Cycle
Treatment of Waste Water
    Sewage Treatment Plants
    Septic Tanks and Oxidation Ponds
Treatment of Drinking Water
    Processing Methods
    Testing Methods
Summary

Teaching Tips

1. Assign the several kinds of questions at the end of the chapter. Encourage your students to answer the questions in their own words. After doing this they can check the chapter for the accuracy of their answers.

2. This chapter is a synthesis of many concepts you have previously taught. Show the students how, for example, basic chemistry (Chapter 2) and the characteristics of different prokaryotic species (Chapter 11) tie in to the information of Chapter 28.

3. Diagram the broad patterns of the biogeochemical cycles explained in this chapter. For example, in the nitrogen cycle show the transition from nitrogen gas - ammonia - nitrite - nitrate. At the end of your lecture, ask the students to also outline the broad patterns of one of the cycles without notes.

4. Invite a representative of the local health department to visit your class and explain the local procedures to treat waste water.

5. Visit the Internet and start with the search terms *biogeochemical cycles*.

Discussion Topics

1. Many principles of ecology are discussed in this chapter. Ecology represents the interrelatedness of organisms. How does phosphorus, for example, act as a limiting factor affect aquatic populations?

2. What are the ecological problems with materials that are not biodegradable?

Correlation Questions

1. During crop rotation, some farmers grow leguminous plants in fields. What is the strategy behind this choice?

2. An ecologist examines several layers of soil in a soil profile. What is the probable composition of the dark, moist layer in the soil?

3. What is the origin of the greenhouse effect in the atmosphere?

4. Where is the placement of the biosphere in the levels-of-organization hierarchy?

Answers: Review Questions

Life and the Evolution of Our Environment

1. Some species of microorganisms are pathogens. However, the majority of microbial species perform beneficial roles. These roles include acting as decomposers in the environment.

2. Biogeochemical cycles involve elements circulating between the biotic and abiotic components of the environment. The oldest fossils were from cyanobacteria that did not require oxygen for their metabolism.

Microorganisms in the Biosphere

3. Microorganisms carry out geochemical transformations that decompose substances in the soil, improving its fertility. By mineralization, organic material is changed to an inorganic form. *Streptomyces* species break down plant and animal remains. Other Gram-positive bacteria also perform this role. Mycorrhizae are fungi forming symbiotic associations with plant roots. The fungus derives nutrients from the plant. The plant also derives some benefits.

4. Phytoplankton in the water are the main source of photosynthesis on the planet. Eutrophication in the water by bacteria produces algal blooms.

The Cycles of Matter

5. The cycles of matter require a variety of organisms, functioning in a particular sequence, to circulate minerals between the living and nonliving parts of the environment.

6. By nitrogen fixation, bacterial species fix nitrogen from the atmosphere into plant species. Some of these bacteria, such as *Azotobacter*, are free-living. It protects its enzyme nitrogenase by respiring oxygen rapidly. *Rhizobium* has its nitrogenase protected by a plant. Heterotrophic bacteria carry out ammonification. By nitrification the fixed nitrogen is converted to nitrite and nitrate ions. Denitrification returns nitrogen to the atmosphere, completing a cyclic flow of nitrogen through the environment.

7. The Haber process industrially fixes nitrogen to produce fertilizers. *Azolla* harbors symbiotic nitrogen-fixing bacteria.

8. Photosynthesis fixes carbon, from carbon dioxide in the atmosphere, into sugars. Herbivores eat plants and a succession of carnivores complete the food chain, passing organic carbon from organism to organism.

    Respiration returns carbon to the atmosphere as carbon dioxide. Combustion also adds this gas back to the atmosphere. This step has upset the balance of the cycle by increasing the burning of fossil fuels. It has increased the level of carbon dioxide in the air and promoted global warming by the greenhouse effect.

9. The phosphorus cycle does not have a gaseous intermediate. Dissolved phosphates enter the waterways from rocks through erosion and weathering. Plants use the phosphate for their metabolism and the phosphorus is passed through the steps of a food chain. Decomposition of plant and animal remains returns the phosphorus to the geological structures.

10. In the sulfur cycle, ions are reduced to hydrogen sulfide. It is reoxidized to sulfate. Elemental sulfur is an intermediate in the cycle.

Treatment of Waste Water

11. Sewage is municipal waste water. A BOD is the amount of oxygen needed for microorganisms to respire all organic material put into a system. It offers knowledge for the amount of time needed to treat sewage.

12. In a municipal sewage plant, primary treatment is mechanical and removes primary sludge. Secondary treatment is biological and uses forced aeration to kill bacteria. Tertiary treatment removes or reduces the concentration of ions in water. By the activity of *Zoogloea ramigera,* sewage is mineralized in the secondary treatment.

13. Small anaerobic digesters degrade sludge by anaerobic bacteria. Septic tanks are small anaerobic digesters. Oxidation ponds use oxygenic phototrophs. Sewage farming involves adding sewage to ditches and allowing it to seep into the ground.

Treatment of Drinking Water

14. Drinking water is first treated with alum, allowing colloidal particles to settle out in flocculation tanks. The water is clarified next by filtering it. Finally it is passed over beds of activated charcoal to remove unwanted compounds.

Answers: Correlation Questions

1. The bubbles could be methane produced in the mud by methanogens. The gas will have a distinct odor.

2. The chemicals inhibit the bacteria that normally carry out the nitrification.

3. The hydrogen sulfide gas from the mud flat has an odor similar to rotten eggs.

4. The chemicals used to remove phosphate could also remove the sulfate. Both should be removed, as either one could be a limiting factor to microbial growth.

5. Both are gases produced by bacterial metabolism.

6. Aerobic respiration evolved after nitrogen fixation, as the original atmosphere of the Earth was reducing and lacked oxygen. Some nitrogen-fixing bacteria do not require oxygen.

Answers: Essay Questions

1. The absence of denitrification would mean the lack of converting nitrate to nitrogen gas. Therefore, nitrogen would not cycle completely.

2. The absence of nitrification would prevent the incorporation of nitrogen gas into ammonia, nitrite, and nitrate. These conversions are necessary for most organisms to metabolically incorporate nitrogen. It cannot be used directly from the atmosphere.

Answers: Discussion Topics

1. Here is one example. Phosphorus is often a limiting factor to plant and microbial growth in waterways. An increase of this element in the water leads to increased growth of plant and microbial populations, depleting the oxygen in the water. This can have an adverse effect on fish life in the water.

2. Materials that are not biodegradable have elements that will accumulate in the environment. They cannot be decomposed by microbial action and, therefore, the elements will not recycle for reuse in the environment.

Answers: Correlation Questions in the Instructor's Manual

1. Some crops deplete nitrogen from the soil to fulfill their metabolic needs. A leguminous plant, through its mutualistic association with bacteria, replenishes this lost nitrogen in the soil.

2. This layer is humus. It is a dark, moist layer of decaying organic matter.

3. A buildup of carbon dioxide in the atmosphere serves to trap heat into the surface of the earth, causing trapped heat buildup similar to the effect of a greenhouse.

4. The biosphere is the largest, most encompassing level.

Chapter 29
Microbial Biotechnology

Learning Goals

To understand:

The traditional uses of lactic acid bacteria to preserve food and make cheese and other dairy products

How yeasts are used to make wine, beer, and bread, and, with acetic acid bacteria, vinegar

The principal methods of slowing or preventing growth of microorganisms to preserve food

How microorganisms are used in insecticides

The industrial fermentations that produce solvents, amino acids, antibiotics, and enzymes

How genetically engineered microbes are used to make new products for medicine, industry, and agriculture

Chapter Outline

Traditional Uses of Microorganisms
    Lactic Acid Bacteria
    Yeasts
    Mixed Cultures
Microbes as Insecticides
Microbes as Chemical Factories
    Anaerobic Fermentations
    Aerobic Processes
    Chemical Reactions
Using Gentically Engineered Microbes
    Medical Uses
    Agricultural Uses
Summary

Teaching Tips

1. Is there a geneticist/microbiologist in your biology department? Invite this faculty member to your class to speak about the advances in the technology with microbes and genetics.

2. Plan a trip for your class to a local brewery or dairy to learn more about the applications of microbes commercially.

3. Review the concepts of metabolism, DNA structure, transcription, and translation to help students understand the information in this chapter.

4. If your course has a lab component, study the bacteria in milk and other commercial products discussed in this chapter.

5. Use a human torso model in class to discuss the structure and function of the anterior pituitary, adrenal cortex, pancreas, etc. Name each structure as you locate it. Explain the function of each hormone secreted by each gland.

Discussion Topics

1. In addition to the applications described in this chapter, what other problems in our society could be solved through the products of genetic engineering?

2. Other scientific investigations take unexpected turns with unexpected discoveries. How was this true in the discovery of antibiotics?

Correlation Questions

1. How does the refrigeration of milk inhibit the souring of milk?

2. How has genetic engineering helped in the treatment of several human disease?

3. A young person, with a genetic basis for pituitary dwarfism is treated with doses of genetically-engineered human growth hormone. However, this person develops dwarfism. What sources should a researcher check to explain this?

4. A protease inhibitor is added to a mixture of rennin and protein. How will this affect chemical activity in the mixture?

Answers: Review Questions

Traditional Uses of Microorganisms

1. Biotechnology is the use of microorganisms for practical purposes.

2. Lactic acid bacteria metabolize sugars to produce substances that add a pleasant taste to food. They are used to make many kinds of dairy products such as yogurt and cheese. They are used to make and preserve sauerkraut.

3. Microorganisms, such as yeasts, produce alcohol by fermentation. Different kinds of yeasts make different kinds of wine. Some species of lactic acid bacteria, however, spoil wine by their metabolism.

4. Cereal grains are saccharified by being hydrolyzed by the enzyme amylase into glucose. Amylase from malt is used to make whiskey and beer. Whiskey is distilled from fermented cereal grains. *Saccharomyces cerevisiae* are used to make beer.

5. Vinegar is made by fermenting sugar in fruit juice. *Saccharomyces cerevesiae* is usually the yeast doing this. Then a species of *Acetobacter* oxidizes the ethanol from the first step into acetic acid. This is the acid in vinegar.

6. Microorganisms, usually *Saccharomyces cerevisiae*, carry out fermentation in dough to produce bubbles of carbon dioxide. This raises the bread.

7. Starter cultures are complex mixtures of bacteria and fungi used to inoculate food. Stable mixed cultures have high growth rates and increased yields. They are highly resistant to contamination.

Microbes as Insecticides

8. *Bacillus thuringiensis* is an insect pathogen that makes Bt. *B. popilliae* is an insect pathogen and makes Bp. *Nosema locustae* is a protozoan that makes spores that combat insects. Baculoviruses make bioinsecticides.

9. Bioinsecticides do not contaminate environments. Insects do no evolve a resistance to them as they do against chemical insecticides.

Microbes as Chemical Factories

10. Fermentation is the anaerobic production of substances. Fermenters are the vessels where these changes take place.

11. Industrial fermentations may at times not be economically efficient. They are abandoned and reused when more profitable.

12. Anaerobic fermentations can produce ethanol, acetone, and butanol.

13. Aerobic fermentation requires vessels with large surface areas. The addition of microbes and the input of substances for fermentation were other challenges. Aerobic fermentations produce antibiotics, amino acids, and enzymes.

14. Microorganisms can be used in sequences to carry out specific chemical reactions of chemical pathways.

Using Genetically Engineered Microbes to Make New Products

15. Recombinant DNA technology uses microorganisms to produce any compound made by other microorganisms.

16. Medical products of DNA technology include hormones and antibiotics. The human growth hormone is produced with a DNA probe that can hybridize with mRNA. From this, message DNA is made by a reverse transcriptase. Recombinant DNA is introduced into a host cell by transfection. Synthesis of the hormone is directed in the cell.

17. Bt toxin protects plant roots. Its production is transferred from bacilli into another bacterium. Ice-minus bacteria seed the atmosphere for rain-making. Silage is protected against damage from certain anaerobic bacteria. Their genes can be cloned. Sheep-shearing protein has been cloned and produced by *E. coli*.

Answers: Correlation Questions

1. A different kind of microorganism, each with a different metabolic capability, is involved in each process.

2. A product is formed that is less acidic.

3. Ethanol is produced in wine and champagne. For this there must be fermentation of cereal grains. Carbon dioxide is produced to leaven bread. Propionic acid is made in Swiss cheese.

4. Penicillin is used as an antibiotic to treat infections. Some microbes can be consumed in beer or wine without harm to the person consuming them.

5. The hGH from bacteria should be free of infection and can be harvested more rapidly, in larger quantities.

6. Although the gene is not normally a part of the *E. coli* genome, it is placed in the bacterial chromosome by genetic engineering. Otherwise, it is not a gene that signals growth in this bacterium.

Answers: Essay Questions

1. *E. coli* can produce a variety of proteins at a rapid rate. The effectiveness of some of these products, however, remains untested. Also, there is always a possible danger of producing a bacterium this way that could produce harmful effects in the environment and be difficult to control.

2. They are not produced and found in the bacteria naturally in the environment but are placed there through genetic engineering.

Answers: Discussion Topics

1. Consider the production of erythropoietin as a recent breakthrough to start this discussion. Are there other human diseases associated with a missing product that could be genetically engineered? Discuss these with your class.

2. Review the research done by Fleming. Emphasize that chance favors the prepared mind and that research can have unexpected turns.

Answers: Correlation Questions in the Instructor's Manual

1. Refrigeration subjects bacteria to a temperature that slows down their metabolism. Therefore, the production of lactic acid proceeds at a very slow pace.

2. Examples include the treatment of type I diabetes with insulin, anemia with EPO, and pituitary dwarfism with human growth hormone.

3. The person still needs the proper environmental components for development , including exercise and proper nutrition.

4. Rennin has protease activity. In the presence of an inhibitor, the chemical breakdown of the protein is curtailed.

Test Bank

Chapter 1
The Science of Microbiology

Multiple Choice

1. Lister used phenol to

   A. disprove the theory of spontaneous generation.
   B. prevent the infection in wounds.
   C. sterilize surgical instruments.
   D. stimulate bacterial growth.

   (Knowledge)

2. The bacterium that causes the bubonic plague is

   A. *Bacillus subtilis*.
   B. *Escherichia coli*.
   C. *Pseudomonas aeruginosa*.
   D. *Yersinia pestis*.

   (Knowledge)

3. The Irish potato famine was caused by a

   A. bacterium.
   B. fungus.
   C. protozoan.
   D. virus.

   (Knowledge)

4. Select the characteristic that all microorganisms have in common.

   A. They are bacteria.
   B. They are organisms used in biological research.
   C. They are pathogens.
   D. They are too small to be seen with the unaided eye.

   (Knowledge)

5. A microbe is used to produce erythropoietin, a hormone that signals the production of red blood cells in the bone marrow of the human body. The production of this hormone is an advance mainly from the field of _____ microbiology.

   A. agricultural
   B. environmental
   C. industrial
   D. pathogenic

   (Comprehension)

6. Select the incorrect association.

   A. algae/eukaryotes
   B. archaea/prokaryotes
   C. bacteria/prokaryotes
   D. protozoa/not microscopic

   (Comprehension)

7. Select the incorrect statement about a virus.

   A. It contains DNA or RNA.
   B. It has a protein coat.
   C. It is a cellular organism.
   D. It is visible through the electron microscope.

   (Comprehension)

8. Select the correct statement about bacteria.

   A. Most are multicellular.
   B. None exhibit motility.
   C. Their cells are filled with uniform, grainy material
   D. Their cells are larger than eukaryotic cells.

   (Comprehension)

9. Bacteria can live at temperature extremes that vary as much as _____ degrees C.

   A. 40 to 60
   B. 20 to 80
   C. 0 to 100
   D. -20 to 110

   (Knowledge)

10. A microbe is discovered in a local waterway. Testing this water reveals its high temperature and high acidity. The microbe produces bubbles in this water. However, tests on the microbe reveal that it does not cause diseases in humans. It probably belongs to the group of

    A. algae
    B. archaea
    C. fungi
    D. viruses

    (Application)

11. Select the correct statement about algae.

    A. Their cells do not contain chloroplasts.
    B. They are eukaryotes.
    C. They do not include kelp, a macroscopic organism.
    D. They lack membrane-bound organelles.

    (Comprehension)

12. The group of fungi does not include

    A. amoeba.
    B. molds.
    C. mushrooms.
    D. yeasts.

    (Knowledge)

13. African sleeping sickness is caused by a(n)

    A. alga.
    B. bacterium.
    C. protozoan.
    D. yeast.

    (Knowledge)

14. The most animal-like microorganisms are

    A. algae.
    B. bacteria.
    C. protozoans.
    D. yeasts.

    (Knowledge)

15. Flatworms and roundworms are

    A. arthropods.
    B. echinoderms.
    C. helminths.
    D. mollusks.

    (Knowledge)

16. Select the disease that is not caused by a virus.

    A. malaria
    B. polio
    C. smallpox
    D. yellow fever

    (Knowledge)

17. Leeuwenhoek's microscopes could magnify to about

    A. 266X.
    B. 400X.
    C. 900X.
    D. 1000X.

    (Knowledge)

18. Redi conducted experiments that discredited the theory of

    A. biogenesis.
    B. cells.
    C. inheritance.
    D. spontaneous generation.

    (Knowledge)

19. In Pasteur's experiments on spontaneous generation, the purpose of the curve in his flasks containing meat broth was to

    A. increase the surface area of the flask.
    B. increase the volume of the flask.
    C. prevent microorganisms from entering the flasks.
    D. promote heating of the broth.

    (Comprehension)

20. A researcher attempts to duplicate the experiments on spontaneous generation conducted by Pasteur. Nutrient broth is sealed in glass flasks with curved necks and is sterilized with heat. The broth is cooled to room temperature. After 48 hours the researcher observes that bacteria populate the broth in the flask. The best explanation for this observation is that the bacteria studied can

    A. change their genetic structure rapidly.
    B. develop from a nonliving source.
    C. form endospores.
    D. pass through pores in the glass.

    (Application)

21. Select the incorrect association.

    A. Jenner/studied smallpox
    B. Koch/anthrax
    C. Pasteur/French chemist
    D. Spallanzani/studied typhoid fever

    (Comprehension)

22. A vaccine can contain a

    A. chemical in high concentration.
    B. chemical in low concentration.
    C. potent form of a microorganism.
    D. weakened form of a microorganism.

    (Knowledge)

23. When Jenner inoculated a child with the fluid from a cowpox blister, it

    A. caused an infection.
    B. had no effect.
    C. stimulated immunity.
    D. worked against a vaccine.

    (Knowledge)

24. To test a drug by selective toxicity is a principle of

    A. chemotherapy.
    B. genetic engineering.
    C. immunology.
    D. virology.

    (Knowledge)

25. The first medically useful antibiotic was

    A. a sulfa drug.
    B. erythromycin.
    C. penicillin.
    D. tetracycline.

    (Knowledge)

26. A researcher attempts to duplicate the experiments by Iwanowski on the tobacco mosaic virus. The researcher pours filtered juice from a plant through a filter. However, he discovers that this filtered fluid contains both bacteria and viruses from the plant. This probably occurs because the filter has pores with a diameter

    A. larger than bacteria but not larger than viruses.
    B. larger than viruses but not larger than bacteria.
    C. larger than both bacteria and viruses.
    D. smaller than both bacteria and viruses.

    (Application)

27. Salvarsan comes from the Latin word that means

    A. disease.
    B. healing.
    C. to save.
    D. to solve.

    (Knowledge)

28. A bacterial culture can double its number of cells every 30 minutes. One bacterial cell placed in nutrient broth leads to the production of _____ cells in one hour.

    A. four
    B. eight
    C. six
    D. ten

(Application)

29. Genetic engineering involves recombinant _____ technology.

    A. carbohydrate
    B. DNA
    C. lipid
    D. protein

(Knowledge)

30. The most common microorganism manipulated for genetic engineering is a

    A. bacterium.
    B. fungus.
    C. protozoan.
    D. virus.

(Knowledge)

True/False

31. The host of the microorganism causing the bubonic plague was a fish.

(Knowledge)

32. *Phytophthora infestans* was the microorganism causing the potato blight in Ireland.

(Knowledge)

33. An organism is discovered growing on the surface of a tree trunk. Studies show it is non-photosynthetic and lives off the decaying matter of the tree. These studies show that the organism cannot be a fungus.

(Comprehension)

34. A cellular organism is studied. The results show that the organism lacks a defined nucleus and most organelles. These results show that the organism could be a prokaryote.

(Comprehension)

35. Some bacteria are photosynthetic.

(Knowledge)

36. The organisms of archaea are not closely related to bacteria or humans.

    (Knowledge)

37. Phytoplankton is algae.

    (Knowledge)

38. Fungi are nonphotosynthetic, prokaryotic, scavengers, and lack mycelia.

    (Comprehension)

39. A microorganism is identified under the microscope. It moves by the beating action of its cilia. This organism is probably a protozoan.

    (Comprehension)

40. A tapeworm is a flatworm.

    (Knowledge)

41. The light microscope in a biology lab has a total magnification of about 1000X. This can be used to study viruses in the lab.

    (Comprehension)

42. The pathogen for AIDS is a bacterium.

    (Knowledge)

43. The organism *Trichinella* is a helminth.

    (Knowledge)

44. Needham's experimental results apparently supported the theory of spontaneous generation. The experiments of Spallanzani and Pasteur disproved this theory.

    (Comprehension)

45. Koch's experiments established a relationship between microorganisms and disease.

    (Knowledge)

Completion

46. The potato blight in Ireland occurred in the _____ century.

    (Knowledge)

47. A local community hires a microbiologist to study the local water supply, testing it for safe human consumption. The training of the microbiologist is mainly in the field of _____ microbiology.

    (Comprehension)

48. DDT is found ineffective at controlling an insect pest that is destroying local crops. A microorganism is tried as a biological control. This is an advance in the field of _____ microbiology.

    (Comprehension)

49. Prokaryotic cells lack structures that are bound by cell _____.

    (Knowledge)

50. You know that a microorganism is a protozoan if it moves by the action of _____, _____, or flagella.

    (Comprehension)

51. _____ are infectious agents that consist exclusively of protein molecules.

    (Knowledge)

52. A large virus is discovered. If the average bacterial cell has a diameter of one micrometer, the diameter of the virus is about _____.

    (Application)

53. The term "vaccination" is derived from the Latin word that means _____.

    (Knowledge)

54. Penicillin was originally referred to as the _____ drug.

    (Knowledge)

55. _____ is the bacterium used most often in studies involving recombinant DNA technology.

    (Knowledge)

Short Essay

56. Most modern classification schemes place the bacteria in a distinct kingdom, one that is apart from the plant or animal kingdoms. However, in the historical two-kingdom scheme of classification, bacteria were classified as plants. Explain the logic of this classification.

    (Analysis)

57. Many biologists described protozoans as "unicellular," as they are one-celled organisms. However, because of their unique cell structure and complexity, other biologists use the term "acellular." Which term do you think is more accurate?

    (Analysis)

58. As a student planning for a career in microbiology, can you assess the other areas of science that are important in preparation for a career in this field?

    (Evaluation)

Correlation Questions

59. Consider the following Case History: A female patient visits an urgent care clinic. Her symptoms include abdominal pain and fever. A small sample of blood is withdrawn from her body. This sample is sent to a microbiology clinic. Microscopic examination of her blood generates data for calculation of her total white blood cell count. This cell count normally falls within the range of 5,000 to 10,000 white blood cells per cubic millimeter of blood. Her count is 20,000. What is the advantage of sampling a small volume of blood for this test?

60. From the Case History cited in question 59, what is the reason for paying close attention to the white blood cell count in this patient?

Answers

Multiple Choice

1. B 2. D 3. B 4. D 5. C 6. D 7. C 8. C 9. D 10. B 11. B
12. A 13. C 14. C 15. C 16. A 17. A 18. D 19. C 20. C 21. D
22. D 23. C 24. A 25. C 26. C 27. C 28. A 29. B 30. A

True/False

31. False 32. True 33. False 34. True 35. True 36. True 37. True
38. False 39. True 40. True 41. False 42. False 43. True 44. True 45. True

Completion

46. nineteenth 47. environmental 48. agricultural 49. membranes
50. cilia and pseudopodia 51. Prions 52. one-tenth of a micrometer 53. cow
54. wonder 55. *Escherichia coli*

Short Essay

56. The bacterial cell has a cell wall. Also, some bacteria are photosynthetic. These are characteristics shared in common with plants.

57. They are one-celled. However, the comparison of protozoan cells to animal cells supports the idea of an acellular makeup, as the protozoan cell is usually more versatile for many functions and less specialized. To perform many functions, a protozoan cell is more complex than the cells of other kinds of organisms.

58. Chemistry offers an important foundation toward understanding the facts and concepts of microbiology. Bacterial cell structure cannot be described without reference to the chemical makeup of cells. Human anatomy and physiology is relevant, as pathogens overcome the human immune system. Various normal floral populations of bacteria inhabit specific regions of the body. Physics is important for understanding the optics of microscopes.

Correlation Questions

59. The human body normally contains 4 to 6 liters of whole blood. Interpreting test results of the patient's blood depends on knowing the concentration of white blood cells throughout this volume. A small sample of the patient's blood indicates the white blood cell concentration throughout the entire volume of the patient's blood. It is impossible to monitor the entire blood volume of the patient. Therefore, the technique of sampling is used. The data from the sample represents the characteristics of the entire blood volume of the patient.

60. White blood cells are the major infection fighters in the blood. As a major component of the immune system of the human body, their changing concentration reflects the changing immune response of the body (See Chapters 16 through 18 in the textbook). An elevated white blood cell count indicates that the body is making more white blood cells, an appropriate response to combat the effects of the microbe infecting the body. More white blood cells are needed to combat these microbes and protect the body.

Chapter 2
Basic Chemistry

Multiple Choice

1. Each of the following was a part of the "chemical soup" in Urey's experiments except
   A. ammonia.
   B. methane.
   C. glucose.
   D. water vapor.
   (Knowledge)

2. Select the incorrect statement about the intact atom.
   A. A proton is not neutral.
   B. An electron has a negative charge.
   C. An intact atom has a net charge.
   D. The number of protons and electrons is equal.
   (Comprehension)

3. An atom has an atomic number of 11 and an atomic weight of 23. The number of neutrons in its nucleus is
   A. 11
   B. 12
   C. 23
   D. 34
   (Comprehension)

4. Which atom has 8 protons in its nucleus?
   A. carbon
   B. hydrogen
   C. nitrogen
   D. oxygen
   (Knowledge)

5. Select the element that is not among the six most abundant elements by weight in living organisms.
   A. carbon
   B. iron
   C. nitrogen
   D. sulfur
   (Knowledge)

6.   An atom has an atomic number of 8. The number of electrons in its outer energy shell is
     A. 2
     B. 4
     C. 6
     D. 8
     (Comprehension)

7.   A molecule of hydrogen peroxide contains two hydrogen atoms and two oxygen atoms. Its molecular weight is
     A. 18
     B. 24
     C. 32
     D. 34
     (Comprehension)

8.   Select the incorrect association.
     A. covalent bond/ions
     B. DNA/molecule
     C. phosphorus/atom
     D. proton/positive
     (Comprehension)

9.   An atom loses two outer-shell electrons. Its charge becomes
     A. minus 1.
     B. minus 2.
     C. plus 1.
     D. plus 2.
     (Comprehension)

10. Select the correct association.
     A. anion/positive
     B. cation/negative
     C. chloride/positive
     D. hydrogen bond/weak
     (Comprehension)

11. Catalysts __1__ the rate of a chemical reaction as they __2__ the activation energy barrier.
     A. 1 - decrease, 2 - lower
     B. 1 - decrease, 2 - raise
     C. 1 - increase, 2 - lower
     D. 1 - increase, 2 - raise
     (Knowledge)

12. Select the best description for the bonding within a water molecule.

    A. sharing of electrons, polar
    B. sharing of electrons, nonpolar
    C. transfer of electrons, polar
    D. transfer of electrons, nonpolar

    (Comprehension)

13. Select the correct characteristic about water.

    A. About 90% of a microbe is water.
    B. It has a high specific heat.
    C. Its boiling point is 100 degrees F.
    D. Its freezing point is 32 degrees C.

    (Comprehension)

14. _____ dissociate in solution to form hydroxide ions.

    A. Acids
    B. Bases
    C. Colloids
    D. Salts

    (Knowledge)

15. Buffers

    A. change the temperature of a solution.
    B. decrease the rate of chemical reactions.
    C. increase the rate of chemical reactions.
    D. stabilize the pH of a solution.

    (Knowledge)

16. A pH of 4 is _____ times more acidic than a pH of 7.

    A. 10
    B. 100
    C. 1000
    D. 10000

    (Comprehension)

17. A solution has a hydrogen ion concentration of 0.0001 moles per liter. It is __1__ times __2__ acidic than a solution with a hydrogen ion concentration of 0.0000001 moles per liter.

    A. 1 - one hundred, 2 - less
    B. 1 - one hundred, 2 - more
    C. 1 - one thousand, 2 - less
    D. 1 - one thousand, 2 - more

    (Application)

18. By a dehydration synthesis water is

    A. added and a chemical bond is broken.
    B. added and a chemical bond is formed.
    C. removed and a chemical bond is broken.
    D. removed and a chemical bond is formed.

    (Knowledge)

19. The most abundant macromolecules in cells are

    A. carbohydrates.
    B. lipids.
    C. proteins.
    D. water molecules.

    (Knowledge)

20. The alpha and beta sheets refer to a protein's _____ structure.

    A. primary
    B. secondary
    C. tertiary
    D. quaternary

    (Knowledge)

21. Select the correct statement about DNA.

    A. It encodes genetic information.
    B. It is usually single-stranded.
    C. Its base pairs include adenine bonded to guanine.
    D. Its bases include uracil.

    (Comprehension)

22. A DNA molecule has 1500 base pairs. 40% of the base pairs are guanine linked to cytosine by hydrogen bonding. The number of adenine bases in this molecule is

    A. 400
    B. 600
    C. 900
    D. 1200

    (Application)

23. Select the molecule with the lowest molecular weight

    A. chitin
    B. lactose
    C. glucose
    D. starch

    (Comprehension)

24. Select the molecule with the highest molecular weight.

    A. galactose
    B. glucose
    C. glycogen
    D. lactose

    (Comprehension)

25. One phospholipid molecule contains _____ bonded fatty acids.

    A. two
    B. three
    C. four
    D. six

    (Knowledge)

True/False

26. An atom has an atomic number of nine. The number of electrons in its outer energy shell is five.

    (Comprehension)

27. An atom has an atomic number of twenty. Its outer energy shell has two electrons.

    (Comprehension)

28. Chlorine atoms have atomic weights of 34 or 35. These are examples of isomers.

    (Knowledge)

29. High-energy bonds require only small amounts of energy to break them.

    (Knowledge)

30. An atom with five electrons in its outer energy shell can form three covalent bonds.

    (Comprehension)

31. The free energy of a chemical reaction determines whether the reaction can occur.

    (Knowledge)

32. A few enzymes are RNA molecules.

    (Knowledge)

33. A sample of water at one degree Celsius is more dense than a sample of water at three degrees Celsius.

    (Comprehension)

34. A macromolecule is soluble in water if its functional groups are hydrophilic.

    (Knowledge)

35. NaCl is the salt of HCl, as they share the same cation in common.

    (Comprehension)

36. The carboxyl group is acidic, as it accepts hydrogen ions in solution.

    (Knowledge)

37. Lactose is a disaccharide consisting of three different elements and 45 atoms per molecule.

    (Comprehension)

38. The hydrolysis of sucrose produces glucose and fructose.

    (Knowledge)

39. Fatty acids join by peptide bonds.

    (Knowledge)

40. Denaturation mainly destroys the primary structure of a protein.

    (Knowledge)

Completion

41. NaCl is formed by _____ bonding.

    (Knowledge)

42. Colloidal suspensions are cloudy or _____.

    (Knowledge)

43. Two carbon atoms unite by a single covalent bond. Each carbon atom in this bond can form (number) more covalent bonds.

    (Comprehension)

44. A glucose molecule consists of six carbon atoms, twelve hydrogen atoms, and six oxygen atoms. Carbon composes (number) percent of the weight of this molecule.

    (Application)

45. A solution is highly acidic. It can become less acidic by removing _____ ions from the solution or by adding _____ ions to the solution.

    (Application)

Matching

46. carbohydrate   A. cholesterol is an example

47. fatty acid   B. consists of polypeptide chains

48. nucleic acid   C. one molecule is the double helix

49. protein   D. chitin is an example

50. sterol   E. saturated or unsaturated

   (Comprehension)

Short Essay

51. Compare a pH of 6 to a pH of 7. Also, compare a pH of 4 or 5 to a pH of 7. Specifically, how does the hydrogen ion concentration of a solution change as the pH decreases unit by unit?

   (Analysis)

52. One molecule of sucrose consists of 12 carbon atoms, 22 hydrogen atoms, and 11 oxygen atoms. Which element contributes the smallest percentage to the molecular weight of sucrose? What is that percentage?

   (Analysis)

53. Compare the energy content, in calories, of a gram of triglyceride to a gram of carbohydrate or protein. Are there differences in the energy content among these molecules? Can you explain these differences?

   (Synthesis)

54. Most proteins denature at temperatures greater than 37 degrees Celsius. However, some bacteria can live in hot springs and their proteins do not denature. Can you explain this by specific characteristics of their levels of protein structure?

   (Synthesis)

55. The element carbon tends to form covalent bonds. By contrast, the elements sodium or chlorine tend to form ionic bonds. What is one reason that carbon reacts differently in forming bonds?

   (Synthesis)

56. Can you assess the molecular weights of various molecules without actual computation? Arrange the following compounds by increasing order of molecular weight: glucose, starch, sucrose, water. Explain your answer.

   (Evaluation)

Correlation Questions

57. There are more kinds of different atoms than different elements. Explain this difference.

58. The pH scale is often described as logarithmic. Explain this pattern of the pH scale.

59. Can the atomic weight of an element be less than its atomic number?

60. An element has an atomic number of 17. Do atoms of this element form cations or anions?

Answers

Multiple Choice

1. C   2. C   3. B   4. D   5. B   6. C   7. D   8. A   9. D   10. D   11. C
12. A   13. B   14. B   15. D   16. C   17. D   18. D   19. C   20. B   21. A
22. C   23. C   24. C   25. A

True/False

26. False   27. True   28. False   29. True   30. True   31. True   32. True
33. False   34. True   35. False   36. False   37. True   38. True   39. False
40. False

Completion

41. ionic   42. turbid   43. three   44. forty   45. remove hydrogen ions; add hydroxyl ions

Matching

46. D   47. E   48. C   49. B   50. A

Short Essay

51. With each one unit decrease on the pH scale, the hydrogen ion concentration increases ten times.

52. The molecular weight of sucrose is 342. The twelve H atoms contribute 12 of these units. 12 divided by 342 equals about 3.5%. The elements carbon and oxygen have atomic weights that are greater than hydrogen.

53. A triglyceride molecule contains many more covalently bonded hydrogen atoms per molecule. The loss of each hydrogen atom by oxidation releases energy. Per gram, a triglyceride stores abound twice as much energy as a gram of carbohydrate or protein.

54. Disulfide bridges tend to stabilize the configuration of the polypeptide chains bonded in the protein molecule. Some bacteria have a high percentage of these bonds for heat stabilization.

55. On a scale of 0 to 8, carbon has four valence electrons. Four is in the middle of this scale. It needs to form four covalent bonds to attain a stable, outer-shell configuration of eight electrons. However, sodium has only one valence-shell electron. It is close to the end of this scale. By losing one electron it attains eight valence-shell electrons. Chlorine is near the other end of the scale and achieves eight valence shell electrons by gaining one more electron.

56. Water is a small molecule. It has a molecular weight of 18. Among the carbohydrates, glucose is a monosaccharide. It has a molecular weight of 180. Sucrose is a larger molecule as a disaccharide, with a molecular weight 342. Starch must be the heaviest molecule, as it is a polysaccharide.

Correlation Questions

57. Atoms of an element can form isotopes. For example, carbon can have an atomic weight of 12, 13, or 14. Therefore, there are at least three atomic forms, isotopes, of this one element. Ten given elements can have twenty or thirty kinds of atoms due to these isotopes.

58. A logarithmic scale has a series of numbers that represent tenfold differences. For the pH scale, a pH of 4 is ten times as acidic as a pH of 5. A pH of 3 is ten times as acidic as a pH of 4. A pH of 9 is ten times more basic than a pH of 8. A pH of 10 is ten times more basic than a pH of 9.

59. The atomic number is the number of protons in the nucleus of an atom. One isotope of hydrogen has only one proton in its nucleus and lacks neutrons. In this isotope the atomic number and atomic weight have the same value, one. However, in all other examples of atoms the atomic weight is the number of protons and the number of neutrons. Adding the number of neutrons to the number of protons makes the atomic weight a higher value than the atomic number.

60. This atom contains 17 electrons. The electron arrangement of this atom is 2 - 8 - 7. Two electrons fill the energy level closest to the nucleus. Eight electrons fill the next energy level. The seven remaining electrons fill the outermost energy level. It needs to gain one electron to fill this shell. As it does this it becomes negative, forming an anion. The element described here is chlorine.

Chapter 3
Methods of Studying Microorganisms

Multiple Choice

1. Visible wavelengths of light are in the range of _____ nanometers.
   A. 100 to 300
   B. 400 to 700
   C. 800 to 1000
   D. 1100 to 1400
   (Knowledge)

2. Select the correct ranking of light rays, from the longest wavelength to the shortest wavelength.
   A. blue - green - yellow - orange - red
   B. green - blue - red - orange - yellow
   C. red - orange - yellow - green - blue
   D. yellow - red - blue - green - orange
   (Comprehension)

3. Diffraction is the
   A. bending of light rays.
   B. conversion of light rays into different colors.
   C. increase in the velocity of light rays.
   D. magnification of images by light rays.
   (Knowledge)

4. The refractive index of pure water at room temperature is __1__, as light travels __2__ in this medium compared to a vacuum.
   A. 1 - 1.02, 2 - faster
   B. 1 - 1.02, 2 - slower
   C. 1 - 1.33, 2 - faster
   D. 1 - 1.33, 2 - slower
   (Knowledge)

5. For magnification by a microscope
   A. concave lenses bring light rays to a single point.
   B. concave lenses separate light rays.
   C. convex lenses bring light rays to a single point.
   D. convex lenses separate light rays.
   (Knowledge)

6. Resolution means that a microscope

    A. distinguishes two points of an image.
    B. magnifies an image.
    C. produces contrast.
    D. stains specimens with different dyes.

    (Knowledge)

7. The wavelength of light in nanometers that produces the least resolving power is

    A. 450
    B. 550
    C. 650
    D. 700

    (Knowledge)

8. The wavelength of light used by a given microscope is 500 nm. If the NA of the objective lens used is 0.5, the resolving power of the microscope is _____ nm.

    A. 250
    B. 500
    C. 50
    D. 1000

    (Application)

9. The maximum magnification of one typical compound microscope is 1000x. The objective lens used for this magnification is probably

    A. 10x
    B. 50x
    C. 100x
    D. 1000x

    (Application)

10. With a typical compound microscope the objective lens that will provide the largest, overall field of view is

    A. 4x for a total magnification 40x.
    B. 4x for a total magnification of 100x.
    C. 10x for a total magnification of 100x.
    D. 10x for a total magnification of 1000x.

    (Application)

11. Petroleum jelly with a coverslip is used in making a

    A. Gram stain.
    B. hanging drop.
    C. simple wet mount.
    D. smear of microorganisms.

    (Knowledge)

12. One species of *Mycobacterium* causes

    A. botulism.
    B. gonorrhea.
    C. syphilis.
    D. tuberculosis.

    (Knowledge)

13. Which substance is the mordant of the Gram stain?

    A. acetone
    B. gentian violet
    C. iodine
    D. safranin

    (Knowledge)

14. A bacterium retains safranin after the decolorizing agent removes the previously applied Gentian violet of the Gram stain. The bacterium is

    A. Gram-positive only.
    B. Gram-negative only.
    C. Gram-positive and Gram-negative.
    D. neither Gram-positive nor Gram-negative.

    (Comprehension)

15. After the four steps of the Gram stain are applied, a bacterium has a somewhat deep violet color. This is because it retained

    A. Gentian violet only and is Gram-positive.
    B. Gentian violet and safranin and is Gram-positive.
    C. Gentian violet and safranin and is Gram-negative.
    D. neither Gentian violet nor safranin and is Gram-negative.

    (Comprehension)

16. The acid-fast stain is specific for

    A. *Bacillus*.
    B. *Escherichia*.
    C. *Mycobacterium*.
    D. *Staphylococcus*.

    (Knowledge)

17. The counterstain for the acid-fast stain is

    A. carbolfuchsin.
    B. gentian violet.
    C. methylene blue.
    D. safranin.

    (Knowledge)

18. Select the last step of the Leifson flagella stain.

    A. air drying before microscopic examination
    B. chemical fixation with formalin
    C. tannic acid/rosaniline dye added
    D. washing off the excess stain

    (Knowledge)

19. Which type of microscopy takes advantage mainly of the difference in refractive indexes of materials?

    A. darkfield
    B. fluorescent
    C. Nomarsky
    D. phase-contrast

    (Knowledge)

20. Phase-contrast microscopy requires

    A. fixing and staining.
    B. fixing but not staining.
    C. staining but not fixing.
    D. neither fixing nor staining.

    (Knowledge)

21. Detection of _____ occurs with fluorescence microscopy.

    A. antibodies
    B. antigens
    C. histamines
    D. histones

    (Knowledge)

22. Most cell structures in one microorganism are three to five nanometers apart. The detailed intracellular makeup of this microbe can be studied with

    A. the SEM only.
    B. the TEM only.
    C. both the SEM and TEM
    D. neither the SEM nor TEM.

    (Comprehension)

23. The requirements for sterilizing most microorganisms by moist heat is

    A. 100C, 15 minutes.
    B. 100C, 20 minutes.
    C. 121C, 15 minutes.
    D. 121C, 20 minutes.

    (Knowledge)

24. Which kind of sterilization procedure takes advantage of the size of microorganisms?

    A. autoclaving
    B. filtration
    C. open flame
    D. use of chemicals

    (Knowledge)

25. Household bleach is

    A. potassium chloride.
    B. potassium hypochlorite.
    C. sodium chloride.
    D. sodium hypochlorite.

    (Knowledge)

26. After three consecutive one-tenth serial dilutions of a culture in nutrient broth, 1 ml of cells is plated on an agar surface and produces 20 colonies. The original cell concentration per ml was

    A. 20
    B. 200
    C. 2000
    D. 20000

    (Application)

27. An original cell concentration in nutrient broth is 3000 per ml. Each step of a serial dilution reduces the concentration of cells in the suspension by one-tenth. After three dilution steps the concentration of cells is _____ per ml.

    A. 0.03
    B. 0.3
    C. 3.0
    D. 30.0

    (Application)

28. A petri dish

    A. is used to hold nutrient agar.
    B. is used to sterilize media.
    C. stores bacterial suspensions.
    D. stores chemical reagents.

    (Knowledge)

29. The purpose of a serial dilution is to

    A. change the growth medium for a bacterial population.
    B. increase bacterial population size.
    C. reduce the number of bacteria for counting purposes.
    D. stain microorganisms.

    (Knowledge)

30. An unknown microorganism grows on a medium with crystal violet. It also changes the appearance of a defined growth medium. By these tests, its identity is revealed by its effect on a

    A. differential medium only.
    B. selective medium only.
    C. differential and selective media.
    D. simple medium.

    (Comprehension)

31. Blood agar is a _____ growth medium.

    A. complex
    B. defined
    C. differential
    D. selective

    (Knowledge)

32. Coliform bacteria makes acid from

    A. lactose, and turns neutral red.
    B. lactose, and turns neutral yellow.
    D. starch, and turns neutral red.
    D. starch, and turns neutral yellow.

    (Knowledge)

33. MacConkey agar contains a _____ indicator.

    A. pH
    B. salinity
    C. sugar
    D. temperature

    (Knowledge)

34. Select the pH that is most favorable for the growth of fungi.

    A. 5.5
    B. 6.5
    C. 7.5
    D. 8.5

    (Knowledge)

35. A bacterial culture is growing in a flask of nutrient broth. The flask is in a shaking machine. Through a malfunction over the next twelve hours, the machine shakes too vigorously and the seal is lost from the top of the flask. The culture becomes contaminated but cannot support the growth of any

    A. aerotolerant anaerobes.
    B. facultative anaerobes.
    C. microaerophiles.
    D. strict anaerobes.

    (Application)

True/False

36. The resolution of a microscope can be improved by increasing the size of the first magnifying lens, decreasing the wavelength of the light, and decreasing the refractive index.

    (Comprehension)

37. For a given wavelength of light, the resolving power of a microscope improves as the NA increases.

    (Comprehension)

38. The total magnification of a compound light microscope increases as the ocular lens is divided by higher and higher powers of objective lenses.

    (Comprehension)

39. The decolorizing step of the Gram stain is not performed thoroughly on a Gram-negative organism. After the application of the counterstain, the bacterium has a distinct red color.

    (Comprehension)

    (Knowledge)

40. Phase-contrast microscopy takes advantage of the interference of light rays.

    (Knowledge)

41. Boiling surgical instruments sufficiently will sterilize the instruments if all potentially contaminating bacteria cannot form endospores.

    (Comprehension)

42. The purpose of the streak plate method is to increase the concentration of colonies growing on a surface of nutrient agar.

    (Knowledge)

43. A nutrient broth culture has a bacterial cell concentration of 50,000 cells per ml. Two consecutive, one-tenth serial dilutions will reduce the cell concentration for easy colony counting when one ml of the diluted broth is plated on a nutrient agar surface.

    (Comprehension)

44. A minimal medium is one kind of defined medium.

    (Knowledge)

45. Strict aerobes are microorganisms killed in the presence of oxygen.

    (Knowledge)

46. A researcher plans to culture a population of facultative anaerobes. Using a shaking machine is necessary to culture these microorganisms in their growth medium.

    (Comprehension)

Completion

47. An opaque object does not transmit _____.

    (Knowledge)

48. Two factors increase the resolving power of a microscope, the use of immersion oil and increasing _____.

    (Knowledge)

49. The NA of the oil immersion lens with a microscope is 0.65. For a resolving power of 400 nm, the wavelength of light that must be used is about _(number)_ nm.

    (Application)

50. Use of a _____ in staining (e.g., Gram stain) increases the cell's affinity for a dye.

    (Knowledge)

51. The steps of the Gram stain are applied to a bacterium. The bacterium appears the color _____ if it accepts the counterstain after not retaining the Gentian violet through the decolorization step.

    (Comprehension)

52. The decolorizing agent for the acid-fast stain is _____.

    (Knowledge)

53. Freeze-fracturing is good for examining _____ as structures in cells.

    (Knowledge)

54. A _____ culture contains different kinds of microorganisms.

    (Knowledge)

55. A _____ medium uses extracts from yeasts.

    (Knowledge)

56. A water sample with populations of *E. coli* was probably contaminated from the _____ of a nearby human population.

    (Comprehension)

Correlation Questions

57. A bacterial population is suspended in a 5 percent solution of NaCl in a test tube. The population is prepared for viewing through a phase-contrast microscope. How will this saline preparation affect the view of these bacteria through a phase-contrast microscope? Study the topic of osmosis in Chapter 4 to help you form your answer.

58. A bacterial population is suspended in a test tube of nutrient broth. The bacteria have a concentration of 3,000 cells per milliliter. From this bacterial population, a microbiologist conducts two consecutive serial dilutions. Each dilution reduces the bacterial population to one-tenth of its former concentration. After the second dilution one ml of the bacterial/broth suspension is spread out completely on a surface of nutrient agar in a petri dish. Was the serial dilution process sufficient for easy counting of the bacterial colonies that will grow on the agar surface?

59. Two different species of bacteria grow well on nutrient agar. Does this indicate that the two species will grow well on a minimal medium?

60. A Gram positive bacterium is grown on nutrient agar in a petri dish. A Gram negative bacterium is grown on nutrient agar in another petri dish. Both bacteria grow under identical conditions for 48 hours. Then, each is subjected to an identical concentration of an antibiotic. The antibiotic limits the growth on one bacterium but does not affect the other population. Can you account for this difference? Read about drug action in the chapter on pharmacology (Chapter 21).

Answers

Multiple Choice

1. B 2. C 3. A 4. D 5. C 6. A 7. D 8. B 9. C 10. A 11. B 12. D
13. C 14. B 15. B 16. C 17. C 18. A 19. D 20. D 21. A 22. B
23. C 24. B 25. D 26. D 27. C 28. A 29. C 30. A 31. C 32. A
33. A 34. A 35. D

True/False

36. False 37. True 38. False 39. False 40. True 41. True 42. False
43. False 44. False 45. False 46. False

Completion

47. light 48. lens size 49. five hundred and twenty 50. mordant 51. red
52. sulfuric acid in ethanol 53. membranes 54. mixed 55. complex
56. waste products

Correlation Questions

57. The bacterial cells will be affected by the hypertonic solution (5% NaCl) around them. They will lose water to their extracellular environment by osmosis (See Chapter 4). Therefore, the cells will become smaller and denser. Light rays will pass through these denser cells differently compared to the environment around them. If the cells are out of phase sufficiently to produce a contrast with their surroundings, the contrast will affect the view of them. The high salt content outside the cells may also affect the passage of light through this area and affect comparable light contrast.

58. The total dilution is 1/100 (1/10 x 1/10). This dilution will reduce the cell concentration from 3,000 to 30. 30 countable colonies produced from these 30 cells produced by the dilution should be a reasonable number for counting on a nutrient agar surface in a Petri dish.

59. Each species may not grow well in minimal media. Nutrient agar supplies a variety of nutrient requirements to the bacteria. In a minimal media, certain vitamins and minerals, for example, may be absent. It one of the bacterial species requires a mineral for growth, the absence of the mineral can limit its growth.

60. Gram positive and negative species differ by their ability to retain crystal violet in their cell walls. Therefore, the chemical composition of their cell walls is different. An antibiotic can affect a bacterium by controlling bacterial cell wall synthesis. Some bacteria can withstand its affect better, depending on the makeup of the cell wall (See Chapter 21).

Chapter 4
Prokaryotic and Eukaryotic Cells

Multiple Choice

1. A bacterial cell is observed under the microscope. Its length is 2 micrometers. Using this to estimate the average length of a eukaryotic cell, the eukaryotic cell is _____ micrometers.
   - A. 0.2
   - B. 2.0
   - C. 20.0
   - D. 200

   (Comprehension)

2. Select the correct characteristic of prokaryotic cells.
   - A. Most have a cell diameter of over 100 micrometers.
   - B. Most of these cells have a cell wall.
   - C. The DNA is located in a well-defined nucleus.
   - D. They contain numerous kinds of organelles.

   (Comprehension)

3. In a bacterial cell the periplasm is/are the
   - A. compartment between two cell membranes.
   - B. composition of the bacterial cell capsule.
   - C. contents of the nucleus.
   - D. specialized liquid part of the cytoplasm.

   (Comprehension)

4. Most bacterial cell capsules are made of
   - A. lipids.
   - B. nucleic acids.
   - C. polysaccharides.
   - D. proteins.

   (Knowledge)

5. Select the incorrect association.
   - A. bacteria/prokaryotic
   - B. LPS/Gram-positive bacteria
   - C. peptidoglycan/cell wall
   - D. RNA polymerase/enzyme

   (Comprehension)

6. Porins in the outer bacterial cell membrane are _____ molecules.

    A. carbohydrate
    B. lipid
    C. nucleic acid
    D. protein

    (Knowledge)

7. Gram-negative bacteria __1__ an outer cell membrane and are __2__ to many toxic substances.

    A. 1 - have, 2 - resistant
    B. 1 - lack, 2 - resistant
    C. 1 - have, 2 - not resistant
    D. 1 - lack, 2 - not resistant

    (Knowledge)

8. Select the correct association.

    A. bacillus/sphere-shaped
    B. coccus/rod-shaped
    C. spirillum/hexagonal-shaped
    D. vibrio/comma-shaped

    (Comprehension)

9. Autolysins are enzymes that

    A. break cross-linked bonds in peptidoglycans.
    B. decrease the transport of substances through membranes.
    C. form bonds in peptidoglycans.
    D. increase the transport of substances through membranes.

    (Knowledge)

10. A bacterial cell is placed in an extracellular environment that has a higher solute concentration compared to its intracellular makeup. Inside the bacterial cell this

    A. lowers its turgor pressure, and the cell will burst.
    B. lowers its turgor pressure, and the cell will shrink.
    C. raises its turgor pressure, and the cell will burst.
    D. raises its turgor pressure, and the cell will shrink.

    (Application)

11. Mycoplasmas

    A. have a cell wall and develop a turgor pressure.
    B. have a cell wall and lack a significant turgor pressure.
    C. lack a cell wall and develop a turgor pressure.
    D. lack a cell wall and lack a significant turgor pressure.

    (Knowledge)

12. A bacterial cell that normally infects the human urinary tract loses its pili. This mainly affects its ability to

    A. gather nutrients.
    B. hold on to body cells.
    C. store nutrients.
    D. transport materials.

(Comprehension)

13. The greatest number of flagella is usually found on a bacterial cell with a(n) _____ arrangement.

    A. amphitrichous
    B. lophotrichous
    C. monotrichous
    D. peritrichous

(Knowledge)

14. Axial filaments are found only in

    A. rod-shaped cells.
    B. spherical cells.
    C. spirochetes.
    D. streptococci.

(Knowledge)

15. The nuclear region of a bacterial cell

    A. has a well-defined membrane with many chromosomes.
    B. has a well-defined membrane with one chromosome.
    C. lacks a well-defined membrane with many chromosomes.
    D. lacks a well-defined membrane but has DNA.

(Knowledge)

16. Most antibiotics interfere with the function of _1_ ribosomes and do not interfere with the function of _2_ ribosomes.

    A. 1 - 60S, 2 - 70S
    B. 1 - 70S, 2 - 80S
    C. 1 - 80S, 2 - 70S
    D. 1 - 80S, 2 - 60S

(Knowledge)

17. Select the correct statement about endospores.

    A. They are absent in species of *Clostridium*.
    B. They are easily decomposed by heat.
    C. They are absent in species causing anthrax.
    D. They have less than 3 percent water.

(Comprehension)

18. Pseudomurein is found in cells of

    A. archaea.
    B. bacteria.
    C. fungi.
    D. protozoans.

(Knowledge)

19. The flagellum of a eukaryotic cell has a microtubule arrangement of

    A. $5 + 2$.
    B. $7 + 3$.
    C. $9 + 2$.
    D. $11 + 4$.

(Knowledge)

20. Which group lacks a cell wall?

    A. algae
    B. bacteria
    C. fungi
    D. mycoplasmas

(Knowledge)

21. The loss of cytoplasmic streaming in a cell would mainly affect the function of the

    A. cilia.
    B. flagella.
    C. pseudopodia.
    D. nucleoids.

(Knowledge)

22. Each somatic (body) cell of an organism normally has 24 chromosomes. The haploid chromosome number in this organism is

    A. 6
    B. 12
    C. 24
    D. 48

(Comprehension)

23. Each gamete of an organism normally has 32 chromosomes. The diploid chromosome number of this organism is

    A. 16
    B. 32
    C. 64
    D. 128

(Comprehension)

24. Solutions A and B are separated by a membrane permeable to water but not permeable to solutes. If solution A has a solute concentration of 0.5% and solution B has a solute concentration of 1.5%, solution B is

    A. hypertonic to A and gains water by osmosis.
    B. hypertonic to A and loses water by osmosis.
    C. hypotonic to A and gains water by osmosis.
    D. hypotonic to A and loses water by osmosis.

    (Application)

25. For a eukaryotic nerve cell, sodium ions tend to diffuse into the cell and potassium ions tend to diffuse out of the cell. By active transport sodium ions __1__ and potassium ions __2__ .

    A. 1 - enter the cell, 2 - enter the cell
    B. 1 - enter the cell, 2 - leave the cell
    C. 1 - leave the cell, 2 - enter the cell
    D. 1 - leave the cell, 2 - leave the cell

    (Application)

True/False

26. Eukaryotic cells have a more complex structure than prokaryotic cells.

    (Knowledge)

27. Gram-negative bacteria have a complete three-layered cellular envelope.

    (Knowledge)

28. Strains of *S. pneumoniae* lacking a capsule are the most life-threatening to humans.

    (Knowledge)

29. Penicillin damages bacterial cell wall structure. Therefore it harms eukaryotic cells without affecting prokaryotic cells.

    (Comprehension)

30. Peptidoglycan molecules consist of protein and nucleic acids.

    (Knowledge)

31. Teichoic acids add to the structural integrity of Gram-positive cell walls.

    (Knowledge)

32. A bacterium is immersed in a solution with a low solute concentration compared to its intracellular makeup. The application of a lysozyme to a bacterial cell reduces the turgor pressure it develops.

    (Application)

33. A single row of 50 eukaryotic cells is observed through a microscope at a magnification of 400x. The diameter of the visual field is 400 micrometers. The cells are side by side, equal in size, and span the entire diameter of the field. The length of each cell is about 20 micrometers.

   (Application)

34. The loss of the hydrophilic tail of a phospholipid molecule in the plasma membrane increases its attraction to water inside and outside the cell.

   (Comprehension)

35. Transmembrane proteins penetrate through the cell membrane.

   (Knowledge)

36. Many Gram-positive bacteria lack pili.

   (Knowledge)

37. Species of *Clostridium* tend to sporulate during harsh environmental conditions.

   (Knowledge)

38. Chloroplasts contain cristae.

   (Knowledge)

39. The cytoskeleton functions for the orderly movement in larger eukaryotic cells.

   (Knowledge)

40. A eukaryotic cell loses its mitochondria. This will affect its ability to carry out active transport.

   (Comprehension)

Completion

41. As a cell's size increases, its surface to _____ ratio changes.

   (Knowledge)

42. An LPS molecule contains a _____ head and a _____ tail.

   (Knowledge)

43. A bacterium is attracted to glucose and a high oxygen concentration. It exhibits the movements of _____ and _____.

   (Knowledge)

44. Mitosis produces body cells in a eukaryotic organism. Each body cell normally has 78 chromosomes. The normal chromosome number in its gametes is _(number)_ .

   (Comprehension)

45. A cell pumps calcium ions out of its cytoplasm by active transport. There is a tendency for this ion to return to the inside of the cell by the transport process of _____.

(Comprehension)

Matching

Label each of the following statements as describing a prokaryotic cell or a eukaryotic cell.

46. Its ribosome function is affected by antibiotics.
47. Its diploid chromosome number is 14.
48. It contains pili.
49. Thylakoid membranes define some of its organelles.
50. Its flagella arrangement is peritrichous.

(Comprehension)

Short Essay

51. At a total magnification of 400x, a neuron spans about one-half the diameter of the circular visual field seen through a microscope. Can you estimate the length of the cell?

(Application)

52. One kind of eukaryotic cell requires ten minutes to carry out mitosis. Which stage do you think requires most of this time? Which stage, or stages, requires the least amount of time?

(Analysis)

53. A bacterium, which is pathogenic to humans, loses its capsule through a mutation. How do you think this will affect its ability to infect humans?

(Analysis)

54. How is the cell volume of a bacterial cell threatened in an extracellular environment that is hypertonic (higher solution concentration) or hypotonic (lower solute concentration)?

(Analysis)

55 What considerations are needed to assure that an antibiotic inhibits bacterial cell growth without harming human host cells? Emphasize the function of cell structures for your answer.

(Synthesis)

56. There is evidence that in humans, the inheritance of DNA in the mitochondria can be traced mainly to the maternal parent and not the male. By comparing human male and female sex cells, can you explain this pattern?

(Evaluation)

Correlation Questions

57. A human white blood cell is capable of engulfment. What characteristics of this cell allow it to engulf things? How does engulfment by a white blood cell give it the ability to protect the human body?

58. Consider this situation in lab: You view a cell under the microscope in lab. List several criteria you would use to decide if the cell is prokaryotic or eukaryotic.

59. List several microorganisms that cannot be treated with antibiotics. List a reason why an antibiotic would be ineffective on each microbe.

60. What evidence exists suggesting that mitochondria descended from bacterial cells that were free-living in the distant past?

Answers

Multiple Choice

1. C 2. B 3. A 4. C 5. B 6. D 7. A 8. D 9. A 10. B 11. D 12. B
13. D 14. C 15. D 16. B 17. C 18. A 19. C 20. D 21. C 22. B
23. C 24. A 25. C

True/False

26. True 27. True 28. False 29. False 30. False 31. True 32. True
33. False 34. False 35. True 36. True 37. True 38. False 39. True 40. True

Completion

41. volume 42. hydrophilic head, hydrophobic tail 43. chemotaxis, aerotaxis
44. thirty-nine 45. simple diffusion

Matching

46. prokaryotic 47. eukaryotic 48. prokaryotic 49. eukaryotic 50. prokaryotic

Short Essay

51. At a total magnification of 400x, the diameter of the circular visual field is 400 micrometers. If the neuron spans about one-half of this length, its estimated length is 200 micrometers.

52. Prophase may require about two-thirds of this time, as time is needed for the shortening of the chromosomes and formation of the mitotic spindle. Telophase requires some time, as it reverses many of the events of prophase. Metaphase, with chromosome attachment, and anaphase, the separation of chromatids, are very rapid stages.

53. Loss of its capsule will not protect the bacterium against antibody attack, rendering it less harmful to the human body.

54. The bacterial cell will shrink away from its cell wall in a hypertonic, extracellular environment. Its cell volume will increase in a hypotonic environment. However, the bacterial cell will probably not burst because of its cell wall.

55. If the antibiotic attacks a cell wall, such as penicillin, it should not affect a human cell. Human cells lack cell walls. If the antibiotic inhibits some step of bacterial protein synthesis, it must inhibit 70S ribosomes (bacterial) without harming 80S ribosomes (human).

56. The human ovum is hundreds of times larger than the human sperm cell. Most of the cytoplasm in the zygote is inherited through the ovum. Therefore, organelles that can duplicate by their own DNA, are inherited from the maternal parent.

Correlation Questions

57. The white blood cell has a flexible cytoplasmic membrane that is not inhibited to move by a surrounding cell wall. The flexibility of this cell membrane allows it to form cell extensions, pseudopodia, that surround a structure external to the cell. By surrounding this external structure, the white blood cell can enclose it and digest it intracellularly. White blood cells can ingest microbes by engulfment, protecting the human body this way if the microbe invades the body.

58. A eukaryotic cell has a defined nucleus and many organelles. It is more complex and larger than a prokaryotic cell.

59. Mycoplasmas lack cell walls and therefore cannot be treated with penicillin. A microorganism lacking ribosomes (e.g., viruses) could not be inhibited by many other antibiotics.

60. Mitochondria have a shape and size similar to some kinds of bacteria. Their organelles also have their own DNA and possibly their own ribosomes.

Chapter 5
Metabolism of Microorganisms

Multiple Choice

1. Select the incorrect association.

    A. assembly/organelles produced
    B. biosynthesis/precursor metabolites used
    C. catabolism/reducing power not produced
    D. polymerization/nucleotides used to make DNA

    (Comprehension)

2. Each of the following is a polymer except

    A. DNA.
    B. glucose.
    C. peptidoglycan.
    D. RNA.

    (Knowledge)

3. Select the correct statement about *E. coli*.

    A. It is Gram-positive.
    B. It lacks cell transporters.
    C. It needs many different nutrients for its metabolism.
    D. Its cell envelope has two layers.

    (Comprehension)

4. Most small nutrient molecules pass through the porins of *E. coli* by

    A. active transport.
    B. facilitated diffusion.
    C. phagocytosis.
    D. simple diffusion.

    (Knowledge)

5. *E. coli* cannot directly convert glucose into glucose-6-phosphate if it lacks

    A. ATP.
    B. fructose-6-phosphate.
    C. glycogen.
    D. potassium.

    (Comprehension)

6. Which metabolic pathway produces the most precursor metabolites in *E. coli*?

   A. aerobic metabolism
   B. glycolysis
   C. pentose phosphate pathway
   D. TCA

   (Knowledge)

7. Oxidation is the __1__ of electrons; reduction is the __2__ of electrons.

   A. 1 - gain, 2 - gain
   B. 1 - gain, 2 - loss
   C. 1 - loss, 2 - gain
   D. 1 - loss, 2 - loss

   (Knowledge)

8. How is a hydrogen atom normally converted to a positive ion?

   A. It gains one proton.
   B. It gains two protons.
   C. It loses one electron.
   D. It loses two electrons.

   (Comprehension)

9. Select the molecule that is reduced.

   A. NAD
   B. NAD(P)
   C. NAD(P)H
   D. NAD(P)O

   (Knowledge)

10. The atom of a copper can lose a maximum of two electrons. The atom of one nonmetal can accept three electrons. By oxidation-reduction, three copper atoms can completely

   A. oxidize two atoms of the nonmetal.
   B. oxidize three atoms of the nonmetal.
   C. reduce two atoms of the nonmetal.
   D. reduce three atoms of the nonmetal.

   (Application

11. Select the incorrect statement about ATP.

   A. It is formed from ADP and a phosphate group.
   B. It is made from catabolic reactions.
   C. Its bonds to phosphate groups are very stable.
   D. Its energy drives other metabolic reactions.

   (Comprehension)

12. Each describes chemiosmosis except that it

    A. involves mitochondrial membranes in *E. coli*.
    B. makes ATP.
    C. uses light in *E. coli*.
    D. uses the active transport of protons.

    (Comprehension)

13. Cytochromes of the electron transport chain accept

    A. electrons only.
    B. hydrogens only.
    C. electrons and hydrogens.
    D. neither electrons nor hydrogens.

    (Knowledge)

14. *E. coli* is located in a low oxygen environment. By chemiosmotic synthesis, it makes about _____ ATP molecules from six pairs of electrons.

    A. three
    B. six
    C. twelve
    D. eighteen

    (Application)

15. During glycolysis, each _1_ molecule starts the process and ends forming two molecules of _2_ .

    A. 1 - glucose, 2 - glycogen
    B. 1 - glucose, 2 - pyruvate
    C. 1 - glycogen, 2 - glucose
    D. 1 - pyruvate, 2 - glucose

    (Knowledge)

16. Without substrate level phosphorylation, for each glucose molecule glycolysis makes _1_ ATP molecules with a net gain of _2_ ATP molecules.

    A. 1 - two, 2 - one
    B. 1 - three, 2 - two
    C. 1 - four, 2 - two
    D. 1 - six, 2 - four

    (Knowledge)

17. In the TCA, citrate is a

    A. four-carbon compound made from oxaloacetate.
    B. four-carbon compound that makes oxaloacetate.
    C. six-carbon compound made from oxaloacetate.
    D. six-carbon compound that makes oxaloacetate.

    (Comprehension)

18. Through a mutation, one microorganism cannot make the amino acid histidine. This prevents it from making some complete
    A. carbohydrates.
    B. lipids.
    C. phosphates.
    D. proteins.
    (Comprehension)

19. The pentose phosphate pathway begins with __1__ and ends with __2__ .
    A. 1 - acetyl CoA, 2 - citrate
    B. 1 - citrate, 2 - acetyl CoA
    C. 1 - glucose-6-phosphate, 2 - phosphoglyceraldehyde
    D. 1 - phosphoglyceraldehyde, 2 - glucose-6-phosphate
    (Knowledge)

20. Humans are unable to make _____ amino acids through their own cell metabolism.
    A. 9
    B. 11
    C. 15
    D. 20
    (Knowledge)

21. The lack of assembly of flagellin in the bacterial cell affects its
    A. anaerobic respiration.
    B. motility.
    C. pigmentation.
    D. reproduction.
    (Comprehension)

22. Without the presence of ATP in its cell, *E. coli*
    A. can synthesize glycogen from glucose.
    B. cannot synthesize glycogen form glucose.
    (Application)

23. Lactic fermentation by bacteria
    A. adds a sweet taste to milk.
    B. does not occur in the muscle tissue of animals.
    C. is used to produce yogurt.
    D. occurs in the presence of oxygen.
    (Knowledge)

24. Which term means "different feeders"?

    A. autotroph
    B. chemotroph
    C. heterotroph
    D. phototroph

    (Knowledge)

25. Effectors control the functioning of allosteric enzymes by changing their

    A. concentration.
    B. location.
    C. pH requirement.
    D. shape.

    (Knowledge)

True/False

26. Disaccharides can pass through the porins in the outer membrane of *E. coli*.

    (Comprehension)

27. Oxygen gas seldom participates in redox reactions.

    (Knowledge)

28. Adenosine triphosphate can be converted to adenosine diphosphate plus a phosphate.

    (Knowledge)

29. Through chemiosmosis ADP is produced from ATP.

    (Knowledge)

30. During chemiosmosis and in *E. coli*, twelve protons pushed out of the cell form six molecules of ATP if sufficient oxygen is present. Assume that NADH and the electron transport chain are involved in this process.

    (Application)

31. A balanced chemical equation represents reactants with chemical bonds that are more stable than the bonds of the stated products. It is unlikely that this reaction will occur.

    (Application)

32. Chemiosmosis uses a proton gradient across a mitochondrial membrane.

    (Knowledge)

33. By chemiosmosis a eukaryotic cell makes eighteen ATP molecules from four pair of electrons.

    (Application)

34. The metabolic pathways in *E. coli* are very similar to the metabolic pathways in other organisms.

    (Knowledge)

35. The compounds in electron transport chains differ in their chemical identity among different kinds of organisms.

    (Knowledge)

36. To form glycogen in bacteria, glucose is first phosphorylated to form glucose-1-phosphate.

    (Knowledge)

37. Oxygen is not the terminal electron acceptor to make ATP in anaerobic respiration.

    (Knowledge)

38. In a research project, a population of autotrophs, that are also phototrophs, are relocated to the deep bottom sediments of a pond. They continue to produce sufficient quantities of glucose.

    (Application)

39. Cyclic photophosphorylation cannot generate reducing power.

    (Knowledge)

40. Pathway A makes B makes C makes D. By allosteric regulation, a decrease in the concentration of D decreases the rate of the reaction where A makes B.

    (Comprehension)

Completion

41. Substance A loses one electron which is accepted by substance B. In this redox reaction, substance B is _____ and substance A is _____.

    (Comprehension)

42. By the process called _____, protons are pumped across membranes by active transport to generate ATP.

    (Knowledge)

43. A eukaryotic cell can produce a net of 38 ATP molecules from the complete metabolism of one glucose molecule. Through glycolysis, it produces about __(number)__ percent of this potential.

    (Application)

44. The term "autotroph" means _____.

    (Knowledge)

45. End-product inhibition is an example of a _____ mechanism.

    (Knowledge)

Matching

46. aspartate

47. glucose

48. NAD(P)H

49. peptidoglycan

50. permease

A. phosphorylated in the beginning steps of glycolysis

B. transporter in the periplasm

C. example of a polymer

D. amino acid

E. measure of a cell's reducing power

(Comprehension)

Short Essay

51. Iron rusts by oxidation reactions. How can you prove this through experimentation?

(Application)

52. One mole of glucose stores about 680 kilocalories of energy. One mole of ATP stores about 7 kilocalories. In terms of useful energy conversion, how can you calculate the efficiency of anaerobic metabolism?

(Application)

53. How can you calculate the efficiency of anaerobic and aerobic metabolism combined? Assume that these phases form 2 ATPs net and 36ATPs net per glucose molecule. How does this efficiency compare to anaerobic metabolism alone?

(Analysis)

54. A researcher wants to promote ethanol production from a population of yeast cells. What are some of the necessary factors that must be introduced into the research project to meet this goal?

(Analysis)

55. The anaerobic and aerobic metabolic pathways producing ATP are very similar in all organisms. Fatty acids enter metabolism for ATP formation at the point of acetyl CoA. If a person wanted to lose body fat by vigorous exercise, what advice would be required to achieve this goal?

(Evaluation)

56. A microorganism has, by evolution, adapted to a habitat in the mud at the bottom of a pond. Predict its pattern of metabolism for ATP formation.

(Evaluation)

Correlation Questions

57. A strict anaerobe is grown on an identical nutrient medium in two different petri dishes. One dish is exposed to a normal atmosphere. The other is isolated from an oxygen source. How will the growth rates of the microbe compare in these two environments?

58. Consider the same situation explained in #57, except that an aerotolerant organism is introduced to each setting. How will the growth rates compare in these two environments?

59. A bacterium is studied for its ability to make an amino acid. The microbe makes the amino acid in a minimal medium. When a new culture of the same organism is given a sufficient quantity of the amino acid, its production ceases. Explain this difference.

60. How is the genetics of microorganisms, presented in the next chapter (Chapter 6), related to their metabolism?

Answers

Multiple Choice

1. C 2. B 3. C 4. D 5. A 6. B 7. C 8. C 9. C 10. C 11. C 12. C
13. A 14. B 15. B 16. C 17. D 18. D 19. C 20. A 21. B 22. B
23. C 24. C 25. D

True/False

26. True 27. True 28. True 29. False 30. True 31. True 32. True
33. False 34. True 35. True 36. True 37. True 38. False 39. True 40. False

Completion

41. B is reduced; A is oxidized.   42. chemiosmosis 43. five 44. self-feeder 45. feedback

Matching

46. D 47. A 48. E 49. C 50. B

Short Essay

51. Test for the presence of rust formation by placing a piece of iron in an oxygen-free environment. It will not form rust. In the presence of oxygen without other substances, weigh a piece of iron before and after it rusts. If it gains weight after rust formation, it probably combined chemically with oxygen.

52. Anaerobic metabolism produces a net gain of 2 ATPs per glucose. 14 divided by 680 equals about a two percent harvest of useful energy.

53. The net yield of ATPs per glucose can be 36: 2 (anaerobic) plus 34 (aerobic). 7 x 36 = 252. 252 divided by 680 equals about 37 percent for an improved efficiency. Some organisms produce 38 ATPs per glucose, 2 (anaerobic) plus 36 (aerobic). In this case, 7 x 38 = 266.266 divided by 680 equals 39 percent.

54. Begin with the requirements of glucose in water in the absence of oxygen.

55. The person exercising needs to know how much vigorous exercise is required before fat-fatty acid metabolism replaces glycogen-glucose metabolism for ATP formation. If, for example, twenty minutes of vigorous exercise is required, then the exercise must surpass this timeframe significantly.

56. This environment presents conditions for anaerobic metabolism. Therefore, the microorganism probably has adapted to form ATP anaerobically. By evolution it may lack the genes and enzymes necessary for aerobic metabolism.

Correlation Questions

57. The presence of oxygen is toxic to a strict anaerobe. A normal atmosphere is about 21 percent oxygen. Therefore, there will be more growth in the setting lacking oxygen.

58. Aerotolerant microbes cannot use oxygen. However, they are not harmed in its presence. In this experiment, there should not be a significant difference in the microbial growth rate observed in the two settings.

59. With a sufficient amount of the amino acid available for the new culture, synthesis of the amino acid is not necessary. Its production is shut down by end-product inhibition.

60. The genetic blueprint for a microorganism is encoded in its DNA. As you will learn in the next chapter, DNA makes RNA which makes protein in the cell's metabolism. By this flow of information, DNA controls the synthesis of the cell's enzymes. Each step of the cell's metabolism is run by an enzyme. Therefore, the DNA can program the production of the enzymes present to run all steps of metabolism or only some of the steps, depending of the genetic makeup of the microbe. These differences in DNA, for example, can determine the molecules a microbe makes, determining whether it can live on a minimal growth medium or requires an enriched medium.

Chapter Six
The Genetics of Microorganisms

Multiple Choice

1. Select the description that is not correct for DNA.

    A. It consists of bonded nucleotides.
    B. It contains base pairs.
    C. It is a polymer.
    D. Its hydrogen bonds connect sugars to phosphates.

    (Comprehension)

2. In a sample of DNA, the concentration of adenine is 30%. The concentration of cytosine in this DNA is _____ percent

    A. 10
    B. 20
    C. 60
    D. 70

    (Application)

3. During replication, a DNA base sequence of ATCG will order a base sequence of

    A. ATCG.
    B. AUCG.
    C. TAGC.
    D. UAGC.

    (Comprehension)

4. During DNA replication, each double helix produced, consists of

    A. two original DNA strands.
    B. one original DNA strand and one new DNA strand.
    C. two new DNA strands.
    D. one DNA strand and one RNA strand.

    (Knowledge)

5. The terminus of the chromosome in *E. coli* is where

    A. the 3 prime end of one DNA molecule begins.
    B. the binding site for SSBP.
    C. the transcription of RNA is initiated.
    D. two completed chromosomes separate after being copied.

    (Knowledge)

6. The function of DNA ligase is to

    A. catalyze the phosphorylation of nucleotides.
    B. guide replication in the 5 prime to 3 prime direction.
    C. seal the gap between segments of DNA.
    D. serve as a primer for DNA replication.

    (Knowledge)

7. Select the incorrect statement about transcription.

    A. DNA is used as a template to make RNA.
    B. DNA is made as a complementary strand to DNA.
    C. Gene expression begins with this process.
    D. Ribonucleoside triphosphates pair with exposed bases.

    (Comprehension)

8. During transcription a DNA sequence of GCTA will order an RNA base sequence of

    A. ATGC.
    B. CGAU.
    C. GCTA.
    D. GCUA.

    (Comprehension)

9. The promoter is where

    A. large segments of mRNA are transcribed.
    B. RNA polymerase binds by signaling.
    C. the repressor protein binds.
    D. the transcript is released from DNA.

    (Knowledge)

10. The role of t-RNA is to

    A. carry amino acids to the ribosome.
    B. synthesize codons at the site of translation.
    C. synthesize the ribosome.
    D. transport DNA nucleotides to the ribosome.

    (Knowledge)

11. For translation the start codon is often __1__ which codes for __2__ .

    A. 1 - ATG, 2 - histidine
    B. 1 - AUG, 2 - methionine
    C. 1 - GTA, 2 - glutamic acid
    D. 1 - GUA, 2 - valine

    (Knowledge)

12. A strand of mRNA is translated into a polypeptide. It consists of 330 bases which include a start codon and a termination codon. If all other bases are transcribed except the one in these two codons, the polypeptide will have _____ amino acids.

    A. 40
    B. 108
    C. 330
    D. 984

    (Application)

13. Inducible enzymes are made

    A. at a constant rate because they are always needed.
    B. only when their signal molecules are present.
    C. only when their substrates are available to the cell.
    D. to catalyze the conversion of DNA into RNA.

    (Knowledge)

14. Select the incorrect description about the lac operon.

    A. Allolactose cannot bind to the lac repressor.
    B. Beta-galactosidase splits a disaccharide.
    C. Galactoside permease brings lactose into the cell.
    D. Transcription is regulated at this operon.

    (Comprehension)

15. One capability of the repressor in the lac operon is to

    A. bind to the lac operator.
    B. remove lactose from the cell.
    C. stimulate transcription.
    D. transport lactose into the cell.

    (Knowledge)

16. The role of the leader protein in the histidine operon is to

    A. add to the protein makeup of the ribosome.
    B. bind with the operator.
    C. determine the cell supply of histidine.
    D. serve as the end product from histidine.

    (Knowledge)

17. Cyclic AMP

    A. regulates the entrance of cell proteins.
    B. regulates the exit of cell proteins.
    C. signals the rate of anabolic reactions.
    D. signals the rate of catabolic reactions.

    (Knowledge)

18. Select the incorrect statement about plasmids.

    A. Their copies are passed to daughter cells.
    B. They are smaller than chromosomes.
    C. They encode functions essential for reproduction.
    D. They have a circular shape.

    (Comprehension)

19. By conjugation,

    A. cells reproduce asexually.
    B. DNA replication is stopped.
    C. genes are destroyed.
    D. plasmids are transferred to cells.

    (Knowledge)

20. A base change in DNA of GGCTAC to GGCCAC is an example of a mutation called the

    A. base substitution.
    B. deletion.
    C. inversion.
    D. transposition.

    (Comprehension)

21. A DNA molecule contains the following order of bases in one strand containing five base pairs: ATACGTACT. If this sequence changes to ATATGCACT, this mutation is an example of a(n)_____.

    A. deletion
    B. duplication
    C. inversion
    D. transposition

    (Comprehension)

22. By a missense mutation, a codon

    A. codes for a new amino acid.
    B. is destroyed.
    C. is lost from the cell.
    D. serves as an initiation codon.

    (Knowledge)

23. Select the incorrect association among mutants.

    A. cold-sensitive/conditionally-expressed
    B. heat-sensitive/temperature
    C. osmotic remedial/temperature intensity
    D. temperature-sensitive/conditionally-expressed

    (Comprehension)

24. Select the technique used in brute-strength examination.

    A. Ames test
    B. clonal selection
    C. replica plating
    D. reversion

    (Knowledge)

25. *Saccharomyces cerevisiae* is a

    A. bacterium.
    B. plant.
    C. virus.
    D. yeast.

    (Knowledge)

True/False

26. A sample of DNA is 28 percent guanine. The percentage of thymine in this sample is 26 percent.

    (Application)

27. By translation RNA makes DNA.

    (Knowledge)

28. A pyrophosphate is one phosphate group split from ATP.

    (Knowledge)

29. During DNA replication in *E. coli* two replication forks move in the same direction along a circular chromosome.

    (Knowledge)

30. The two strands of a DNA double helix are antiparallel, meaning that they are aligned in opposite directions.

    (Knowledge)

31. A double-stranded molecule is produced in a bacterial. It was not produced by transcription.

    (Comprehension)

32. RNA polymerase is solely responsible for transcription in prokaryotes.

    (Knowledge)

33. The anticodon is a base triplet on mRNA.

    (Knowledge)

34. An anticodon of ATG is complementary to a codon of UAC.

    (Comprehension)

35. Attenuation is a regulatory mechanism of translation.

    (Knowledge)

36. Catabolite repression is one example of global regulation.

    (Knowledge)

37. *E. coli* has about 4288 genes on its one circular chromosome.

    (Knowledge)

38. Spontaneous mutations occur in the natural course of microbial growth.

    (Knowledge)

39. A strand of DNA nucleotides has the following order of bases: ATGGCCATG. A change of this to ATGGATG is an example of an inversion.

    (Comprehension)

40. In direct selection conditions are created that prevent the growth of a desired mutant strain.

    (Knowledge)

Completion

41. The range of G-C base pairs in the DNA of different organisms can range from 25 percent to (number) percent.

    (Knowledge)

42. A DNA double helix has 1500 base pairs. 700 of these base pairs are AT. The total number of G and C bases from the remaining base pairs is (number) .

    (Application)

43. The linkage of an amino acid to a tRNA is called amino acid _____.

    (Knowledge)

44. _____ enzymes are made in a cell only when a signal molecule is scarce.

    (Knowledge)

45. The genotype describes the cell's genetic plan. The _____ describes the effect of the plan on the appearance and function of the cell.

    (Knowledge)

Matching

Each description matches to only one letter. A letter can be used more than once throughout the match.

46. can be natural or artificial   A. conjugation
47. involves F+ and F- cells   B. transduction
48. a phage mediates this process   C. transformation
49. plasmid and pilus are involved
50. the virus involved can be virulent

(Comprehension)

Short Essay

51. A DNA molecule consists of 2000 base pairs. 40% of the base pairs are A-T. How many bases in the DNA molecule are guanine?

    (Application)

52. From the DNA base sequence of ATACCGTAC, write one example of a deletion mutation and an inversion mutation.

    (Application)

53. An antibiotic is spread over a plate of bacteria growing on nutrient agar. After this treatment, only a small percentage of cells remain to produce colonies. Is this an example of direct selection or indirect selection?

    (Analysis)

54. An HFr cell consistently introduces its chromosome into the recipient cell at the same point. How can the length of time for its conjugation be used to map the genes on this chromosome?

    (Analysis)

55. Explain one strategy for an experiment proving that the replication of DNA is semiconservative.

    (Synthesis)

56. Spontaneously, a bacterium acquires a mutation that prevents it from utilizing glucose. Many bacteria descend from this original mutant. However, experiments reveal that only 90 percent of the mutants with the genotype actually express this trait in their phenotype. Why?

    (Evaluation)

Correlation Questions

57. In the early 1900s scientists thought that either DNA or proteins could be the genetic material. Some thought that DNA lacked the necessary complexity to encode genetic information. The conclusion was that proteins had this complexity. Can you explain this viewpoint.

58. There are some viruses (Chapter 13) that carry out the following process: RNA makes DNA. How do you think they are different metabolically in order to carry off this unique process?

59. Early studies on human DNA led to estimates of 100,000 different human genes. Data for this conclusion included the total number of DNA base pairs in the human genome and the average number of base pairs per human gene. Recent studies have shown that this estimate of 100,000 human genes was high. If the number is 40,000, can you explain the reason for the difference (40,000 genes to 100,000 genes)?

60. The lactose operon is an inducible operon. Another type of operon is a repressible operon. The tryp operon is one example. It involves a metabolic pathway in which a bacterium makes tryptophan. As this synthesized amino acid builds up in concentration, it binds to an operator gene directly, turning off the switch controlling the genes that make enzymes for its production. How is this type of operon different from an inducible operon?

Answers

Multiple Choice

1. D   2. B   3. C   4. B   5. D   6. C   7. B   8. B   9. B   10. A   11. B   12. B
13. C   14. A   15. A   16. C   17. D   18. C   19. D   20. A   21. C   22. A
23. C   24. C   25. D

True/False

26. False   27. False   28. False   29. False   30. True   31. True   32. True
33. False   34. True   35. False   36. True   37. True   38. True   39. False   40. False

Completion

41. eighty   42. sixteen hundred   43. activation   44. repressible   45. phenotype

Matching

46. C   47. A   48. B   49. A   50. B

Short Essay

51. By subtraction, 60% of the 2000 base pairs are G-C. Within each pair, one of the bases is guanine. 60% of 2000 equals 1200.

52. As one example, the chromosome could lose its last three bases, TAC. If TAC remains detached, it is a deletion. If these bases reattach as CAT at the exposed C end, this is one example of an inversion.

53. It is direct selection, as the only surviving mutants are the ones that are resistant to the antibiotic.

54. Over short time intervals, the genes at the beginning or origin of the chromosome will be introduced. Genes that are further away from the origin will require more time to be introduced into the recipient cell. By relating changing time intervals to the frequency at which genes are transferred, the order of genes from the origin can be plotted.

55. The nucleotides used for making the new half of each DNA molecule can be tagged radioactively. When a DNA double helix duplicates, each daughter molecule produced will consist of one old strand (nonradioactive) and one new strand (radioactive).

56. One possibility is that the genotype only sets the potential for the expression of the phenotype. Perhaps the proper environmental influence for this expression, such as the correct temperature, is not always present. Therefore, a genotype is not translated into the expected phenotype 100 percent of the time.

Correlation Questions

57. DNA consists of only four different nucleotide building blocks. Proteins consist of 20 different building blocks, offering more possible combinations by which the building blocks can be bonded together. However, scientists later learned that the DNA bases are transcribed in groups of three, increasing the complexity as that molecule functions to make RNA and proteins. Four DNA bases, read in groups of three, has sixty-four different combinations.

58. These viruses must have an enzyme that runs transcription in reverse when RNA makes DNA. In fact these viruses have a reverse transcriptase.

59. One assumption was that all of the human DNA is transcribed and serves as active genetic material. In fact, there are regions between the actively transcribing regions of DNA that do not function genetically to make RNA and proteins.

60. A repressible operon is simpler. A molecule binds directly to the operator gene (e.g., tryptophan) in the repressible operon, turning off the activity of the operon. In the inducible operon, the appearance of the inducer substance (.e.g, lactose) binds to a repressor that normally turns off the operon. With the repressor tied up by the inducer, the operon is not inhibited and makes the RNA and enzymes needed to run the associated metabolic pathway. In the case of the lac operon, the enzymes to metabolize lactose are made when lactose enters the cell and binds with the repressor.

Chapter 7
Recombinant DNA Technology

Multiple Choice

1. Genetic recombination involves

   A. artificial means only.
   B. natural means only.
   C. artificial and natural means.
   D. neither artificial nor natural means.

   (Knowledge)

2. During meiosis in eukaryotes, crossing-over usually occurs between chromosomes that are

   A. homologous only.
   B. nonhomologous only.
   C. homologous and nonhomologous.
   D. neither homologous nor nonhomologous.

   (Knowledge)

3. Recombinant DNA technology occurs in vitro. This means it occurs

   A. only in bacterial cells.
   B. outside cells.
   C. spontaneously in the environment.
   D. with homologous chromosomes.

   (Knowledge)

4. Select the incorrect description about cloning.

   A. One cell produces a group of cells.
   B. It can reproduce only a few copies of a gene.
   C. It is used in recombinant DNA technology.
   D. It produces copies from a single gene.

   (Comprehension)

5. A cloning vector is a(n)

   A. DNA molecule that a cell can replicate.
   B. insect used in recombinant DNA technology.
   C. mutated microorganism.
   D. virus used to insert a gene.

   (Knowledge)

6. The weight of a bacterial cell is 200 units. The DNA in this cell comprises about _____ weight units of this cell.

    A. 2
    B. 6
    C. 14
    D. 20

    (Application)

7. To purify DNA, a cell extract is the

    A. genome of eukaryotic cells.
    B. genome of prokaryotic cells.
    C. group of chemicals used to sterilize a culture.
    D. liquid content of ruptured cells.

    (Knowledge)

8. In eukaryotic genes the segments of noncoding DNA are the

    A. exons.
    B. introns.
    C. mutons.
    D. transposons

    (Knowledge)

9. By the action of reverse transcriptase,

    A. DNA makes DNA.
    B. DNA makes RNA.
    C. RNA makes DNA.
    D. RNA makes protein.

    (Knowledge)

10. Select the characteristic that is not preferable for a good cloning vector.

    A. It has an origin of replication.
    B. It has genes that identify host cells with the vector.
    C. It must be relatively large.
    D. It should not unduly tax the host cell's metabolism.

    (Comprehension)

11. Restriction endonucleases

    A. cut DNA molecules for insertion into cells.
    B. influence the transport of messengers into cells.
    C. make bacterial cells resistant to viral infection.
    D. speed up the rate of DNA replication.

    (Knowledge)

12. The restriction enzyme Eco RI is named by the
    A. antibodies it can make.
    B. environment where it lives.
    C. organism producing it.
    D. sequence of genes on its chromosome.
    (Knowledge)

13. Type II restriction enzymes cut asymmetrically within base sequences that are _____ bases long.
    A. 4 to 7
    B. 8 to 10
    C. 11 to 13
    D. 14 to 18
    (Knowledge)

14. Select the palindromic sequence.
    A. ATAGGT
    B. ACACCT
    C. ATATGT
    D. ATTGCA
    (Comprehension)

15. Under certain conditions the ends of DNA cut by restriction enzymes are _____ ends.
    A. adhesive
    B. cohesive
    C. enzymatic
    D. mutated
    (Knowledge)

16. Two DNA strands anneal. This means that they
    A. join together.
    B. mutate.
    C. recombine genetically.
    D. separate.
    (Comprehension)

17. Ethidium bromide is used to _____ DNA on a gel medium.
    A. clone
    B. mutate
    C. separate
    D. stain
    (Knowledge)

18. Ligation means to _____ the ends of DNA.

    A. fluoresce
    B. seal
    C. separate
    D. transport

    (Knowledge)

19. Transformation, transfection, microinjection, and electroporation are all means to

    A. combine DNA in an electrophoretic field.
    B. extract DNA from host cells.
    C. put DNA molecules into host cells.
    D. separate DNA in an electrophoretic field.

    (Knowledge)

20. *E. coli* will take up DNA from solution in an environment with calcium chloride that is chilled to _1_
    Celsius and suddenly heated to _2_ Celsius.

    A. 1 - zero, 2 - twenty
    B. 1 - zero, 2 - forty-two
    C. 1 - ten, 2 - twenty
    D. 1 - ten, 2 - forty-two

    (Knowledge)

21. Select the incorrect description about electroporation.

    A. It exposes a DNA solution to high voltages.
    B. It introduces DNA to animal cells.
    C. It introduces DNA in plant cells.
    D. It makes a cell membrane impermeable to DNA.

    (Comprehension)

22. For prior purification a short DNA molecule that is complementary to its corresponding mRNA is
    called a(n)

    A. exon.
    B. intron.
    C. probe.
    D. transposon.

    (Knowledge)

23. 150 kilobases contains _____.

    A. 15,000 base pairs
    B. 15,000 bases
    C. 150,000 base pairs
    D. 150,000 bases

    (Comprehension)

24. In *E. coli* there are normally _____ plasmids (PBR type) per cell.

    A. 1 to 5
    B. 20 to 40
    C. 80 to 125
    D. 500 to 1000

    (Knowledge)

25. Through PCR 10 milligrams of DNA is increased to 200,000 milligrams. Through this process, there is about a _____- fold change in the amount of DNA.

    A. 2,000
    B. 20,000
    C. 200,000
    D. 2,000,000

    (Application)

True/False

26. Two short DNA molecules recombine by crossing over. Their base sequences are ATTACTGCG and GTGCCAATC. By a crossover, the new base sequences could be GCGTCTTTG and GAAACCGAA.

    (Application)

27. Each somatic (body) cell of a sexually reproducing, eukaryotic organism has 54 chromosomes. It probably inherited 27 of these chromosomes from each parent.

    (Comprehension)

28. Most bacterial cells have introns on their chromosomes.

    (Knowledge)

29. Most microbiologists think that endonucleases evolved to protect bacteria from viruses.

    (Knowledge)

30. Eco RI is produced by *Serratia marcescens*.

    (Knowledge)

31. The RFLP is a specific restriction endonuclease of *E. coli*.

    (Knowledge)

32. T4 ligase is an enzyme formed by bacteriophage T4 when it infects a protozoan.

    (Knowledge)

33. In the process of transfection, a virus is used as a cloning vector.

    (Comprehension)

34. The surgical removal of the adrenal gland from a laboratory mouse will significantly reduce the production of insulin in this organism.

    (Comprehension)

35. Shot gun cloning is used to produce a gene bank.

    (Knowledge)

36. _B. subtilis_ was the host cell first used to make the hormone insulin by genetic engineering.

    (Knowledge)

37. By proteomics, an organism is identified by the lack of proteins in its makeup.

    (Comprehension)

38. PCR is a technique used to multiply genes.

    (Knowledge)

39. Microarray technology is used to induced mutations in bacteria.

    (Comprehension)

40. PCR can be used to search for the genes of the AIDS virus.

    (Knowledge)

Completion

41. One cell of _E. coli_ has a length of one micrometer. Using this statistic as an estimate, the length of its DNA molecule is about __(number)__ micrometers.

    (Application)

42. _Thermus aquaticus_ is a highly _____ bacterium, as it thrives in a select temperature range.

    (Knowledge)

43. Sma I is a _____ endonuclease that forms blunt ends directly.

    (Knowledge)

44. Fifty percent of the chromosomal DNA in a eukaryotic cell consists of introns. About _____ percent of its DNA consists of noncoding regions that make enzymes.

    (Comprehension)

45. _____ is the process of converting a genome, with a complete known sequence of bases, into useful information.

    (Knowledge)

Matching

46. cell extract   A. enzyme that can seal DNA gaps

47. clone   B. restriction endonucleases

48. Eco RI   C. liquid fraction

49. HGH   D. all cells are genetically identical

50. ligase   E. hormone produced by the pituitary gland

(Comprehension)

Short Essay

51. Write one example of a palindrome, using a sequence of eight DNA bases. Illustrate how it is a palindrome.

    (Application)

52. Write one example of a DNA base sequence that is not a palindrome. Use a sequence of eight DNA bases. Illustrate how it is not a palindrome.

    (Application)

53. Outline the steps taken to splice genes into a cloning vector.

    (Knowledge)

54. One particular plasmid from *E. coli* has a DNA mass of about 10 micrograms. From this amount, how many doubling processes must occur to produce a mass of this plasmid of about ten milligrams?

    (Analysis)

55. Without bacterial transformation or a virus cloning vector, what do you think are some of the steps required to put recombinant DNA into an *E. coli* host cell?

    (Synthesis)

56. Until the advances in recombinant DNA technology, HGH was obtained mainly from the pituitary glands of cadavers. How have the advances in DNA technology changed the potential to treat individuals with pituitary dwarfism?

    (Evaluation)

Correlation Questions

57. A pair of homologous chromosomes is studied in a eukaryotic cell. On one homolog, the sequence of genes is ABCDE. On the other homolog the sequence of corresponding genes is abcde. Write one example of how crossing over can change the identity of the gene sequences on these chromosomes.

58. Bacterial cells do not have homologous chromosomes and therefore cannot experience crossing over. How can they form genetic recombinants aside from conjugation, transduction, or transformation?

59. The streak plate method, used to isolate different species of microorganisms, was discussed earlier in the text. How does the formation of isolated colonies by this method relate to the concept of cloning?

60. A human hormone known as erythropoietin (EPO) has been produced through genetic engineering. This hormone is produced naturally in the human body by the kidney. The hormone signals the red bone marrow to produce red blood cells. How can the administration of this hormone, produced by genetic engineering, be used to treat humans?

Answers

Multiple Choice

1. C   2. A   3. B   4. B   5. A   6. B   7. D   8. B   9. C   10. C   11. A   12. C
13. A   14. C   15. B   16. A   17. D   18. B   19. C   20. B   21. D   22. C   23. C
24. B   25. B

True/False

26. False   27. True   28. False   29. True   30. False   31. False   32. False
33. True   34. False   35. True   36. False   37. False   38. True   39. False   40. True

Completion

41. one thousand   42. thermophilic   43. restriction   44. fifty percent   45. Annotation

Matching

46. C   47. D   48. B   49. E   50. A

Short Essay

51. A palindrome reads the same way in either direction. One example is A-G-G-A-T-A-A-T.

52. A nonpalindromic sequence does not read the same way in both directions. One example is A-T-C-T-G-G-C-A.

53. Start with the steps outlined in the book: cutting the cloning vector, sealing the fragments of DNA, etc.

54. There are many possibilities. As one example, from 10 micrograms, one doubling produces 100 micrograms. A doubling of this produces 10,000 micrograms. This is equal to 10 milligrams.

55. Start by reviewing the steps listed in the text. What substance must be in high concentration in the extracellular environment? What temperature changes are required?

56. The use of cadavers resulted in the harvesting of small amounts of the human growth hormone over long time intervals. By recombinant DNA technology, larger amounts can be produced in given time intervals. The rapid DNA copying and metabolic rates of bacterial cells are an advantage in this production.

Correlation Questions

57. If the homologs break and exchange chromosomal segments between the second and third genes, the recombinants are ABcde and abCDE.

58. A DNA fragment could enter a bacterial cell from a distantly related organism, perhaps a mammalian cell. For example a bacterial cell with the gene sequence of ABCDE could receive a fragment with the genes pqr. Integrating this segment, the new bacterial chromosome could be ABCpqrDE, a recombinant.

59. The streak plate method separates cells sufficiently that, now unmixed, each isolated cell, forms its own local population of cells, a colony. Each colony is a clone, all cells from this group arising from asexual reproduction (without recombination) from one isolated cell.

60. EPO can be used to treat different kinds of anemia due to diminished red blood cell production. The hormone serves as a signal to stimulate this process, make more red blood cells, and increase the oxygen-carrying power of the blood.

Chapter 8
The Growth of Microorganisms

Multiple Choice

1. Select the incorrect statement about binary fission.
    A. It is also called budding.
    B. It is the cleavage of a cell.
    C. It occurs after the cell elongates.
    D. It produces two cells of approximately equal size.
    (Comprehension)

2. In a rich laboratory medium, the doubling time for *E. coli* is about _____ minutes.
    A. 4
    B. 12
    C. 18
    D. 32
    (Knowledge)

3. With a normal doubling time for *E. coli* in the intestinal tract of a vertebrate, the doubling time is about _____ hours.
    A. 6
    B. 12
    C. 24
    D. 48
    (Knowledge)

4. When graphing the exponential growth of a bacterial population, the slope is directly related to the
    A. growth rate.
    B. initial size of the population.
    C. size of the individual cells.
    D. synchronization of population increase.
    (Knowledge)

5. The doubling time for a bacterium is 25 minutes. The growth rate for a population of this bacterium is
    A. 2.0
    B. 2.4
    C. 25
    D. 250
    (Application)

6. The most rapid rate of population growth is in the _____ phase.

    A. death
    B. lag
    C. log
    D. stationary

    (Knowledge)

7. The beginning phase of population growth is usually the _____ phase.

    A. death
    B. lag
    C. log
    D. stationary

    (Knowledge)

8. The inoculum is the

    A. area where a population grows.
    B. cells used to start a culture.
    C. depletion of nutrients in a culture.
    D. rate of population increase.

    (Knowledge)

9. A batch culture means that a population

    A. grows in a closed container.
    B. is cultivated at a constant temperature.
    C. is free of toxins.
    D. undergoes a constant rate of increase.

    (Knowledge)

10. A microorganism requires equal concentrations of the nutrients W, X, Y and Z in its growth medium. Reduction of the concentration of X stops population growth. X is the _____ nutrient for population growth.

    A. abiotic
    B. biotic
    C. limiting
    D. nonlimiting

    (Comprehension)

11. A chemostat

    A. decreases population size.
    B. has no effect on population size.
    C. increases population size.
    D. stabilizes population size.

    (Knowledge)

12. Cells in the center of a colony on a solid growth surface are usually in the _____ phases.

    A. death or stationary
    B. lag or log
    C. log or stationary
    D. stationary or lag

    (Knowledge)

13. *E. coli* grows about _____ times faster on a rich medium than it does on a poor medium.

    A. two
    B. ten
    C. one hundred
    D. five hundred

    (Knowledge)

14. Biofilms are

    A. assemblages of microbes in nature.
    B. grown on surfaces of nutrient agar.
    C. photographed images of microbes in nature.
    D. produced only in artificial lab environments.

    (Comprehension)

15. Oxygenases

    A. add oxygen directly to organic molecules.
    B. break down an organic carbon source.
    C. build an organic carbon source.
    D. remove oxygen from organic molecules.

    (Knowledge)

16. For bacteria, the enzyme nitrogenase

    A. enhances denitrification.
    B. enhances nitrogen fixation.
    C. inhibits denitrification.
    D. inhibits nitrogen fixation.

    (Knowledge)

17. A helminth organism has a body mass of 10 grams. The element nitrogen probably contributes about _____ grams of this mass.

    A. 0.5
    B. 1.5
    C. 2.5
    D. 3.5

    (Application)

18. Sulfur is a component of each of the following except

    A. a few species of tRNA.
    B. certain essential metabolites.
    C. glucose and sucrose.
    D. two specific amino acids.

    (Comprehension)

19. A mesophilic bacterium grows best at normal room temperature. Its total temperature range for growth is probably about _____ degrees Celsius.

    A. 25 to 35
    B. 20 to 30
    C. 5 to 45
    D. 0 to 80

    (Comprehension)

20. Psychrophiles grow best at a temperature of _____ degrees Celsius.

    A. zero
    B. 25
    C. 37
    D. 100

    (Knowledge)

21. Alkaliphiles grow best at a pH of

    A. 1
    B. 5
    C. 7
    D. 9

    (Comprehension)

22. If the concentration of solutes increases in the external environment, a bacterial cell will probably pump

    A. potassium ions into the cell.
    B. potassium ions out of the cell.
    C. water into the cell.
    D. water out of the cell.

    (Application)

23. A spectrophotometer measures the _____ of a culture.

    A. dry weight
    B. pH
    C. temperature
    D. turbidity

    (Knowledge)

24. The Petroff-Hauser chamber is used to
    A. count cells.
    B. measure cell diameter.
    C. remove cells from a culture.
    D. stain cells.
    (Knowledge)

25. After being diluted to 0.001 of its original concentration, one ml of a bacterial culture in broth is plated for counting. 300 colonies are produced on the nutrient agar surface in a Petri dish. The original cell concentration in the broth was about _____ cells per ml.
    A. 30,00,000,000
    B. 30,000,000
    C. 300,000
    D. 300
    (Application)

True/False

26. Microbial growth refers to a population and not to an individual cell.
    (Knowledge)

27. For bacterial culture growth, synchronous cultures are common.
    (Knowledge)

28. The death phase of a microbial population is a highly dynamic state.
    (Knowledge)

29. The lag phase is a no-growth phase for a microbial population.
    (Knowledge)

30. A trace element is needed in small amounts for microbial growth.
    (Knowledge)

31. A strain of *E. coli*, requiring glucose for growth, fails to grow on a nutrient medium containing maltose as a carbon source. The growth of this population can be improved by digesting this disaccharide into its monosaccharides.
    (Application)

32. A population of nitrogen-fixing bacteria grows rapidly. Its growth rate can be inhibited by increasing its availability to oxygen and decreasing its concentration of nitrogenase.
    (Application)

33. Bacterial colonies on a nutrient agar surface are tested for catalase activity in lab. The surface is flooded with a dilute solution of hydrogen peroxide. Gas bubbles do not form. Catalase activity is probably absent.

    (Application)

34. *Salmonella typhimurium* decreases its number of ribosomes per cell on a growth medium. This probably means it is growing on a poor growth medium.

    (Comprehension)

35. A researcher wants to inhibit the growth rate of a population of mesophilic bacteria. This can be achieved by growing the population at 37 degrees Celsius in an incubator.

    (Comprehension)

36. Barophiles are prokaryotes that live under high-pressure conditions.

    (Knowledge)

37. A researcher wants to inhibit the growth rate of a population of acidophilic bacteria. This can be achieved by adding HCl to the growth medium.

    (Comprehension)

38. Total cell counts can be done electronically with a Coulter counter.

    (Knowledge)

39. The MPN method involves making a series of tenfold dilutions from an original bacterial culture.

    (Knowledge)

40. A tube of nutrient broth, with low osmotic strength, is innoculated with a sample of a bacterium that is a mesophile and is a halophile. The broth tube is incubated for 48 hours at five degrees Celsius. After 48 hours the broth in the tube will show high turbidity.

    (Application)

Completion

41. A bacterial population of facultative anaerobes is growing on a nutrient agar surface. As it grows, all oxygen is removed from its environment. This will _____ its growth.

    (Comprehension)

42. One cell produces sixteen cells. By exponential growth this is two raised to the _____ power.

    (Application)

43. OH - is the _____ radical.

    (Knowledge)

44. Siderophores are compounds that release the element _____ through chemical reactions.

    (Knowledge)

45. A _____ is a salt-loving bacterium.

    (Knowledge)

46. A tube of nutrient broth is sterilized and placed in an incubator at 37 degrees for 48 hours. The sterilization procedure is probably successful if the broth is _____ in its appearance.

    (Application)

Matching

47. death phase   A. exponential rate of growth

48. lag phase   B. nutrients are depleted

49. log phase   C. beginning phase of population growth

50. stationary phase   D. a plateau on a graph

    (Knowledge)

Short Essay

51. A small population of *E. coli* inhabits the intestine of a vertebrate. Assuming the absence of cell death, how much time will be required to increase the population cell concentration eightfold? How will cell death change this computation?

    (Application)

52. A bacterium normally lives in the human oral cavity. Describe its temperature, pH, and nutrient requirements.

    (Analysis)

53. Compare the different stages of bacterial population growth. In which stage do you think a hazardous change in the environment will affect the population most adversely?

    (Analysis)

54. The concentration of ribosomes in the cells of a population of *Salmonella typhimurium* is measured and plotted over time. This time study reveals significant increases in the ribosome concentration. What reasons could account for this change?

    (Analysis)

55. A bacterial population consists of a number of mutants that have a long list of mineral requirements. How, through experimentation, can a researcher determine the mineral that is the limiting nutrient?

    (Synthesis)

56. Select the method of measuring microbial growth that is the most accurate. Defend your choice.

    (Evaluation)

Correlation Questions

57. Principles of population dynamics, relevant to all kinds of organisms, can be demonstrated by the growth patterns of a bacterial population in a test tube of nutrient broth. For example, this growth tube can support a finite, maximum number of organisms. Many population biologists think that planet earth can support a finite, upper limit of humans. What are some other patterns of microbial growth that are relevant to all species?

58. Many principles of chemistry and physics support the understanding of microbial growth patterns. What are some of these principles?

59. Many principles of cell biology support an understanding of microbial growth patterns. What are some of these principles?

60. The phosphate ion is often a limiting nutrient to algae populations in streams. Increased phosphate runoff into a stream can change this situation and affect the fish life in a stream. How can an increase in phosphate in a stream affect, for example, a trout population? Most species of trout require clean, fast-moving, well-oxygenated water in order to survive.

Answers

Multiple Choice

1. A 2. C 3. B 4. A 5. B 6. C 7. B 8. B 9. A 10. C 11. D 12. A
13. B 14. A 15. A 16. B 17. B 18. C 19. C 20. A 21. D 22. A
23. D 24. A 25. C

True/False

26. True 27. False 28. True 29. True 30. True 31. True 32. True
33. True 34. False 35. False 36. True 37. False 38. True 39. True 40. False

Completion

41. not affect 42. fourth 43. hydroxyl 44. iron 45. halophile 46. clear

Matching

47. B 48. C 49. A 50. D

Short Essay

51. The *E. coli* population doubles its size in 12 hours. It increases by four times its original size in 24 hours and doubles again, for a final eightfold increase, in 36 hours. With cell death the time requirement will be longer, as cells dying off will subtract from the number being added each cycle.

52. It is a mesophile that thrives in a neutral pH environment. Its nutrients probably include most common molecules in human diets, such as some of the simple sugars.

53. Due to the rapid rate of population increase during the log phase, rapid changes and effects also occur during this stage of population growth.

54. The cells are increasing their rate of protein synthesis, probably because of an increase in the concentration of amino acids in the microbe's growth medium.

55. Each individual mineral can be lowered in concentration from the environment as the other minerals are held constant. The one measured in shortest supply that inhibits population growth is the limiting factor.

56. This is an evaluation. Review the different techniques described at the end of the chapter. For example, the plate count could be the most accurate with excellent technique. Measurement using turbidity may not be as accurate.

Correlation Questions

57. Many populations, when colonizing a new environment, carry out the same phases of population growth that microbes demonstrate in a test tube: lag - log - stationary - death. Their maximum population size is controlled by limits in space and raw materials. Usually a factor, such as a limiting nutrient, determines the maximum population size. The overutilization of space and raw materials can lead to the demise of the population in a closed environment, either in a test tube or on a planet.

58. The principles of chemistry/physics include the following: concentration and identity of molecules serving as a source of nutrients, the effect of pH on population growth, and the effect of temperature on population growth.

59. The principles of cell biology include the following: cell division, cell structures (e.g., ribosome concentration based on amino acid availability in the growth medium), cell metabolism (e.g., facultative anaerobes), and osmosis.

60. Without phosphates limiting population growth, there will be increased growth of the algae in the stream. This increase of algae will increase the use of oxygen in the stream, affecting its availability for other life forms in the stream. The subsequent algal bloom will slow down the flow of water. These changes can convert a well-oxygenated, fast-moving stream into a slow-moving, warm stream deprived of oxygen to support a trout population.

Chapter 9
Controlling Microorganisms

Multiple Choice

1. Which term refers to the destruction of all microbial life?

    A. antisepsis
    B. decontamination
    C. disinfection
    D. sterilization

    (Knowledge)

2. _____ means to specifically kill microorganisms on living tissue.

    A. Antisepsis
    B. Decontamination
    C. Disinfection
    D. Sterilization

    (Knowledge)

3. A microbiostatic treatment controls population size as it

    A. increases the numbers of a population.
    B. inhibits but does not kill a population.
    C. kills a population.
    D. produces mutations in a population.

    (Knowledge)

4. The D-value of a population is 20 minutes. If a microbial population consists of 1000 cells, it is highly probable that the environment with this population will be sterile in about _____ minutes.

    A. 10
    B. 20
    C. 40
    D. 60

    (Application)

5. A researcher wants to sterilize a microbial population with prolonged heat. He needs to know that these cells in a __1__ phase are more susceptible to thermal killing than the cells in the __2__ phase.

    A. 1 - death, 2 - log
    B. 1 - log, 2 - stationary
    C. 1 - lag, 2 - log
    D. 1 - stationary, 2 - log

    (Comprehension)

6. If 90 percent of the microbes in a population is killed every 10 minutes, after 20 minutes about
   _____ percent of the original microbes will still be alive.

   A. 1
   B. 5
   C. 10
   D. 11

   (Application)

7. Select the genus with species that produce endospores.

   A. *Aerobacter*
   B. *Clostridium*
   C. *Escherichia*
   D. *Staphylococcus*

   (Knowledge)

8. The thermal death point of a microbial population is 50 degrees Celsius. The time required to sterilize
   a medium with this population is _____ minutes.

   A. 5
   B. 10
   C. 30
   D. 60

   (Comprehension)

9. Select the incorrect statement about using moist heat as a physical control for microorganisms.

   A. It is a method that denatures proteins.
   B. It is effective.
   C. It kills vegetative cells.
   D. It sterilizes only the surface that it contacts.

   (Comprehension)

10. An autoclave usually maintains a pressure of _1_ pounds per square inch at a temperature of _2_
    degrees Celsius.

    A. 1 - fourteen, 2 - one hundred
    B. 1 - fourteen, 2 - one hundred and twenty-one
    C. 1 - fifteen, 2 - one hundred
    D. 1 - fifteen, 2 - one hundred and twenty-one

    (Knowledge)

11. Refrigeration preserves food by

    A. dehydrating microbial cells.
    B. denaturing proteins.
    C. inhibiting the growth of populations.
    D. killing many microorganisms.

    (Knowledge)

12. Among the following choices, select the wavelength of UV light that is most effective at damaging the DNA in microorganisms.

    A. 150
    B. 275
    C. 350
    D. 500

    (Comprehension)

13. Select the incorrect statement about using UV light to kill microorganisms.

    A. It can penetrate glass.
    B. It has wavelengths shorter than visible light.
    C. It is lethal to microorganisms.
    D. It presents a health hazard to humans.

    (Comprehension)

14. Select the microorganism that cannot be removed from a liquid medium by filtration.

    A. alga
    B. bacterium
    C. protozoan
    D. virus

    (Knowledge)

15. By sublimation

    A. gases are directly converted to solids.
    B. liquids are directly converted to solids.
    C. solids are directly converted to gases.
    D. solids are directly converted to liquids.

    (Knowledge)

16. Germistats

    A. accelerate the growth of microbial populations.
    B. kill microorganisms.
    C. inhibit microbial growth.
    D. stain cells.

    (Knowledge)

17. A laboratory scientist is using a germicide to control a microbial population. The end point of this germicide is a dilution of 1:10000. For phenol it is 1:100. The germicide is _____ powerful than phenol.

    A. 10 times less
    B. 100 times more
    C. 1000 times less
    D. 1000 times more

    (Application)

18. Phenols are distinguished chemically by the presence of _____ groups.

    A. acid
    B. aldehyde
    C. hydroxyl
    D. sulfur

(Knowledge)

19. A tincture of iodine contains a(n)

    A. acid.
    B. alcohol.
    C. base.
    D. salt.

(Knowledge)

20. Select the agent that is not an alkylating agent.

    A. ethanol
    B. ethylene oxide
    C. formalin
    D. glutaraldehyde

(Knowledge)

21. A laboratory scientist decides to make up a 37% formalin solution from a stock solution of 100 % formaldehyde. Using 7.4 grams of this solution, the scientist must dilute it with about _____ grams of distilled water.

    A. 2.6
    B. 6.3
    C. 12.6
    D. 18.4

(Application)

22. The spoiling of food in a refrigerator is usually due to the action of

    A. barophiles.
    B. mesophiles.
    C. psychrophiles.
    D. thermophiles.

(Knowledge)

23. For canning, a _____ treatment of *C. botulinum* is usually applied.

    A. 4D
    B. 6D
    C. 8D
    D. 12D

(Knowledge)

24. One standard treatment of pasteurization in the United states is

    A. 63 degrees C at 10 minutes.
    B. 63 degrees C at 30 minutes.
    C. 80 degrees C at 10 minutes.
    D. 80 degrees C at 30 minutes.

    (Knowledge)

25. Calcium propionate is commonly used to preserve

    A. bread.
    B. cheese.
    C. milk.
    D. pickles.

    (Knowledge)

True/False

26. Treatments that only inhibit microbial growth are microbiostatic.

    (Knowledge)

27. Stationary-phase cells of *E. coli* are killed by cold shock.

    (Knowledge)

28. Beginning at room temperature, the TDT probably decreases as the temperature used for sterilization increases.

    (Comprehension)

29. Dry heat kills microorganisms mainly by denaturing proteins.

    (Knowledge)

30. A bacterial population that cannot form endospores withstands prolonged boiling. The population probably consists of psychrophiles.

    (Comprehension)

31. A dairy scientist wants to store one pint of milk and prevent the milk from decomposing by bacterial metabolism. The milk contains populations of mesophiles. Storing the milk in a refrigerator at 5 degrees Celsius is a good choice.

    (Comprehension)

32. Photoreactivation is a DNA repair mechanism.

    (Knowledge)

33. Ionizing radiation is commonly used as a physical control method in microbiology laboratories.

    (Knowledge)

34. Lyophilization removes water by sublimation.

    (Knowledge)

35. High extracellular concentrations of sugar damage microbial cells by plasmolysis.

    (Comprehension)

36. Chlorhexidine is a phenolic.

    (Knowledge)

37. Chlorine must be bound to organic chemicals to kill microorganisms.

    (Knowledge)

38. Ethylene oxide kills endospores.

    (Knowledge)

39. Very few microorganisms can grow in a deep freeze.

    (Knowledge)

40. UHT sterilized milk is popular for consumption in the United States.

    (Knowledge)

Completion

41. Microbiocidal treatments _____ microorganisms.

    (Knowledge)

42. A 95 % solution of ethanol is stored in a person's home. To make it more effective as a skin disinfectant, it must be diluted to 50%. This can be done by diluting 100 grams of the 95% ethanol with _____ grams of distilled water.

    (Application)

43. A laboratory scientist wants to make up a 3 percent solution of hydrogen peroxide from a 100 percent stock solution. To do this, 1.5 grams of the stock solution must be diluted with _____ grams of distilled water.

    (Application)

44. *Salmonella* species are pathogens of the _____ in the human body.

    (Knowledge)

45. The effectiveness of a germicide can be determined by the _____ disc method.

    (Knowledge)

Matching

46. chlorine

47. formalin

48. hydrogen peroxide

49. isopropanol

50. phenol

(Comprehension)

A. It is an alkylating agent.

B. It was called carbolic acid by Lister.

C. Its atom forms one ionic bond.

D. It forms oxygen from catalase.

E. Its molecule has the OH group.

Short Essay

51. In previous generations of human populations, a simple abscessed tooth could lead to the death of the human infected. Many people currently consider the treatment of this condition routine. Why was this considered such a life-threatening situation at one time?

(Knowledge)

52. How does the changing atmospheric pressure in an autoclave affect the boiling point of water? How is this used as an advantage to sterilize bacterial from a medium?

(Application)

53. How can you determine the thermal death point for a bacterial population in a liquid suspension in the lab?

(Analysis)

54. The cells of a bacterial population lose the genetic ability to synthesize mitochondria. How will this affect the capacity of the bacteria to survive extracellular environments of changing osmotic strength?

(Analysis)

55. Outline some of the steps in lab used to compare the effectiveness of different germicides by the filter-paper disc method.

(Synthesis)

56. Compare the different methods for preserving food. Which one do you think is most effective?

(Evaluation)

Correlation Questions

57. A population consists of 10,000 bacterial cells. It is treated with a sterilizing agent. The environment with this population becomes sterile in two hours. What is its D-value?

58. An undergraduate student wants to make microbiology the focus of his undergraduate major. In addition to calculus, he is advised to take several courses in mathematics. Why is this additional background in mathematics needed for his undergraduate major?

59. One ancient approach to preserving meat was to salt it and dry it in the sunlight. How did this approach utilize some of the control methods explained in this chapter?

60. The meaning of the term "death", when studying microorganisms, is different compared to the meaning of the term, when studying multicellular organisms. What is the difference?

Answers

Multiple Choice

1. D   2. A   3. B   4. D   5. B   6. A   7. B   8. B   9. D   10. D   11. C   12. B
13. A   14. D   15. C   16. C   17. B   18. C   19. B   20. A   21. C   22. C
23. D   24. B   25. A

True/False

26. True   27. False   28. True   29. False   30. False   31. True   32. True
33. False   34. True   35. True   36. False   37. False   38. True   39. True   40. False

Completion

41. kill   42. ninety grams   43. forty-eight and one half grams   44. intestine   45. paper

Matching

46. C   47. A   48. D   49. E   50. B

Short Essay

51. Antibiotics were not present in ancestral human populations. Without this chemical control method, the infection caused by an abscess could infect the human body sufficiently to cause death.

52. As the atmospheric pressure increases, the boiling point of water increases. By increasing this temperature, a temperature is reached that also destroys bacterial endospores and removes all life.

53. Sterilize a bacterial population at a given temperature. Record the amount of time needed for sterilization. Next, conduct new experiments. With new equivalent bacterial populations, continue to progressively reduce the temperature until the lowest temperature is reached that kills all bacteria in ten minutes.

54. Surviving the changing osmotic environments outside the bacterial cells requires active transport mechanisms. Ions must be pumped into or out of the cells by this transport process. Active transport requires energy from ATP molecules produced by mitochondria. With the absence of these powerplants, the ability to conduct active transport and survive is reduced.

55. The cells of a bacterial population is grown on the surface of nutrient agar. Filter paper discs, impregnated with the different germicides, are placed on this surface. The zone of inhibition produced around each disc is measured. The greater this zone, the greater the effectiveness of the germicide.

56. The answer to this question requires an appraisal. Study the methods described in the chapter. Temperature control may have some limitations. How can chemical or osmotic controls overcome these limitations? There are advantages and disadvantages to each method.

Correlation Questions

57. The population must be reduced in size to 10 percent through five cycle to be eradicated. The pattern of size reduction is: 10,000 - 1,000 - 100 - 1 - 0. Five cycles are needed for elimination of all cells. Two hours (120 minutes) divided by 5 cycles equals a D value of about 24 minutes.

58. Calculus presents the patterns of exponential growth, important for understanding the log phase of microbial population increase. Understanding the patterns of population size and growth requires applying statistical analysis.

59. The salt creates a high osmotic strength outside the microbial cells. The heat and UV light from the sun are physical control methods.

60. The death of a multicellular organism refers to the loss of life of one individual. The death of a microbial population means eradication of all members (often billions) of individual cells. Each microbial cell is a living organism.

Chapter 10
Classification

Multiple Choice

1. The classification scheme for the different kinds of organisms is hierarchical. From species to kingdoms its groups are

   A. broader and less inclusive.
   B. broader and more inclusive.
   C. narrower and less inclusive.
   D. narrower and more inclusive.

   (Comprehension)

2. Select the broadest taxonomic category from the following list:

   A. class
   B. family
   C. order
   D. phylum

   (Comprehension)

3. Select the most specific taxonomic category from the following list:

   A. class
   B. genus
   C. order
   D. phylum

   (Comprehension)

4. In the binomial name *Bacillus subtilis*, *subtilis* refers to the _____ name.

   A. class
   B. family
   C. genus
   D. species

   (Knowledge)

5. In the binomial name *Homo sapiens*, *Homo* refers to the _____ name.

   A. family
   B. genus
   C. order
   D. species

   (Knowledge)

6. *Staphylococcus aureus* is named by the

   A. environment it inhabits.
   B. Gram reactions and type of motility.
   C. grouping and color of its cells.
   D. kind of metabolism it conducts.

   (Knowledge)

7. *Shigella etousae* is named

   A. after a microbiologist.
   B. after a nation.
   C. by the environment it inhabits.
   D. by the kind of metabolism it conducts.

   (Knowledge)

8. The fossil record to study evolution is limited to the past _____ million years.

   A. 200
   B. 400
   C. 600
   D. 800

   (Knowledge)

9. Stromatolites are the fossilized remains of

   A. heterotrophic eukaryotes.
   B. heterotrophic prokaryotes.
   C. phototrophic eukaryotes.
   D. phototrophic prokaryotes.

   (Knowledge)

10. In eukaryotes, a species is a group of organisms capable of

    A. competing for the same resources.
    B. interbreeding.
    C. living in the same area.
    D. not exchanging genes.

    (Knowledge)

11. Microorganisms that belong to the same species can be subdivided into

    A. divisions.
    B. domains.
    C. kingdoms.
    D. strains.

    (Knowledge)

12. Select the correct statement about classifying viral species.

    A. Species are not grouped into genera.
    B. The ICTV uses a Linnaean scheme.
    C. They present less problems than classifying bacteria.
    D. Viral species are given ordinary English names.

    (Comprehension)

13. Early schemes classified bacteria as

    A. animals.
    B. fungi.
    C. plants.
    D. protozoans.

    (Knowledge)

14. Early schemes classified protozoans as

    A. animals.
    B. bacteria.
    C. fungi.
    D. plants

    (Knowledge)

15. An organism is heterotrophic and has an absorptive mode of nutrition. It has a eukaryotic cell structure. It belongs to the kingdom of

    A. Animalia.
    B. Fungi.
    C. Monera.
    D. Protista.

    (Comprehension)

16. Chatton proposed a classification scheme of

    A. bacteria and nonbacteria.
    B. eukaryotes and prokaryotes.
    C. microbes and nonmicrobes.
    D. plants and animals.

    (Knowledge)

17. Which taxonomic category from the following has the lowest similarity coefficient in a dendogram?

    A. class
    B. family
    C. genus
    D. species

    (Comprehension)

18. A simple test classifies bacteria as Gram-positive or Gram-negative. This method mainly emphasizes

    A. biochemistry.
    B. morphology.
    C. physiology.
    D. serology.

    (Knowledge)

19. Tetrazolium dye is a(n)

    A. Gram-staining dye.
    B. medium for electrophoresis.
    C. oxidation-reduction indicator.
    D. simple stain dye.

    (Knowledge)

20. Phage typing uses

    A. bacteria to classify protozoa.
    B. bacteria to classify viruses.
    C. viruses to classify bacteria.
    D. viruses to classify plants.

    (Knowledge)

21. A sample of DNA consists of 2000 base pairs. The percentage of G-C base pairs in an organism is 38%. The number of adenine bases in this sample is

    A. 160
    B. 310
    C. 1240
    D. 2480

    (Application)

22. Heating DNA

    A. causes its two strands to bond.
    B. increases the mutation rate.
    C. melts it.
    D. stimulates transcription.

    (Knowledge)

23. A dichotomous key is a series of questions offering _____ alternatives. The questions proceed from more _____.

    A. two, general to specific
    B. two, specific to general
    C. four, general to specific
    D. four, specific to general

    (Comprehension)

24. The genome of a microbe has three billion base pairs. In one research experiment, about one billion DNA base pairs are mapped in the genome of this microbe. This represents about _____ percent of that total genome.

    A. 25
    B. 33
    C. 50
    D. 75

    (Application)

25. SSU rRNA is a(n)

    A. DNA probe.
    B. enzyme for protein synthesis.
    C. ribosomal subunit.
    D. strand of mRNA.

    (Knowledge)

True/False

26. A class is a broader and more inclusive taxonomic category than an order.

    (Comprehension)

27. The Linnaean system of classification is a natural system.

    (Knowledge)

28. The Earth is twice as old as the oldest microbial fossils.

    (Comprehension)

29. The definition of a species for eukaryotes can be applied to prokaryotes.

    (Knowledge)

30. K12 is a well-known species of *B. subtilis*.

    (Knowledge)

31. Virus species can be subdivided into strains.

    (Knowledge)

32. An organism has a eukaryotic cell structure. It is phototrophic with a cell wall. By this description it could be a member of the kingdom of Protista or Plantae.

    (Comprehension)

33. Whittaker proposed a two-kingdom scheme.

    (Knowledge)

34. Members of the Archaea live in normal environments.

    (Knowledge)

35. In a dendogram, a genus has a higher similarity coefficient than a family.

    (Comprehension)

36. Fermentation of a carbon source can produce an acid or gas.

    (Knowledge)

37. Serum antibodies are protein molecules.

    (Knowledge)

38. A nosocomial infection is acquired in aquatic environments.

    (Knowledge)

39. An organism has a G+C percentage of 22%. This means it cannot be a protozoan but that it could be a bacterium.

    (Comprehension)

40. Sequencing of ribosomal RNA bases has become the foundation of modern taxonomy for sequencing macromolecules.

    (Knowledge)

Completion

41. In the binomial name, the second name is the _____ epithet.

    (Knowledge)

42. From stromatolites, microbial _____ were layered masses of cells.

    (Knowledge)

43. A dendogram groups organisms with the highest _____.

    (Knowledge)

44. In plants, the range of % G+C is 33 to 48 percent. Therefore, the range of % A+T is _____ to _____ percent. In a sample of 1500 base pairs, the number of A+T base pairs in the plant is _____ to _____.

    (Comprehension)

45. If a similarity coefficient of 0.80 could define a genus, then a similarity coefficient of 0.70 could not define a _____.

    (Comprehension)

Matching

46. Haeckel
47. Linnaeus
48. Stanier
49. Wheelis
50. Whittaker

A. Swedish biologist first developed widely hierarchy

B. first to put fungi in separate kingdom

C. supported eukaryote/prokaryote grouping in the 1940s

D. suggested three kingdoms in 1866

E. introduced a new scheme in 1990 featuring domains

(Knowledge)

Short Essay

51. A sample of DNA contains 6000 bases. The percentage of A-T base pairs is 52%. What is the number of cytosine bases in the sample?

(Application)

52. How is it difficult to apply the species concept when classifying bacteria?

(Application)

53. Through advanced technology, sequencing DNA in bacteria has replaced sequencing the bases in RNA and the amino acids in proteins. How can this approach still be used to account for the biochemical differences and similarities among organisms?

(Analysis)

54. Two bacterial species are compared for twenty different characteristics. Sixteen of these characteristics are the same in this comparison. What taxonomic category do these two species probably define?

(Analysis)

55. Compose a dichotomous key that leads to the classification of *B. subtilis*.

(Synthesis)

56. Assess the historical classification scheme that has been used for bacteria. What are its strengths? What are its limitations? How are these limitations being removed?

(Evaluation)

Correlation Questions

57. Many biologists think that the subspecies of humans are the result of evolution. Geographical barriers separated human populations. Each local group had its own unique mutations subject to different environmental selection pressures. Many biologists also think that the subspecies of humans will disappear in the next 100 years. Explain this line of thought.

58. New variations of microorganisms are discovered on a planet through space exploration. A biologist is asked to classify these life forms in a meaningful way. Most of these microbes have unique pigments. What are the strengths of using the pigment systems of these microbes as a basis for classification? What are the weaknesses?

59. The chairman of a biology society wants to mail a microbiology research article to all faculty members in this professional society. He sorts out their addresses, from state to local address. How can the addresses of these faculty members be viewed as part of a hierarchy?

60. Distinct fossil imprints of microbes are discovered in a geological layer in South America. How can carbon-dating be used to estimate the age of the fossil?

Answers

Multiple Choice

1. B   2. D   3. B   4. D   5. B   6. C   7. A   8. C   9. D   10. B   11. D   12. D
13. C   14. A   15. B   16. B   17. A   18. B   19. C   20. C   21. C   22. C
23. A   24. B   25. C

True/False

26. True   27. False   28. False   29. False   30. False   31. True   32. True
33. False   34. False   35. True   36. True   37. True   38. False   39. False   40. True

Completion

41. species   42. mats   43. similarity coefficient   44. 52 to 67 percent; 780 to 1005 base pairs
45. species

Matching

46. D   47. A   48. C   49. E   50. B

Short Essay

51. 6000 bases represent 3000 base pairs. 48% of the base pairs are G-C. 48% of 3000 equals 1440. In each of these base pairs, one base is guanine. Therefore, the number of G bases is 1440.

52. The modern-day definition of a species depends on the potential for interbreeding. Two different species cannot interbreed. Members of the same species can interbreed. Many kinds of bacteria do not reproduce sexually in order to test this concept.

53. By the genetic code, the sequence of bases in DNA is decoded into a sequence of bases in RNA. The base sequence in mRNA is translated into the sequence of amino acids specified by the DNA genetic blueprint. Therefore, there is a colinear correlation as DNA makes RNA which then in turn, makes protein.

54. 16 divided by 20 equals a similarity coefficient of 0.80. This value is closer to revealing a species than a genus (0.65).

55. From Figure 10.12 in the text, use the dichotomous key for *E. coli* as a guide. Start with the composition of the cell wall and the Gram staining result. For example, the cell wall makeup of *B. subtilis* means that it cannot belong to the archaebacteria. *B. subtilis* is Gram-positive.

56. The historical scheme emphasizes morphological and physiological criteria. This approach is useful for the staining procedures and tests (e.g., fermentation of glucose) that have been conducted in lab for years. However, this approach often does not emphasize phylogeny for meaningful similarities and differences. The current undertaking of sequencing DNA and RNA bases for comparisons, however, does seek this meaningful information.

Correlation Questions

57. Through improved methods of communication and transportation, formerly-existing geographical barriers are disappearing. The resultant interbreeding among human subspecies will lead to the loss of unique mutations and distinctive traits within each subspecies.

58. Classifying organisms based on superficial characteristics (e.g., color of pigment) is not a sound approach phylogenetically. However, if the pigment systems can be related to genetic similarities and differences (e.g., DNA or RNA comparisons), the basis for classifying will be on a more phylogenetic basis.

59. The address of each faculty member ranges from broad categories to very specific categories: state - county - township - town - street - number.

60. Carbon - 14 is a radioactive isotope of carbon. It decays to N-14. Originally all the carbon in an organism is C-14. Its half-life is the time required for one half of the carbon in an organism to change to N-14. If, for example, the half-life is 1,000,000 years, the fossilized organism is 1,000,000 years old if it has equal amounts of C-14 and N-14. If 75% is N-14, this change required another 1,000,000 years. The age is this case is 2,000,000 years. By this pattern the age of the organism can be deduced.

Chapter 11
The Prokaryotes

Multiple Choice

1. The most complete and widely accepted scheme of natural, prokaryotic classification uses
   A. cell wall composition.
   B. staining reactions.
   C. the sequence of bases in DNA and mRNA.
   D. the sequence of bases in 16S ribosomal RNA.
   (Knowledge)

2. The prokaryotes in *Bergey's Manual* are currently classified into _____ domains.
   A. 2
   B. 3
   C. 4
   D. 5
   (Knowledge)

3. The halophilic archaea are named because they are
   A. attracted to acids.
   B. attracted to salts.
   C. repelled by acids.
   D. repelled by salts.
   (Knowledge)

4. Select the phylum that has only one species.
   A. *Chlorobi*
   B. *Chrysiogenetes*
   C. *Cyanobacteria*
   D. *Deinococcus*
   (Knowledge)

5. Select the phylum that has the largest number of species
   A. *Alphaproteobacteria*
   B. *Chlorobi*
   C. *Cyanobacteria*
   D. *Proteobacteria*
   (Knowledge)

6. Which bacterium produces vinegar?

   A. *Acetobacter*
   B. *Azospirillum*
   C. *Leptospira*
   D. *Treponema*

   (Knowledge)

7. Select the correct association.

   A. *Acetobacter*/member of Chlorobi
   B. *Bradyrhizobium*/not symbiotic
   C. *Neisseria*/meningitis
   D. *Rhizobium*/forms a capsule

   (Comprehension)

8. *Rhozibium* is important for

   A. genetic engineering.
   B. nitrogen fixation.
   C. wine fermentation.
   D. yogurt production.

   (Knowledge)

9. The term "enteric" means

   A. intestinal
   B. luminescent
   C. nitrogen-fixing
   D. pathogenic

   (Knowledge)

10. All members of the *Enterobacteriales* have a cell shape that is the

    A. bacillus or rod-shaped
    B. coccus or spherical
    C. spirillum.
    D. vibrio or comma-shaped.

    (Knowledge)

11. A Gram-negative bacterium is isolated for identification. It can ferment lactose but cannot use citric acid as a carbon source. It converts tryptophan to indole. This species belongs to the genus

    A. *Escherichia*.
    B. *Salmonella*.
    C. *Staphylococcus*.
    D. *Yersinia*.

    (Application)

12. Luminescent bacteria are associated with

   A. anaerobic respiration.
   B. botulism.
   C. enteric diseases.
   D. marine life.

   (Knowledge)

13. *P. aeruoginosa* produces a _____ pigment.

   A. blue-green
   B. brown
   C. red-orange
   D. yellow

   (Knowledge)

14. *Xanthomonas* is often cultivated for its

   A. capsule.
   B. cell wall.
   C. DNA.
   D. ribosomes.

   (Knowledge)

15. There are _____ recognized genera of bacteria that form endospores.

   A. 2
   B. 3
   C. 4
   D. 5

   (Knowledge)

16. Gliding bacteria can move only when contacting a _____ surface

   A. frozen
   B. gaseous
   C. liquid
   D. solid

   (Knowledge)

17 Select the genus that is not included with lactic acid bacteria.

   A. *Bacillus*
   B. *Leuconostoc*
   C. *Pediococcus*
   D. *Streptococcus*

   (Knowledge)

18. Anthrax is caused by a species of the genus

    A. *Azobacter.*
    B. *Bacillus.*
    C. *Clostridium.*
    D. *Pseudomonas.*

    (Knowledge)

19. Species of *Mycobacterium* cause

    A. anthrax and rheumatic fever.
    B. gonorrhea and syphilis.
    C. leprosy and tuberculosis.
    D. tooth decay.

    (Knowledge)

20. Members of the rickettsias and chlamydias were once through to be

    A. fungi.
    B. plants.
    C. protozoa.
    D. viruses.

    (Knowledge)

21. Select the incorrect association.

    A. *Sarcina*/cubical packets
    B. *Staphylococcus*/cluster of cells
    C. *Streptococcus*/strict anaerobe
    D. *Streptococcus*/string of beads

    (Knowledge)

22. Select the incorrect characteristic about the *Mollicutes*.

    A. Almost all are obligate fermenters.
    B. Their cells burst easily
    C. They are closely related to Gram-positive bacteria.
    D. They lack a cell wall.

    (Knowledge)

23. Select the incorrect, overall description about the spirochetes.

    A. They are long and helical.
    B. They are not decolorized in the Gram staining process.
    C. They can live with or without oxygen.
    D. They move through media with high viscosity.

    (Knowledge)

24. A bacterium is located in an environment of thick mud. Its flagellum consists of two axial filaments. The bacterium has a corkscrew shaped and is Gram negative. It could belong to the genus
    A. *Bacillus*
    B. *Escherichia*
    C. *Treponema*
    D. *Vibrio*
    (Knowledge)

25. Species of *Bacteroides* live mainly in the _____ of animals
    A. blood and upper respiratory tract
    B. blood and skin
    C. mouth and intestinal tract
    D. respiratory and reproductive tracts
    (Knowledge)

True/False

26. The current scheme of classification in Bergey's Manual relies mainly on superficial, morphological characteristics of microbes.

    (Knowledge)

27. Two of the biological world's three domains share the same prokaryotic cell structure.

    (Knowledge)

28. A bacterium can form endospores. This means that it could be a species of the genus *Xanthomonas* or genus *Clostridium*, but not a member of the genus *Bacillus*.

    (Comprehension)

29. Many prokaryotic species are halophiles.

    (Knowledge)

30. Thermoacidophiles thrive in comparitively mild, safe environments.

    (Knowledge)

31. Cyanobacteria are algae.

    (Knowledge)

32. Members of the genus *Agrobacterium* cause cancer.

    (Knowledge)

33. Prosthecae decrease the surface to volume ratio of microbial cells.

    (Knowledge)

34. Caulobacters prosper in nutrient-poor environments.

    (Knowledge)

35. A bacterium is isolated from the soil. It can form endospores and is a strict anaerobe. This bacterium could be a member of the genus *Clostridium* and cannot be a member of the genus *Escherichia*.

    (Application)

36. Species of *Mycobacterium* are acid-fast bacteria.

    (Knowledge)

37. The deltaproteobacteria include a group of anaerobes.

    (Knowledge)

38. All species of the genus *Bacillus* are strict anaerobes.

    (Knowledge)

39. Species of *Staphylococcus* are facultative anaerobes.

    (Knowledge)

40. Species of actinomycetes are abundant in most soils.

    (Knowledge)

Completion

41. All species of the *Crenarchaeota* share the common property of being extremely _____.

    (Knowledge)

42. Species of *Rhizobium* and *Azotobacter* conduct nitrogen _____ in the soil.

    (Knowledge)

43. Sulfur-reducing bacteria produce the gas _____.

    (Knowledge)

44. A bacterium is isolated from a hot, dry environment. It has a thin peptidoglycan cell wall and is Gram-negative. It is a carbon-fixer and nitrogen-fixer, needing only a few minerals to complete its nutritional requirements. This bacterium probably belongs to the group of _____.

    (Application)

45. Butanediol fermentation can be detected by a simple chemical test for the presence of the substance _____.

    (Knowledge)

Matching/Labeling

Label each of the following as Gram-positive or Gram-negative.

46. cyanobacteria

47. *Bacillus*

48. *Staphylococcus*

49. *Clostridium*

50. *Chlamydia*

   (Knowledge)

Short Essay

51. A bacterium is isolated from the mucous membranes of an animal. It is studied in lab for identification. It is motile and its flagella consist of two axial filaments. It is also Gram-negative. What group of bacteria contains this species?

   (Application)

52. Some species of bacteria ferment substances to form the alcohol in wine. Other species destroy wine. At the genetic level, how can you account for this difference?

   (Analysis)

53. A plot of farmland is covered with asphalt during the construction of a small shopping center. Years later, the asphalt is removed. A farmer tries to grow alfalfa on the exposed land and is unsuccessful. Why? What could be done to improve the productivity of this land?

   (Analysis)

54. Explain how rickettsias are bacteria and not viruses. Explain how they could have been mistaken for viruses at one time.

   (Analysis)

55. *E. coli* has evolved numerous adaptations to live in the human large intestine. Describe some of these adaptations.

   (Synthesis)

56. How has the current edition of *Bergey's Manual* changed its approach to classify microorganisms?

   (Evaluation)

Correlation Questions

57. A biologist submits a scheme to classify bacteria into two kingdoms. One kingdom contains Gram-positive bacteria. The other kingdom contains Gram-negative bacteria. Is this a logical approach to classify bacteria?

58. Thermoacidophiles tolerate extreme environmental conditions that kill many other kinds of cells. What biochemical adaptations do they have that allows them to withstand harsh environments?

59. Light production is often associated with heat production. However, luminescent bacteria can produce light without the byproduct of heat. How can they do this?

60. A pathogen attacks the mucous membranes of the human upper respiratory tract. In the winter, many people use dry heating systems in their homes. How does the use of this type of heat make humans more susceptible to invasion by this pathogen?

Answers

1. D 2. A 3. B 4. B 5. D 6. A 7. C 8. B 9. A 10. A 11. A
12. D 13. A 14. A 15. A 16. D 17. A 18. B 19. C 20 D. 21. C
22. B 23. B 24. C 25. C

True/False

26. False 27. True 28. False 29. True 30. False 31. False 32. True
33. False 34. True 35. True 36. True 37. True 38. False 39. True 40. True

Completion

41. themophilic 42. fixation 43. hydrogen sulfide 44. cyanobacteria 45. acetoin

Matching/Labeling

46. negative 47. positive 48. positive 49. positive 50. negative

Short Essay

51. Read about the spirochetes, B 17.

52. Different species of bacteria have different DNA genetic blueprints. Through transcription and translation, they make different enzyme systems and have different biochemical abilities. Some, metabolically, can make ethyl alcohol. Other species produce substances that break down wine.

53. The land has probably lost its population of nitrogen-fixing bacteria. Establishing the land with new populations of these bacteria could make it more productive.

54. They have the organelles and biochemical abilities associated with bacteria. However, they are very small in size.

55. It probably thrives in an alkaline environment, a pH of 8 to 9. Its optimal temperature for growth is about 37 degrees Celsius and it can survive at low concentrations of oxygen.

56. It emphasizes less about morphological and physiological characteristics. It relies more on phylogeny through ribosomal RNA studies and meaningful evolutionary relationships.

Correlation Questions

57. This scheme has a weak phylogenetic basis. It centers on a morphological trait, namely a difference in cell wall morphology.

58. The adaptation centers on the secondary and tertiary structure of proteins in organisms. Harsh temperature and pH conditions disrupt proteins at these levels. Bonds that can stabilize protein structure at these levels (e.g., disulfide bonds), assist in withstanding the denaturation of a protein.

59. A enzyme called luciferase catalyzes a chemical reaction that liberates light. The reaction it controls does not liberate great amounts of heat. Generally, enzymes allow reactions to occur in the "cold chemistry" of living organisms. Without enzymes, more heat is involved in similar chemical reactions.

60. Dry heat can also dry out the mucous membranes in the human body, making these less effective as a major line of defense to withstand pathogens that attack the body.

Chapter 12
Eukaryotic Microorganisms, Helminths, and Arthropod Vectors

Multiple Choice

1. In a five-kingdom scheme of classification, eukaryotic microorganisms are divided into two kingdoms:
    A. fungi and monerans.
    B. fungi and protists.
    C. monerans and protists.
    D. plants and protists.
    (Knowledge)

2. Select the correct description about fungi.
    A. None are pathogens.
    B. The yeasts are members.
    C. They are phototrophic organisms.
    D. They have a prokaryotic cell structure.
    (Comprehension)

3. The specific name for the entire, multinucleate mass of cytoplasm among fungi is
    A. acellular.
    B. mycelium.
    C. saprophyte.
    D. septa.
    (Knowledge)

4. Fungi are classified by their
    A. ecological preferences.
    B. kind of metabolism.
    C. means of reproduction.
    D. metabolic specializations.
    (Knowledge)

5. Among yeasts, budding is a means of
    A. energy storage.
    B. feeding.
    C. movement.
    D. reproduction.
    (Knowledge)

6. Select the class that is not a member of the lower fungi.

    A. Basidiomycetes
    B. Chytridiomycetes
    C. Oomycetes
    D. Zygomycetes

    (Knowledge)

7. A mold is discovered growing on stale bread. Select the characteristic of its life cycle that excludes it from being *Rhizopus nigricans*.

    A. It grows as a haploid mycelium.
    B. It has a nonresistant, diploid zygospore.
    C. It produces air-born sporangiospores.
    D. It produces swimming cells.

    (Comprehension)

8. Each of the following is a group of higher fungi except

    A. Ascomycetes.
    B. Basidiomycetes.
    C. Deuteromycetes.
    D. Zygomycetes.

    (Knowledge)

9. The species of Ascomycetes differ by the

    A. arrangement of the asci.
    B. means of sexual reproduction.
    C. presence or absence of conidia.
    D. presence or absence of septa.

    (Knowledge)

10. Each is a member of the Basidiomycetes except the

    A. mushrooms.
    B. puffballs.
    C. shelf fungi.
    D. yeasts.

    (Knowledge)

11. A scientist discovers a fungus that forms long chains of conidia on branching conidiophores. It has a brush-like appearance. It belongs to the genus of

    A. *Aspergillus*.
    B. *Candida*.
    C. *Mucor*.
    D. *Penicillium*.

    (Application)

12. A yeast is studied for identification in a lab. It is *Saccharomyces cerevisiae* if it ferments sugars to ethanol and

   A. carbon dioxide and is a facultative anaerobe.
   B. carbon dioxide and is a strict anaerobe.
   C. oxygen and is a facultative anaerobe.
   D. oxygen and is a strict anaerobe.

   (Comprehension)

13. The fungi are the major cause of infectious diseases in

   A. arthropods.
   B. bacteria.
   C. mammals.
   D. plants.

   (Knowledge)

14. Phalloidin is a(n)

   A. antibiotic.
   B. part of a mycelium.
   C. reproductive structure in algae.
   D. toxin produced by a fungus.

   (Knowledge)

15. Select the incorrect characteristic about algae.

   A. Some are microscopic.
   B. They carry out oxygenic photosynthesis.
   C. They exhibit a tissue structure.
   D. They reproduce differently than plants.

   (Comprehension)

16. For every five liters of oxygen produced by photosynthesis on the Earth, on average about _____ liters is produced by the activity of phytoplankton.

   A. one
   B. two
   C. three
   D. four

   (Application)

17. Algae are divided into six groups by their

   A. habitat selection.
   B. means of reproduction.
   C. thallus forms.
   D. type of metabolism.

   (Knowledge)

18. A microorganism is observed under the microscope. It has an eyespot and moves toward light. It moves by a flagellum. It is probably a species of

    A. *Amoeba.*
    B. *Euglena.*
    C. *Paramecium.*
    D. *Roccella.*

    (Application)

19. A lichen is a mutualistic association between a

    A. fungus and alga.
    B. fungus and protozoan.
    C. protozoan and bacterium.
    D. protozoan and virus.

    (Knowledge)

20. Protozoans are divided into four groups based on their means of

    A. cell structure.
    B. locomotion.
    C. metabolism
    D. reproduction.

    (Knowledge)

21. A *Paramecium* moves by the action of its

    A. cilia.
    B. contractile vacuoles.
    C. lysosomes.
    D. smooth and rough ER.

    (Comprehension)

22. The trypanosomes include members that cause

    A. African sleeping sickness.
    B. dysentery.
    C. encephalitis.
    D. malaria.

    (Knowledge)

23. Members of Mastigophora move by the action of

    A. cilia.
    B. flagella.
    C. parapodia.
    D. pseudopodia.

    (Knowledge)

24. Select the correct characteristic about members of Sarcodina.

    A. They are limited to marine environments.
    B. They lack pseudopodia.
    C. They move by cilia.
    D. Very few members cause human diseases.

(Knowledge)

25. Compared to flagella, cilia have a

    A. different structure and are larger.
    B. different structure and are smaller.
    C. similar structure and are larger.
    D. similar structure and are smaller.

(Knowledge)

26. The macronucleus and micronucleus are found in the cells of a

    A. ciliate.
    B. flagellate.
    C. sarcodine.
    D. sporozoan.

(Knowledge)

27. Select the incorrect characteristic about most members of Platyhelminthes.

    A. Earthworms are not members of this group.
    B. Most species lack a digestive tract.
    C. They have bilateral symmetry.
    D. They have specialized organ systems.

(Comprehension)

28. Proglottids are structures that

    A. attach tapeworms to a host.
    B. digest food.
    C. make eggs.
    D. synthesize pigment.

(Knowledge)

29. Cysticerci encyst is the _____ of mammals.

    A. blood
    B. muscles
    C. nerves
    D. reproductive organs

(Knowledge)

30. A scientist studying the life cycle of a fluke attempts to control this parasite by destroying its snail host. This directly prevents the development of the fluke's _____ larva.

    A. cercaria
    B. metacercariae
    C. miracidia
    D. redia

    (Application)

True/False

31. Fungi are heterotrophic, nonphototrophic, and absorptive.

    (Comprehension)

32. Yeasts do not form hyphae.

    (Knowledge)

33. A researcher wants to prevent the spread of a fungus of Oomycetes. This can be accomplished by removing all water from its environment.

    (Application)

34. The higher fungi are coenocytic.

    (Knowledge)

35. A basidium is a single, club-shaped cell.

    (Knowledge)

36. Most yeasts are members of Ascomycetes or Deuteromycetes.

    (Knowledge)

37. A scientist from an industrial company is studying local ecosystems to find a natural source of cephalosporin production. The filamentous, green pond growth in the pond is one good source for this antibiotic.

    (Comprehension)

38. Phycology is the study of algae.

    (Knowledge)

39. A microorganism is discovered in a local stream. It is studied in the lab. It has a prokaryotic cell structure. It cannot produce oxygen and glucose from carbon dioxide and water. These characteristics mean that it cannot be a protozoan.

    (Application)

40. The cellular slime molds are phylogenetically related to red algae.

    (Knowledge)

Completion

41. _____are organisms that transmit diseases between hosts.

    (Comprehension)

42. The slime molds are divided into two groups, the _____ slime molds and _____ slime molds.

    (Knowledge)

43. The two phyla of the helminths are the _____ and _____ .

    (Knowledge)

44. A human patient is ill. Tests reveal proglottids in the feces of this person. This indicates infection by a

    _____ .

    (Comprehension)

45. The members of Trematoda have flattened segments. However, unlike earthworms, their bodies lack

    _____ .

    (Knowledge)

Matching

46. arthropod   A. root-like structure
47. cercari   B. Platyhelminthes
48. flatworm   C. free-swimming larva
49. protozoa   D. animal with jointed appendages
50. rhizoid   E. *Plasmodium*

    (Knowledge)

Short Essay

51. One species of Basidiomycetes has a basidiocarp in which cells have nuclei that fuse and undergo meiosis. How does meiosis change the chromosome number in this species?

    (Application)

52. A researcher wants to eradicate a liver fluke population from the environment. He wants to use a biological means of control. How can he achieve this without treating the adult stage of the fluke directly?

    (Application)

53. The arthropods are probably the most successful phylum of animals on the Earth. Analyze this claim.

    (Analysis)

54. Through evolution tapeworms have lost their digestive system. How is this adaptive?

    (Analysis)

55. Can you classify the four groups of protozoan on a criterion other than locomotion? What criterion would you use?

    (Synthesis)

56. A lichen is classified as a mutualistic association. Why?

    (Evaluation)

Correlation Questions

57. Slime molds are currently classified in the kingdom Protista. Do you think their unique characteristics warrant a separate kingdom for their classification?

58. On initial inspection, some fungi could be mistakenly identified as plants. How could this mistake be made?

59. A researcher claims that the exoskeleton of a newly-discovered invertebrate is a polysaccharide. However, it does not consist of cellulose or other familiar polysaccharides. How can he prove that these polysaccharides do not compose the exoskeleton?

60. A new, plantlike organism, is discovered by a researcher. The researcher wants to learn if the organism's highest level of organization is at the tissue level or the organ level. How can the researcher decide this?

Answers

Multiple Choice
1. B 2. B 3. B 4. C 5. D 6. A 7. B 8. D 9. A 10. D 11. D 12. A 13. D
14. D 15. C 16. D 17. C 18. B 19. A 20. B 21. A 22. A 23. B 24. D
25. D 26. A 27. B 28. C 29. B 30. D

True/False

31. True 32. True 33. True 34. False 35. True 36. True 37. False 38. False
39. True 40. True

Completion

41. vectors 42. true, cellular 43. flatworms, roundworms 44. tapeworm 45. segments

Matching

46. D   47. C   48. B   49. E   50. A

Short Essay

51. Meiosis usually produces haploid structures from diploid structures. This reduces the chromosome number by one-half.

52. He should concentrate on eradicating one of the required intermediate hosts: an intermediate host (snail or clam) and/or a secondary host (fish/crab/water plant).

53. They are the most successful based on species diversity. There are probably more species of insects, still many undiscovered, than all other species, combined. Overall, there are more different kinds of arthropods that are successfully occupying a wide variety of ecological niches.

54. The use of resources and energy to maintain a digestive system would be wasteful, as the tapeworms gain their nutrients in finished form from the host. Without a digestive system, more resources and energy can be used for reproduction.

55. One possible approach is the complexity and specialization of cell structure. Ciliates, for example, have the most complex cells. The sporozoans have specializations for a parasitic existence.

56. The alga gains a substrate and habitat from the fungus. The fungus gains a source of nutrition from the photosynthetic alga.

Correlation Questions

57. Some of their characteristics resemble algae. Others are similar to protozoa. Other traits, such as the grex and unique pigment systems, are not shared with other phyla.

58. Some have a leafy appearance and pigment systems that superficially resemble plants. Many grow on a substrate. They do not exhibit motility.

59. Administer different enzymes to samples of the exoskeleton. Known enzymes can digest cellulose, chitin, etc. If the exoskeleton is not digested by these enzymes, associated with specific polysaccharide substrates, the exoskeleton is not composed of these better-known polysaccharides.

60. Study the responses of the groups of cells in the organism. Do the cells work separately or do they maintain function only when working as an integrated group (tissues)? Do the cell groups work interdependently (organ) or separately?

Chapter 13
The Viruses

Multiple Choice

1. Select the incorrect statement about viruses.

    A. All cellular organisms are attacked by them.
    B. They are parasites.
    C. They contain nucleic acids inside a protein coat.
    D. They show signs of life outside of host cells.

    (Comprehension)

2. Which scientist purified and crystallized the tobacco mosaic virus?

    A. Beijerinck
    B. Griffith
    C. Iwanowsky
    D. Stanley

    (Knowledge)

3. Virions are

    A. intact, nonreplicating virus particles.
    B. intact, replicating virus particles.
    C. the DNA core of the viruses.
    D. the protein coat of the viruses.

    (Knowledge)

4. Each of the following is used to classify viruses except

    A. carbohydrate makeup.
    B. host range.
    C. life cycle.
    D. size.

    (Knowledge)

5. A bacteriophage is (a)

    A. bacterium that infect bacteria.
    B. bacterium that infect viruses.
    C. virus that infects bacteria.
    D. virus that infects viruses.

    (Knowledge)

6. One virus has a diameter of 0.15 micrometers. This is _____ nanometers.

    A. 15000
    B. 1500
    C. 150
    D. 15

    (Application)

7. The virus capsid consists of

    A. carbohydrate.
    B. lipid.
    C. nucleic acid.
    D. protein.

    (Knowledge)

8. Which viral nucleic acid has either a plus or minus strand?

    A. dsDNA
    B. ssDNA
    C. dsRNA
    D. ssRNA

    (Knowledge)

9. The most common polyhedral virus has _____ triangular surfaces.

    A. 10
    B. 20
    C. 30
    D. 50

    (Knowledge)

10. In the viral life cycle, uncoating is the

    A. attachment to the host cell.
    B. entrance of the viral genome into the host cell.
    C. removal of the capsid and envelope.
    D. rupturing of the host cell.

    (Knowledge)

11. One characteristic first used to name viruses was

    A. capsid structure.
    B. DNA composition.
    C. disease type.
    D. host range.

    (Knowledge)

12. The methods to count and study bacteriophages are based on their
    A. analysis of RNA composition.
    B. effects on different growth media.
    C. host range and organ system preferences.
    D. mode of infecting and destroying host cells.

    (Knowledge)

13. The latent period is when viruses
    A. do not increase in number.
    B. escape from their host.
    C. increase in number substantially.
    D. rupture their capsids.

    (Knowledge)

14. The life cycle of the temperate phage lambda is
    A. either the lytic or lysogenic pathway.
    B. neither the lytic nor lysogenic pathway.
    C. the lysogenic pathway only.
    D. the lytic pathway only.

    (Knowledge)

15. A substance is added to a bacteriophage sample. The substance destroys the activity of the lysozymes in the viruses. This prevents their ability to
    A. change their nucleic acid genetically.
    B. decrease their metabolism.
    C. dissolve the bacterial cell wall.
    D. increase their metabolism.

    (Comprehension)

16. A drop of a bacterial culture is added to an undiluted viral sample. This mixture is spread over a solid agar surface. After incubation, 20 circular plaques develop on the lawn of bacterial cells. The number of viruses in the sample was probably
    A. 2
    B. 20
    C. 200
    D. 2000

    (Application)

17. T4 and lambda bacteriophages contain
    A. dsDNA.
    B. ssDNA.
    C. dsRNA.
    D. ssRNA.

    (Knowledge)

18. The tail fibers of an animal virus are destroyed. This will directly interfere with the _____ stage of the life cycle of this virus.

    A. absorption
    B. adsorption
    C. penetration
    D. uncoating

    (Comprehension)

19. RNA-dependent RNA polymerase is needed by

    A. double-strand DNA viruses.
    B. single-strand DNA viruses.
    C. double-strand RNA viruses.
    D. triple-strand RNA viruses.

    (Knowledge)

20. Shingles is a disease mainly affecting the

    A. blood.
    B. bones.
    C. muscles.
    D. skin.

    (Knowledge)

21. Plus-strand RNA in an HIV is used exclusively as a template for

    A. DNA replication.
    B. reverse transcription.
    C. transduction.
    D. translation.

    (Knowledge)

22. Of the influenza virus, only types _____ infect humans.

    A. A and B
    B. B and C
    C. A and C
    D. A, B, and C

    (Knowledge)

23. Oncogenes in cells will cause the cells to

    A. develop pigmentation.
    B. divide too rapidly.
    C. divide too slowly.
    D. lose pigmentation.

    (Comprehension)

24. Plant viruses are normally named by the
    A. disease they cause.
    B. genetic mutations.
    C. host range.
    D. size of their particles.
    (Knowledge)

25. The TMV infects
    A. animal cells.
    B. bacteria.
    C. fungi.
    D. plants.
    (Knowledge)

True/False

26. Viruses contain some of the same macromolecules found in cellular organisms.
    (Knowledge)

27. A suspension with viruses and bacteria is passed through a filter. Each pore has a diameter of 500 nanometers. The viruses will probably pass through the filter but the bacteria will be trapped by it.
    (Comprehension)

28. The minus strand in viruses is specialized DNA.
    (Knowledge)

29. The envelope of a virus can be denatured by heat.
    (Comprehension)

30. The ICTV scheme has only three hierarchical levels.
    (Knowledge)

31. It is necessary to dilute a viral suspension before plating it.
    (Knowledge)

32. A viral mutation blocks the ability of the virus to remove its capsid and envelope. This directly inhibits the uncoating stage of its life cycle.
    (Comprehension)

33. Prophage DNA is the nucleic acid core in a virus when it is not infecting a host.
    (Knowledge)

34. A temperate phage can act like a virulent phage or exist in host cells without harming the cells.

    (Comprehension)

35. Adsorption is responsible for the tissue specificity of animal viruses.

    (Knowledge)

36. A virus infects a host cell lacking ribosomes. In the absence of this organelle, the viruses can adapt and make their own proteins independently.

    (Comprehension)

37. Animal cells do not contain latent viruses.

    (Knowledge)

38. AZT inhibits reverse transcription in the AIDS virus.

    (Knowledge)

39. Antigenic drift can produce highly dangerous strains of the influenza virus.

    (Knowledge)

40. A viroid is a circular molecule of ssRNA with a capsid.

    (Knowledge)

Completion

41. A viral suspension is diluted to 0.001 of its original virus concentration. It is mixed with nutrient agar and a bacterial population which is then poured into a petri dish. After incubation, twelve plaques develop on the lawn in the dish. The original viral population consisted of _(number)_ viruses.

    (Application)

42. _____ are proteins that protrude from the viral envelope.

    (Knowledge)

43. A virus that is enteric infects the human _____ tract.

    (Comprehension)

44. _____ are clear, circular regions on a nutrient agar surface that contain few or no bacteria after phage infection.

    (Knowledge)

45. During the _____ stage of its life cycle, the intact virion or its nucleic acid enters a host cell.

    (Knowledge)

46. _____ are the most thoroughly studied group of viruses.

    (Knowledge)

Matching/Labeling

Label each of the following as describing a virulent or temperate phage

47. It enters the lytic or lysogenic pathway.
48. It enters only the lytic pathway.
49. The phage combines with the host cell without damage.
50. Its attack is swift and deadly.

    (Comprehension)

Short Essay

51. One particular virus has a diameter of 0.02 micrometers. Express this diameter in nanometers.

    (Application)

52. How can a microbiologist use a bacterial lawn on the surface of nutrient agar to calculate the viral concentration from a liquid suspension?

    (Application)

53. One RNA virus loses its ability to produce its reverse transcriptase. How does this affect its ability to reproduce?

    (Analysis)

54. How can a temperate phage, carrying out a lysogenic life cycle, be converted to a virulent phage?

    (Analysis)

55. Outline the steps required for a plant virus to successfully infect its host.

    (Synthesis)

56. A scientist claims that viruses are not alive. What evidence can he use to support this claim?

    (Evaluation)

Correlation Questions

57. Antibiotics usually attack a microbial cell structure, such as a cell wall or ribosome. A prescribed antibiotic is not effective for treating a viral disease. Explain the reason for this.

58. Viruses have been used recently to treat humans with the disease cystic fibrosis. These viruses introduce their "good DNA" into human host cells with the cystic fibrosis gene (autosomal recessive).

The viral gene replaces the defective human gene. How do these viruses serve as a unique kind of vector?

59. In this chapter on viruses, references are made to taxonomy and nomenclature. How are they different? How are they related?

60. Currently, viruses are not part of the six-kingdom classification scheme used to classify living organisms. If viruses were classified, how would you develop a scheme to classify them?

Answers

Multiple Choice

1. D 2. D 3. A 4. A 5. C 6. C. 7. D 8. D 9. B 10. C 11. D
12. D 13. A 14. A 15. C 16. B 17. A 18. B 19. C 20. D
21. B 22. B 23. B 24. A 25. D

True/False

26. True 27. True 28. False 29. True 30. True 31. True 32. True
33. False 34. True 35. True 36. False 37. False 38. True 39. True 40. False

Completion

41. twelve thousand 42. spikes 43. digestive 44. plaques 45. penetration 46. retroviruses

Matching/Labeling

47. temperate 48. virulent 49. temperate 50. virulent

Short Essay

51. There are 1000 nanometers in one micrometer. Multiply 0.02 times 1000. The viral diameter is 20 nanometers.

52. After the viral suspension is spread over the bacterial lawn, each virus will produce a plaque on the bacterial lawn. The number of plaques produced equals the number of viruses in the suspension. If the suspension was diluted before plating, this dilution must be considered to calculate the original virus concentration. For example, if 12 lawns were formed from one ml, but the original suspension was diluted by 0.01, 12 must be multiplied by 100 to calculate the original viral concentration: 12 x 100 = 1200.

53. It will not be able to make DNA from RNA due to the loss of this enzyme. Therefore, its ability to reproduce will be lost.

54. As a temperate phage, the virus is incorporated into the bacterial chromosome and is copied during each cycle of bacterial cell division. Some type of stimulus must change its latency into a virulent form. For example, high-energy radiation from the environment may cause this

conversion and change the virus to a virulent form. Then the phage will cause lysis of the bacterial cell.

55. It will carry out the steps of adsorption and penetration. However, there will not be uncoating because the plant virus lacks such a coat. Once inside the host cell it will take over the metabolism of the host plant cell. For example, it will use the host ribosomes for viral protein synthesis. It will use the host cell ATP as a source of energy. Once replicated, the new viruses will burst from the plant host cell.

56. Outside the host cell the virus does not display the properties of life. The virus crystallizes into two substances, protein and nucleic acid. It displays the properties of life only when it is inside the host cell, but not independently.

Correlation Questions

57. Antibiotics usually attack a bacterial cell wall or inactivate ribosomes. These structures are not a part of viral structure.

58. The virus is used to carry the DNA into a host cell, in this case to produce the desired result of treating a human disease.

59. Taxonomy classifies an organism into a series of hierarchical categories. Nomenclature is the scientific name used to identify the organism into each category. A bacterium is classified into a genus and species. *Staphylococcus aureus* are the genus and species names for a unique kind of bacterium occupying these categories, setting it apart from a bacterium with a different genus and species name.

60. This question has several possible answers. Start with the biochemical makeup of the virus: its nucleic acid core and protein coat.

Chapter 14
Microorganisms and Human Health

Multiple Choice

1. If a human body contains an average of 100 trillion cells, the estimated number of bacterial cells using this body as a host is

    A. an undetermined number.
    B. greater than 100 trillion.
    C. less than 100 trillion.
    D. one hundred trillion.

    (Application)

2. Select the internal human body structure that does not support a normal biota.

    A. mouth
    B. heart
    C. intestinal tract
    D. urethra

    (Knowledge)

3. Select the internal human body structure that does support a normal biota.

    A. bone
    B. brain
    C. muscle
    D. vagina

    (Knowledge)

4. Opportunists are microorganisms that

    A. always cause disease.
    B. cause disease when the proper condition arises.
    C. constantly produce beneficial effects in the host.
    D. never cause disease.

    (Knowledge)

5. Select the incorrect statement about *Bifidobacterium* species in the human body.

    A. They are favored to grow in the presence of bifidus.
    B. They ferment sugars to acetic acid.
    C. They ferment sugars to lactic acid.
    D. They inhibit infant health.

    (Comprehension)

6. A species of bacterium lives on the surface of the human skin. It does not help or harm the human host. However, it gains a habitat. This symbiotic relationship is

   A. commensalism.
   B. mutualism.
   C. parasitism.
   D. predation.

   (Comprehension)

7. By microbial antagonism, one microbe

   A. changes the effect on another microbe.
   B. has no effect on another microbe.
   C. helps the growth of another microbe.
   D. interferes with the growth of another microbe.

   (Knowledge).

8. In clinical medicine the term "parasite" refers to each of the following except

   A. bacterium.
   B. insect.
   C. protozoan.
   D. worm.

   (Knowledge)

9. Through opportunism among microbes,

   A. commensals change to mutualistic species.
   B. commensals change to pathogens.
   C. mutualistic species change to commensals.
   D. parasites change to commensals.

   (Comprehension)

10. The function of epithelium of the human body is to

    A. contract.
    B. cover surfaces.
    C. send impulses.
    D. transport substances.

    (Knowledge)

11. The mucociliary system in the human body is mainly a _____ defense.

    A. biochemical
    B. mechanical
    C. transport
    D. vascular

    (Knowledge)

12. Select the incorrect association.

    A. keratin/protein
    B. keratin/skin
    C. lysozyme/enzyme
    D. lysozyme/intestine

    (Comprehension)

13. Adhesins help bacteria to

    A. destroy antibiotics.
    B. produce acids.
    C. stick to surfaces.
    D. transport substances.

    (Knowledge)

14. Select the incorrect statement about the skin.

    A. It contains lysozymes.
    B. It contains microbiocidal fatty acids.
    C. It is usually a dry environment.
    D. Its salt concentration promotes bacterial growth.

    (Comprehension)

15. *Staphylococcus* species are

    A. aerobic organisms.
    B. facultative anaerobes.
    C. microaerophiles.
    D. strict anaerobes.

    (Knowledge)

16. Select the incorrect statement about the diphtheroids.

    A. *Corynebacterium* species are members.
    B. Most species are commensals.
    C. They are a major skin floral group.
    D. They are Gram-negative rods.

    (Comprehension)

17. The conjunctiva is a _____ membrane.

    A. cutaneous
    B. mucous
    C. serous
    D. synovial

    (Knowledge)

18. Select the genus with frequent, normal biota inhabitants of the nasal cavity.

    A. *Bacillus*
    B. *Enterobacter*
    C. *Escherichia*
    D. *Staphylococcus*

    (Knowledge)

19. Select the correct statement about the oral cavity.

    A. It contains the enzyme trypsin.
    B. It is not readily colonized by microbes.
    C. It has *Pseudomonas* species as normal biota members.
    D. It is warm and moist.

    (Comprehension)

20. Through a disease, the stomach secretes lower quantities of HCl. The main result of this in the stomach is to produce

    A. a comparatively more acidic pH.
    B. a comparatively more basic pH.
    C. decreased peristalsis.
    D. increased peristalsis.

    (Application)

21. Select the facultative anaerobe(s) normally found in the large intestine.

    A. *Bacteroides species*
    B. *Clostridium botulinum*
    C. *Escherichia coli*
    D. *Fusobacterium species*

    (Knowledge)

22. A fungus, which is an opportunist living in the vagina, belongs to the genus

    A. *Bacillus*
    B. *Candida*
    C. *Eschirichia*
    D. *Staphylococcus*

    (Knowledge)

23. The _____ is the last part of the urinary tract where urine passes through when eliminated.

    A. bladder
    B. kidney
    C. ureter
    D. urethra

    (Comprehension)

24. Vitamin K is important in the human body for

    A. blood clotting.
    B. bone formation.
    C. mineral storage.
    D. phosphorus formation.

    (Knowledge)

25. Thrush is an infection of the

    A. brain.
    B. heart.
    C. oral cavity.
    D. small intestine.

    (Knowledge)

True/False

26. Transient flora tend to persist as populations in the human body.

    (Knowledge)

27. *Candida albicans* can become an opportunist in the human body during antibiotic therapy.

    (Knowledge)

28. Mutualism and commensalism are different kinds of symbiosis.

    (Comprehension)

29. A bacterium lives in the intestine of a mammal where it makes essential vitamins while gaining a habitat. This is an example of mutualism.

    (Comprehension)

30. Acne is caused by a viral infection.

    (Knowledge)

31. The skin is a hostile environment to some microorganisms.

    (Knowledge)

32. A bacterium is part of the normal biota on the human skin. A wound to the skin allows it to enter the human bloodstream. This allows it to become an opportunist.

    (Comprehension)

33. Lysozyme inhibits bacterial growth but does not kill bacteria.

    (Knowledge)

34. Normally the conjunctiva is constantly lubricated by tears.

    (Knowledge)

35. *Staphylococcus epidermidis* is found in the nasal cavities of most humans.

    (Knowledge)

36. Blockage of the cystic duct prevents the gallbladder from secreting its products into the upper small intestine. This will not affect the normal floral population in this part of the digestive tract.

    (Application)

37. *Staphylococcus aureus* can cause opportunistic vaginal infections.

    (Knowledge)

38. The urethra has a wide variety of normal biota.

    (Knowledge)

39. A deficiency of vitamin B12 in the human body can lead to the development of anemia.

    (Application)

40. Opportunists tend to be virulent in strong, healthy hosts.

    (Comprehension)

Completion

41. The term _____ generally refers to organisms living together.

    (Knowledge)

42. _____ surface defenses act against most all microorganisms.

    (Knowledge)

43. Lack of pili on *E. coli* cells prevents these cells from _____ to cell surfaces.

    (Comprehension)

44. _____ are proteins that kill bacteria competing for space in the intestine.

    (Knowledge)

45. One type of tissue in the human body contains erythrocytes and leukocytes. It lacks normal biota. This tissue is the _____.

    (Comprehension)

46. A sample of the human skin reveals a microbial concentration of 25,000 per square centimeter. This indicates that the skin was not recently _____.

    (Application)

Matching

47. *Demodex*   A. one species causes infections in burns

48. *Pseudomona*   B. one species causes tooth decay

49. *Staphylococcus*   C. one species causes blepharitis

50. *Streptococcus*   D. one species normally inhabits the skin

    (Knowledge)

Short Essay

51. What evidence exists that intestinal flora can enter this body region only via the oral cavity?

    (Application)

52. One strain *E coli* is a normal biota species of the large intestine of one person. How can this same strain cause food poisoning in a different individual?

    (Application)

53. Why is it an unsuccessful strategy for a pathogen or parasite population to completely kill its host population?

    (Analysis)

54. Explain how an infection of the sinuses can reach the middle ear.

    (Analysis)

55. Explain how information of human anatomy and physiology, combined with the concepts of microbiology, is necessary in order to understand the principles of this chapter.

    (Synthesis)

56. Are normal biota helpful or harmful? Support your choice.

    (Evaluation)

Correlation Questions

57. Space travelers are checked for their normal biota upon their return to earth from a space flight. Why is this procedure necessary?

58. Most observers view the stomach or heart as an organ of the body. However, the skin is also an organ. How does this structure meet the definition of a true organ?

59. How is the term *microbiota* more appropriate for describing the microbial inhabitants of the human body than *microflora*?

60. The disease cystic fibrosis prevents the action of cilia lining the upper respiratory tract. How does this make the human body more vulnerable to microbial infection?

Answers

Multiple Choice

1. B 2. B 3. D 4. B 5. D 6. A 7. D 8. A 9. B 10. B 11. B 12. D
13. C 14. D 15. B 16. D 17. B 18. D 19. D 20. B 21. C 22. B
23. D 24. A 25. C

True/False

26. False 27. True 28. True 29. True 30. False 31. True 32. True 33. False
34. True 35. True 36. False 37. False 38. False 39. True 40. False

Completion

41. symbiosis 42. nonspecific 43. adhering 44. bacteriocins 45. blood
46. washed or cleansed 47. C 48. A 49. D 50. B

Short Essay

51. Infants, with blockages at GI tract sites for food passage before the intestine, did not establish a normal biota in the intestine.

52. The immune system of the first person can defend against this *E. coli* strain. The second person probably has a different immune mechanism. Also, this bacterium will have effects on the human bloodstream of the second person by absorption in the small intestine. This event precedes the arrival of *E. coli* into the large intestine.

53. The survival and propagation of the pathogen or parasite depends on the survival of the host. The eradication of the host population would lead to the eradication of the pathogen.

54. The cavities of the sinuses are continuous with the internal region of the nose. The nasopharynx is posterior and continuous with the internal nose. Therefore, microbes from the sinuses can reach the nasopharynx from the sinuses. Via the eustachian tube in this region of the throat (nasopharynx), microbes can enter the middle ear.

55. A knowledge of human anatomy is needed to describe the location and environment of the normal biota of the human body. Physiology is necessary to describe the other conditions these microbes encounter and must overcome, such as the mucociliary action of the respiratory tract.

56. The major argument for the beneficial effects rests on the phenomenon of microbial antagonism. However, there is evidence that germ-free animals can remain healthy.

Correlation Questions

57. There is a possibility that a new microbe could have infected the space travelers during their trip to outer space. Humans on planet earth may not have evolved a line of defense against this microbe. Also, a means of treating a disease from this microbe would not exist for this exotic microbial species. Therefore, its release into the environment on earth could be a disaster, threatening human life.

58. By definition an organ is two or more tissues integrated, working with common functions. A skin meets this definition and description as do the heart, stomach, and other organs.

59. *Flora* is a term that pertains more to plants. *Biota* is a more inclusive term that is more appropriate for the wide diversity of microbes inhabiting the human body.

60. The cilia of the upper respiratory tract beat opposite to the inflow of air, serving as a filter to trap invading microbes that could enter the body through this tract. A layer of mucous works with this ciliary action, serving to rid the body of invading microbes. In the absence of this ciliary-mucous membrane activity, microbes can invade the body.

Chapter 15
Microorganisms and Human Disease

Multiple Choice

1. A pathogen must have a reservoir in order to

    A. attach to a substrate
    B. gain a food source.
    C. overcome the action of antibiotics.
    D. survive outside the human host.

    (Knowledge)

2. Almost any _____ can be a reservoir for rabies.

    A. bird
    B. fish
    C. mammal
    D. reptile

    (Knowledge)

3. Influenza is a _____ disease of humans.

    A. gastrointestinal
    B. genitourinary
    C. nervous system
    D. respiratory

    (Knowledge)

4. Select the incorrect association.

    A. *Bordetella*/cholera
    B. *Clostridium*/endospores
    C. *Salmonella*/typhoid fever
    D. *Streptococcus*/strep throat

    (Comprehension)

5. Rabies attacks the human _____ system.

    A. endocrine
    B. nervous
    C. skeletal
    D. urinary

    (Knowledge)

6. In one experiment, the relationship between numbers and a specific infection is measured quantitatively with experimental animals. For a computation of the LD, _____ of 500 animals die from the disease.

    A. 50
    B. 150
    C. 250
    D. 400

    (Application)

7. The reservoir for *Clostridium tetani* is the

    A. atmosphere.
    B. human blood.
    C. oceans.
    D. soil.

    (Knowledge)

8. The portal of entry for *Bordetella pertussis* is usually the

    A. broken skin.
    B. nose.
    C. reproductive tract.
    D. urinary tract.

    (Comprehension)

9. Each of the following is a fomite except

    A. bedding.
    B. blood.
    C. cups.
    D. towels.

    (Knowledge)

10. More human diseases are transmitted by the _____ system than through any other system.

    A. circulatory
    B. reproductive
    C. respiratory
    D. urinary

    (Knowledge)

11. Most of the primary cases of Herpes simplex virus, type one, are seen in

    A. older adults.
    B. teenagers.
    C. small children.
    D. younger adults.

    (Knowledge)

12. Select the incorrect association.

    A. biological vector/Lyme disease
    B. biological vector/malaria
    C. mechanical vector/nonliving fomites
    D. mechanical vector/flies for cholera

    (Comprehension)

13. *Coccidiodes immitis* is a(n) _____ microorganism.

    A. airborne
    B. food-inhabiting
    C. viral
    D. water-borne

    (Knowledge)

14. Parenteral transmission occurs by each of the following ways except

    A. a break in the mucous membrane.
    B. a break in the skin.
    C. intravenous fluid injection by sterile conditions.
    D. penetration of the skin by a contaminated needle.

    (Knowledge)

15. FHA allows *Bordetella pertussis* to

    A. attach to the respiratory tract.
    B. live in its abiotic reservoir.
    C. lyse red blood cells.
    D. react against antibodies.

    (Knowledge)

16. By __1__ a microbe enters __2__ .

    A. 1 - exocytosis, 2 - body cells
    B. 1 - exocytosis, 2 - body tracts
    C. 1 - phagocytosis, 2 - body cells
    D. 1 - phagocytosis, 2 - body tracts

    (Comprehension)

17. In lab, a student studies a prepared slide of *Plasmodium* infecting the tissues of an organism. This slide is probably found in a _____ lab.

    A. botany
    B. hematology
    C. neurology
    D. urology

    (Application)

18. Select the incorrect association.

    A. *Bordetella*/whooping cough
    B. *Cryptococcus*/typhoid
    C. *Neisseria*/gonorrhea
    D. *Streptococcus*/pneumonia

    (Comprehension)

19. *Trypanosoma brucei* evades host defenses by _____ variation.

    A. antibody
    B. antigenic
    C. monobody
    D. monogenic

    (Knowledge)

20. If a microbe __1__ its B exotoxin subunit, it __2__ .

    A. 1 - contains, 2 - alters a cell component.
    B. 1 - contains, 2 - attaches to a host cell.
    C. 1 - loses, 2 - alters a cell component.
    D. 1 - loses, 2 - attaches to a host cell.

    (Comprehension)

21. Ptx directly interferes with the human body's ability to

    A. form sex cells.
    B. protect itself with epithelium
    C. send signals inside cells.
    D. transport oxygen.

    (Comprehension)

22. Select the incorrect association.

    A. coagulase/fibrin formation
    B. cytolysin/forms cell membranes
    C. hyaluronidase/degrades polysaccharide
    D. kinases/split fibrin

    (Comprehension)

23. Streptokinase is used to

    A. dissolve blood clots.
    B. inhibit neurotransmitters.
    C. lyse erythrocytes.
    D. stimulate muscle contraction.

    (Knowledge)

24. Lytic infections affect host cells by
    A. blocking muscle contraction.
    B. breaking cells apart.
    C. disrupting neuron function.
    D. stimulating enzyme activity.
    (Knowledge)

25. A student plans to study Negri bodies by preparing slides in lab. One source from a mammal would be its
    A. bone marrow.
    B. brain.
    C. liver.
    D. pancreas.
    (Comprehension)

True/False

26. HIV-infected people who have not yet developed AIDS are incubatory carriers.
    (Knowledge)

27. Lyme disease is an example of a zoonosis.
    (Comprehension)

28. The oral cavity and urinary tract of the human body are portals of entry for microbiota.
    (Comprehension)

29. In a recent study of whooping cough, 200 people per 1000 people in a population that are exposed to *B. pertussis* develop whooping cough. This is a normal frequency of infection.
    (Application)

30. Fomites are a common reservoir for human pathogens.
    (Knowledge)

31. The genus *Clostridium* has species causing tetanus and gas gangrene.
    (Knowledge)

32. *Coxiella burnetii* is destroyed by phagolysosomes in white blood cells.
    (Knowledge)

33. The presence of a capsule around a bacterial cell makes the microbe more vulnerable to phagocytosis.
    (Knowledge)

34. Siderophores tend to release iron to transferrin in the human body.

    (Knowledge)

35. All Gram-negative bacteria contain endotoxin.

    (Knowledge)

36. Endotoxins are the lipopolysaccharide component of the outer member of Gram-negative bacteria.

    (Knowledge)

37. Adenylate cyclase produces a lingering effect of the pertussis exotoxin in eukaryotic cells.

    (Knowledge)

38. Leukocidins stimulate the production of white blood cells.

    (Knowledge)

39. A mammal's clotting time is six minutes. A student withdraws blood from a mammal in lab. Immediately, the student studies the normal coagulation of blood in a capillary tube. By breaking the tube after eight minutes, the student does not discover threads of fibrin.

    (Comprehension)

40. Mucous membranes tend to line the inside free surfaces of cavities that are sealed off from the environment outside the human body.

    (Comprehension)

Completion

41. A successful pathogen must maintain a _____ in the environment to live before and after infection.

    (Knowledge)

42. In the urinary tract, a successful pathogen must _____ to the surface of a host.

    (Knowledge)

43. A successful pathogen must invade the body of a _____ and evade the body's _____.

    (Knowledge)

44. A successful human pathogen must exit from the body and return to its _____.

    (Knowledge)

Matching

45. avirulent	A. term for a harmless microbe
46. FHA	B. caused by a species of *Neisseria*
47. gonorrhea	C. general term for transmitting agent
48. lactoferrin	D. refers to vertical transmission of an infection
49. perinatal	E. iron transport protein
50. vector	F. hematoglutinin

(Comprehension)

Short Essay

51. Some respiratory diseases can be prevented if people sleep at night with a cool mist humidifier. How is this a means of prevention?

(Application)

52. One influenza strain of a microbe infects an animal host. Analysis of the blood of the host after death reveals numerous virulent strains, with different genetic variations. How did this occur?

(Analysis)

53. What common characteristics do the soil and human body tissues have to promote the multiplication of *Clostridium tetani*?

(Analysis)

54. What provisions are taken in medical labs to prevent the development and survival of fomites?

(Analysis)

55. Explain all of the factors in the life cycle of a microorganism that are necessary for its success in the environment.

(Synthesis)

56. One species of bacterium attacks the human body by producing kinases. Another species attacks the body by producing coagulases. Compare these two strategies for overcoming the defenses of the human body.

(Evaluation)

Correlation Questions

57. A human population has both incubatory carriers and chronic carriers for a disease. A certain percentage of the population represents the chronic carriers. How can this percentage be calculated?

58. Diseases with wild animal reservoirs can be difficult to eradicate. What are the difficulties?

59. The layers of the skin are the epidermis (its most external layer), the underlying dermis, and the highly -vascular hypodermis, which resides under the dermis. If an injected vaccine does not penetrate to the hypodermis of the skin, it may not protect the subject being injected. Why?

60. Blood vessels wear out and are always rupturing in a human body. Some bacterial species produce coagulase, preventing the ability of an infected person to form blood clots. If a person does not suffer an injury producing bleeding, how does the loss of blood-clotting ability threaten a person's health?

Answers

Multiple Choice

1. D 2. C 3. D 4. A 5. B 6. C 7. D 8. B 9. B 10. C 11. C 12. C 13. A
14. C 15. A 16. C 17. B 18. B 19. B 20. B 21. C 22. B 23. A 24. B 25. B

True/False

26. True 27. False 28. True 29. False 30. False 31. True 32. False
33. False 34. False 35. True 36. True 37. True 38. False 39. False 40. False

Completion

41. reservoir 42. adhere 43. host/defenses 44. reservoir

Matching

45. A 46. F 47. B 48. E 49. D 50. C

Short Essay

51. The mucous membranes are not as effective as a line of defense if they become dry. The use of a cool mist humidifier prevents the drying of mucous membranes.

52. The viral strains multiply in the host. Genetic recombination produces new strains. Various selective pressures favor the survival of some of these strains, which survive and multiply in the blood of the host.

53. Both provide warm, moist environments.

54. Some fomites are discarded. Nonperishable items are sterilized. For example, surgical instruments can be autoclaved.

55. Use the list at the beginning of the chapter. Start with the reservoir and continue with leaving the reservoir, adherence, invasion, etc.

56. Both strategies are effective for the microbes. Kinases split the fibrin of clots. This is dangerous in the human body, as the clotting of the blood is a normal repair process for aging, broken blood vessels. Coagulases promote clot formation. Too many clots can block bloodflow. Too many clots can lead to the formation of emboli. This can be fatal.

Correlation Questions

57. The chronic carriers must be tabulated (e.g. 300,000 subjects in one study). The incubatory carriers must also be counted (e.g. tests reveal 700,000 subjects). These two statistics allow calculation of the desired percentage.

58. A wild animal often has a wide ecological range. It can be difficult to identity. Unless every member of the animal species is identified and eradicated, it cannot be removed as a reservoir for the disease.

59. The hypodermis contains the blood flow. The vaccine must enter the blood of the subject. The circulatory system serves as the vehicle to spread the vaccine to the immune sites of the body. Without introduction into the blood the developing immunity cannot occur.

60. Blood vessels are always rupturing on a microscopic level. They must be plugged by developing clots. Therefore the clotting process is a normal part of the repair process in the human body.

Chapter 16
The Immune System: Innate Immunity

Multiple Choice

1. Select the characteristic that is not a clinical sign of swelling in an area of the body.

   A. heat production from the area
   B. pain in the area
   C. redness in the area
   D. shrinkage of the area

   (Knowledge)

2. The human body has _____ line of defense against infection.

   A. two
   B. three
   C. four
   D. five

   (Knowledge)

3. Each of the following is a surface line of defense except

   A. adaptive
   B. biochemical
   C. mechanical
   D. structural

   (Knowledge)

4. The two parts of the human immune system are

   A. adaptive and nonadaptive.
   B. artificial and natural.
   C. biochemical and structural.
   D. innate and adaptive.

   (Knowledge)

5. There are about _____ kinds of leukocytes. The plasma is the _____ part of the blood.

   A. 1 - five, 2 - cellular
   B. 1 - five, 2 - noncellular
   C. 1 - ten, 2 - cellular
   D. 1 - ten, 2 - noncellular

   (Comprehension)

6. Select the cell that is a type of white blood cell.

   A. eosinophil
   B. erythrocyte
   C. neuron
   D. thrombocyte

   (Knowledge)

7. Phagocytosis is performed by

   A. muscle cells.
   B. neurons.
   C. red blood cells.
   D. white blood cells.

   (Knowledge)

8. Select the most common type of white blood cell in the human body.

   A. basophil
   B. lymphocyte
   C. monocyte
   D. neutrophil

   (Knowledge)

9. Select the cell that is not a type of white blood cell.

   A. eosinophil
   B. neutrophil
   C. monocyte
   D. thrombocyte

   (Knowledge)

10. Select the white blood cell that protects the human body against parasites.

    A. eosinophil.
    B. erythrocyte
    C. lymphocyte
    D. neutrophils

    (Knowledge)

11. Select the incorrect association.

    A. basophil/leukocyte
    B. monocyte/red blood cell
    C. neutrophil/leukocyte
    D. phagosome/psedopodia

    (Comprehension)

12. Neutrophils compose about 60% of the total white cell count in the human body. If a neutrophil concentration of 6000 per cubic mm is measured in a subject, the total number of white blood cells per cubic mm is closest to

    A. 3000.
    B. 6000.
    C. 8000.
    D. 10,000.

(Application)

13. Eosinophils compose about 2 percent of the total white cell count in the human body. If an eosinophil concentration of 250 per cubic mm is measured in a subject, the total number of white blood cells per cubic mm is closest to

    A. 1000.
    B. 2000.
    C. 12,500.
    D. 15,000.

(Application)

14. Select the leukocyte that gives rise to macrophages.

    A. basophil
    B. eosinophil
    C. lymphocyte
    D. monocyte

(Knowledge)

15. Select the cell that makes antibodies.

    A. basophil.
    B. eosinophil.
    C. neutrophil.
    D. plasma

(Knowledge)

16. The first step in phagocytosis is

    A. activation.
    B. adherence.
    C. engulfment.
    D. recognition.

(Knowledge)

17. Erythema of a tissue results when blood vessels supplying this tissue

    A. constrict and decrease blood flow to the tissue.
    B. constrict and increase blood flow to the tissue.
    C. dilate and decrease blood flow to the tissue.
    D. dilate and increase blood flow to the tissue.

    (Comprehension)

18. Inflammatory mediators affect capillaries by

    A. decreasing permeability and allowing leukocytes to enter tissues.
    B. decreasing permeability and not allowing leukocytes to enter tissues.
    C. increasing permeability and allowing leukocytes to enter tissues.
    D. increasing permeability and not allowing leukocytes to enter tissues.

    (Comprehension)

19. Each of the following is a characteristic of phagocytes except

    A. chemotaxis.
    B. diapedesis.
    C. margination.
    D. thrombocytosis.

    (Knowledge)

20. The first step of inflammatory repair is

    A. activating complement proteins.
    B. cleaning up the inflamed area.
    C. phagocytosis.
    D. production of antibodies.

    (Knowledge)

21. Absence of interferon in the body makes it more vulnerable to _____ attack.

    A. bacterial
    B. fungal
    C. protozoan
    D. viral

    (Comprehension)

22. Select the incorrect statement about the interferons.

    A. Alpha interferon is produced by T lymphocytes.
    B. Gamma interferon is produced by B lymphocytes.
    C. There are three main classes.
    D. They are a group of small proteins.

    (Comprehension)

23. Interferons are

    A. bacteria-nonspecific.
    B. bacteria-specific.
    C. virus-nonspecific.
    D. virus-specific.

    (Knowledge)

24. Natural killer cells are

    A. erythrocytes.
    B. leukocytes.
    C. neurons.
    D. platelets

    (Knowledge)

25. NK cells fight

    A. neither bacterial nor viral infections.
    B. only bacterial infections.
    C. only viral infections.
    D. viral and other kinds of infections.

    (Knowledge)

True/False

26. The molecules of the complement pathway are proteins.

    (Knowledge)

27. Leukocytes are produced by the liver.

    (Knowledge)

28. The last step of the alternative pathway for complement is spontaneous hydrolysis.

    (Comprehension)

29. Molecules of C3 are split into C3b only if microbes are not invading the human body.

    (Comprehension)

30. C3 convertase rapidly forms molecules of C3a.

    (Knowledge)

31. Lymphocytes compose 25% of the total white blood cell count per cubic mm. If the total count is about 9000 leukocytes, lymphocytes compose about 2250 cells of this total.

    (Application)

32. Neutrophils have a long lifespan.

    (Knowledge)

33. Phagocytes have cell-surface receptors on their outer surface.

    (Knowledge)

34. A human is infected by a parasitic worm. Measurement of the eosinophil concentration during the infection reveals a rising concentration of this white blood cell type.

    (Application)

35. Macrophages develop from differentiated monocytes.

    (Knowledge)

36. Cytokines are released from macrophages.

    (Comprehension)

37. A phagosome is a membrane-bound vacuole within a phagocyte.

    (Knowledge)

38. Inflammatory mediators are not released by mast cells.

    (Comprehension)

39. Inflammatory mediators can stimulate nerve endings.

    (Knowledge)

40. Inflammation does not damage human tissues.

    (Knowledge)

Completion

41. Vasodilation of a blood vessel tends to change the resistance to blood flow through the vessel by _____ it.

    (Application)

42. Erythema will subside in an area of the body when the supplying blood vessels change their diameter by _____.

    (Application)

43. _____ tissue in the human body cannot regenerate.

    (Knowledge)

44. Interferons are distinguished by _____ and _____ rather than by function.

    (Knowledge)

45. Leukemias are cancers of _____ (cell type).

(Knowledge)

46. Interferons regulate the functions, motility, and division of _____.

(Knowledge)

Matching

47. B cell

48. dendritic cell

49. eosinophil

50. macrophage

A. attacks helminths

B. differentiates into plasma cell

C. large cell wandering through tissues

D. star-shaped cell

(Knowledge)

Short Essay

51. A person has a severe skin rash. An antihistamine is prescribed to treat it. Explain the strategy behind this treatment.

(Application)

52. A total white blood cell count in the human body ranges from 5000 to 10,000 per cubic millimeter. However, this statistic does not convey all needed information about the body's line of defense through leukocyte activity. What additional calculation is needed about leukocytes?

(Analysis)

53. A person's total white blood cell count per cubic millimeter is 9800. Calculate the number of each of the following leukocytes in this total, based on the following percentages: neutrophils, 65%; lymphocytes, 25%; monocytes, 6%; eosinophils, 3%; and basophils, 1%.

(Analysis)

54. How do you think chemotaxis develops between a leukocyte and human body cell?

(Analysis)

55. Considering the roles of heredity and environment, how do the different kinds of leukocytes develop unique morphologies and functions when they are derived from the same group of stem cells?

(Synthesis)

56. Compare the mobility and roles of erythrocytes and leukocytes. Relate this to their functions.

(Evaluation)

Correlation Questions

57. What is the relationship between erythema and phagocytosis as responses in the human body?

58. The skin is often referred to as a first line of defense. The innate immune system is a second line of defense. Explain the labeling for each of these lines of defense.

59. All cells of the human body have the same genome, conferred to them by mitosis. However, there are about ten different kinds of white blood cells. Each cell has unique characteristics. Explain this variation.

60. Aspirin is an anti-inflammatory substance to the human body. It is known to target the activity of prostaglandins. How does aspirin have its effect of the body?

Answers

Multiple Choice

1. D 2. B 3. A 4. D 5. D 6. A 7. D 8. D 9. D 10. A 11. B
12. D 13. C 14. D 15. D 16. D 17. D 18. C 19. D 20. B 21. D
22. B 23. C 24. B 25. D

True/False

26. True 27. False 28. False 29. False 30. False 31. True 32. False 33. True
34. True 35. True 36. True 37. True 38. False 39. True 40. False

Completion

41. decreasing 42. vasoconstriction 43. nervous 44. chemical, genetic
45. leukocytes 46. cells

Matching

47. B 48. D 49. A 50. C

Short Essay

51. The skin rash probably results from an overactive response mediated by histamine. The use of a substance to inhibit histamine should reduce this activity.

52. A differential white blood cell count is also needed to express the percentage of neutrophils, eosinophils, etc. Specific white blood cell types increase in response to specific kinds of body infections. These changes can be noted only through specific measurements of each white blood cell type.

53. Multiply the percentage of each white blood cell type by the total. Neutrophils = 6370; lymphocytes = 2450; monocytes = 588; eosinophils = 294; basophils = 98.

54. The chemical attraction is probably based on a biochemical affinity between the leukocyte and body cell. A specific receptor protein on the body cell membrane attracts a chemical component on the surface of the white blood cell.

55. All of the white blood cell types have the same genetic makeup through mitosis. However, only certain genes in each white blood cell type are activated. Differential gene activation explains the specialization of the white blood cell types. These different activities are probably based on different environmental influences. Perhaps one kind of white blood cell develops at a different temperature or is signaled by a different hormone.

56. Erythrocytes are not motile but flow through the blood vessels as the blood circulates. This is sufficient for their function of carrying oxygen and carbon dioxide. White blood cells, however, have the ability to squeeze through the openings in the walls of blood vessels through diapedesis. Without this ability they cannot carry out their role of defending the body. Much of their activity is in the intercellular spaces.

Correlation Questions

57. Erythema indicates increased blood flow to tissues of the body. This increased flow of blood brings more phagocytic cells to the tissue area. These phagocytes can leave the capillaries of the circulation and enter the tissue area. More blood flow brings more phagocytic cells to a tissue area to defend it.

58. The skin is one of the first defenses to protect the body against attacking microbes. However, if it is defeated (e.g., broken by a wound), second immune lines are next to protect the body and prevent further microbial invasion.

59. The variety of white blood cell types is due to differential gene activation. Although a cell can potentially develop into any cell kind (all genes are present), it will take a specific line of development depending on which genes in its total genome are activated. Different environmental signals are in part responsible for activating (depressing) some genes and repressing others.

60. Prostaglandins are inflammatory mediators. By inhibiting their action, aspirin prevents them from carrying out their response. This can be helpful if the inflammatory response is unwanted or too powerful.

Chapter 17
The Immune System: Adaptive Immunity

Multiple Choice

1. Select the cell that is not a kind of lymphocyte.

    A. NK cell
    B. B cell
    C. neutrophil
    D. T cell

    (Knowledge)

2. B cells are the agents of

    A. cellular immunity.
    B. humoral immunity.
    C. nondifferentiated white blood cells.
    D. the fourth line of defense.

    (Knowledge)

3. The spleen is a __1__ found in the __2__ .

    A. 1 - primary lymphoid organ, 2 - abdomen
    B. 1 - primary lymphoid organ, 2 - thorax
    C. 1 - secondary lymphoid organ, 2 - abdomen
    D. 1 - secondary lymphoid organ, 2 - thorax

    (Knowledge)

4. Select the incorrect association.

    A. adenoids/nose
    B. appendix/intestinal tract
    C. Peyer's patches/esophagus
    D. tonsils/throat

    (Comprehension)

5. An epitope is a(n)

    A. antibody.
    B. antigenic determinant.
    C. entire antigen molecule.
    D. specialized lymphocyte.

    (Knowledge)

6. Different epitopes are recognized by lymphocyte receptors by complementary

    A. locations in the human body.
    B. processing by the thymus gland.
    C. shapes of the molecules.
    D. sites of synthesis in the body.

    (Knowledge)

7. B cells become immunocompetent. This means they produce

    A. antigens that are ineffective.
    B. many kinds of antigens.
    C. many kinds of antibodies.
    D. one kind of antibody.

    (Knowledge)

8. The human genome has about _____ different genes

    A. 10,000
    B. 30,000
    C. 100,000
    D. 1,000,000

    (Knowledge)

9. The human body can make about _____ million different antibodies.

    A. ten
    B. thirty
    C. fifty
    D. one hundred

    (Knowledge)

10. Plasma cells

    A. make antibody molecules.
    B. make antigen molecules.
    C. transport carbon dioxide.
    D. transport oxygen.

    (Knowledge)

11. T lymphocytes are named from an organ located in the _____ cavity.

    A. abdominal
    B. cranial
    C. pelvic
    D. thoracic

    (Comprehension)

12. Which class of antibodies is mainly found on the surface of mast cells?

    A. IgA
    B. IgD
    C. IgE
    D. IgG

    (Knowledge)

13. A sample of a person's antibodies is analyzed to detect the development of an allergy. An increased concentration of the _____ class indicates an allergy.

    A. IgA
    B. IgD
    C. IgE
    D. IgM

    (Application)

14. All antibody monomers has a shape resembling the letter

    A. A
    B. B
    C. Y
    D. Z

    (Knowledge)

15. One person's body makes about 105 million different antibodies. About _____ million of these antibodies are IgG antibodies.

    A. 25
    B. 50
    C. 78
    D. 100

    (Application)

16 A person's body makes about 105 million different antibodies. About _____ million of these are IgM antibodies.

    A. 5
    B. 11
    C. 48
    D. 76

    (Application)

17. Through clonal selection

    A. B cells become less numerous.
    B. B cells become more numerous.
    C. T cells become less numerous.
    D. T cells become more numerous.

    (Knowledge)

18. Class II MHC proteins hold

    A. antibody fragments on antibody presenting cells.
    B. antibody fragments on antibody presenting cells.
    C. antigen fragments on antibody presenting cells.
    D. antigen fragments on antigen presenting cells.

    (Knowledge)

19. Perforins are

    A. carbohydrates.
    B. lipids.
    C. nucleic acids.
    D. proteins.

    (Knowledge)

20. The administration of antibodies to a person to fight diphtheria is _____ immunity.

    A. artificially acquired active
    B. artificially acquired passive
    C. naturally acquired active
    D. naturally acquired passive

    (Comprehension)

True/False

21. NK cells participate in the innate immune system.

    (Knowledge)

22. B cells produce defensive proteins called antibodies.

    (Comprehension)

23. Phagocytes destroy antigens by opsonization.

    (Knowledge)

24. T cells respond to antigens by humoral immunity.

    (Comprehension)

25. Lymph drains into the kidneys through the thoracic duct.

    (Knowledge)

26. A human has more different genes than different kinds of antibodies produced in the human body.

    (Knowledge)

27. Proteins are stronger antigen molecules compared to polysaccharide antigens.

    (Knowledge)

28. Immune tolerance is the ability to destroy one's own molecules in the human body.

    (Knowledge)

29. Lymphocytes have antigen receptors on their cell surface to recognize antigens.

    (Knowledge)

30. By immunocompetence, each individual B cell can produce one particular kind of antibody molecule.

    (Knowledge)

31. Clonal selection produces a group of identical B cells capable of fighting an infection.

    (Knowledge)

32. Interleukin-1 actives TH1 cells but does not activate B cells.

    (Knowledge)

33. The absence of interleukin-1 in the body leads to fever production.

    (Knowledge)

34. A secondary immune response generates a smaller quantity of antibody compared to the primary immune response.

    (Knowledge)

35. Antibodies are not toxic to pathogens.

    (Knowledge)

36. The membrane-attack complex is restricted to fighting infections against *Clostridium*.

    (Knowledge)

37. T cells kill virus-infected cells and bacterial-infected cells.

    (Knowledge)

38. MHC are proteins on the surface of mature erythrocytes in the human body.

    (Comprehension)

39. Apoptosis is programmed cell death.

    (Knowledge)

40. Artificially acquired passive immunity is stimulated by vaccination.

    (Knowledge)

Completion

41. The bone marrow contains _____ cells, rapidly dividing cells that produce blood cells.

    (Knowledge)

42. Lymph is derived from the _____, the liquid part of whole blood.

    (Comprehension)

43. Selective lymphocyte stimulation occurs through _____ selection.

    (Knowledge)

44. Two antigen-binding sites are on the arms of the _____ -shaped antibody molecule.

    (Knowledge)

45. Vaccines stimulate the production of _____ lymphocytes.

    (Knowledge)

Matching

46. IgA

47. IgD

48. IgE

49. IgG

50. IgM

    (Knowledge)

A. found on the surface of basophils

B. mainly on the surface of B cells

C. secreted forms are pentamers

D. dimer in body secretions

E. enters fetal circulation to protect newborns

Short Essay

51. A physician wants to withdraw a sample of bone marrow from a patient for a study of lymphocyte production. Name one site in the human body to logically withdraw this tissue.

    (Application)

52. The lymphatic system is often described as a backup system to prevent edema in the body. How is this an accurate description?

    (Analysis)

53. How does the human body make a number of antibodies that far exceeds the number of different genes in the body?

    (Analysis)

54. A person suspects the development of a parasitic worm infection in his body. How can a quantitative serum analysis of his Ig antibodies confirm this diagnosis?

    (Analysis)

55. A person develops glomerulonephritis through an autoimmune reaction. How could this diagnosis be confirmed and explained?

    (Synthesis)

56. Is passive immunity mainly cellular immunity or humoral immunity?

    (Evaluation)

Correlation Questions

57. An antibody has a pentamer structure. How is this an advantage when fighting antigen molecules through precipitation reactions?

58. A medical technologist is studying the different kinds of immune cells under the microscope. How does a knowledge of cell structure help her in identifying the different cell types?

59. Recently stem cell research has been in the news, often as a controversial topic. How does the phrase *stem cell* in this context differ from its meaning in Chapter 17 on the immune system?

60. Can the administration of a vaccine be dangerous to a person's health. Explain.

Answers

Multiple Choice

1. C   2. B   3. C   4. C   5. B   6. C   7. D   8. B   9. D   10. A   11. D   12. C   13. C
14. C   15. C   16. B   17. B   18. D   19. D   20. B

True/False

21. True   22. True   23. True   24. False   25. False   26. False   27. True   28. False
29. True   30. True   31. True   32. False   33. False   34. False   35. True   36. False
37. True   38. False   39. True   40. False

Completion

41. stem   42. plasma   43. clonal   44. Y   45. memory

Matching

46. D   47. B   48. A   49. E   50. C

Short Essay

51. The sternum contains this type of tissue. This bone is easy to locate and its bone marrow tissue is accessible. The sternum has a thin layer of compact bone surrounding the softer, inner marrow.

52. Tissue fluid derived from the blood plasma is returned to the blood. Most of this fluid return to the blood occurs at the venous ends of systemic capillaries. However, this return is not 100 percent effective. Lymphatic capillaries, next to the systemic capillaries, capture the fluid not collected back into the blood. Eventually they combine this fluid with the blood. Without this backup, the fluid would remain in the tissue spaces, causing edema.

53. Lymphocytes make these antibodies. They have a great capacity to cut and paste gene fragments into new combinations. Therefore, they make this variety of antibodies by genetic recombination.

54. IgE antibodies defend against parasitic worm infections. With this kind of infection, IgE antibody concentration will increase to carry out this role. This can be confirmed through a quantitative analysis.

55. Plasma proteins and blood cells are not normally filtered at the glomerulus in the kidney nephrons. The passage of whole blood into the urinary tract occurred across the leaky capillaries of the glomeruli, possibly damaged through an autoimmune response. Reacting against the makeup of one's own nephrons probably occurred through clonal deletion.

56. Humoral immunity refers to substances dissolved or suspended in the blood plasma, such as antibodies. Passive immunity depends on antibodies only.

Correlation Questions

57. A pentamer molecule has numerous binding sites. It can bond with numerous antigen molecules, removing them from sites where they can attack body tissues. Large amounts of precipitate are formed, protecting the body.

58. The immune cells have distinctive appearances. The neutrophil, for example, has a multi-lobed nucleus with blue-staining granules in the cytoplasm. The nucleus of the eosinophil is less distinct, with red-stained granules in the cytoplasm. T and B lymphocytes lack stained cytoplasmic granules. The plasma cell is a small, nondescript cell.

59. Stem cell research in the news refers mainly to stem cells from a fetus. These are nondifferentiated cells that have not specialized during prenatal development. The stem cells in the bone marrow are located in a specific body region. However, they are also nonspecialized, committing to form the different kinds of blood cells.

60. A vaccine often contains an attenuated or weakened form of a microorganism. Normally, it is not virulent but retains enough properties to stimulate the human immune system. However, occasionally the microbe may retain enough virulence to cause an infection.

Chapter 18
Immunologic Disorders

Multiple Choice

1. The symptoms of immediate hypersensitivity develop within
   A. 10 to 20 seconds.
   B. 10 to 20 minutes.
   C. 30 to 60 seconds.
   D. 30 to 60 seconds.
   (Knowledge)

2. An injection of epinephrine is used to counteract a(n) _____ reaction in the body.
   A. anaphylactic shock
   B. cell-mediated
   C. cytotoxic
   D. immune complex
   (Knowledge)

3. The production of Ig antibodies is stimulated by
   A. bee venom.
   B. milk.
   C. starch.
   D. vinegar.
   (Knowledge)

4. Allergic rhinitis affects the _____ tract.
   A. digestive
   B. reproductive
   C. respiratory
   D. urinary
   (Comprehension)

5. Describe the correct responses in asthma.
   A. The bronchioles' smooth muscle contracts with edema.
   B. The bronchioles' smooth muscle contracts without edema.
   C. The bronchioles' smooth muscle relaxes with edema.
   D. The bronchioles' smooth muscle relaxes without edema.
   (Comprehension)

6. Respiratory allergies are diagnosed by tests on the

    A. blood.
    B. neurons.
    C. skin.
    D. urine.

    (Knowledge)

7. Ingestion of peanuts or shellfish can cause systemic _____ reactions.

    A. anaphylactic
    B. cell-mediated
    C. cytotoxic
    D. immune complex

    (Knowledge)

8. Goodpasture's syndrome involves antibody production that binds proteins to the

    A. brain that activates complement.
    B. brain that inhibits complement.
    C. kidney that activates complement.
    D. kidney that inhibits complement.

    (Knowledge)

9. From the ABO antigen-antibody system, a person with blood type B normally develops the

    A. A antigen and A antibody.
    B. A antigen and B antibody.
    C. B antigen and A antibody.
    D. B antigen and B antibody.

    (Comprehension)

10. Within the ABO antigen-antibody system, a person with bloodtype B can receive _____ without causing agglutination of the person's blood.

    A. bloodtypes A and O only
    B. bloodtypes B and O only
    C. bloodtypes A and B only
    D. neither bloodtypes A nor B

    (Application)

11. A person's blood is tested for Rh typing. The blood reacts with the anti-Rh antibody in a typing serum, causing agglutination of the person's blood. The person's blood probably

    A. has the Rh antigen and has the Rh antibody.
    B. has the Rh antigen but lacks the Rh antibody.
    C. lacks the Rh antigen but has the Rh antibody.
    D. lacks the Rh antigen and lacks the Rh antibody.

    (Application)

12. SLE is an example of a type _____ hypersensitivity reaction.

    A. I
    B. II
    C. III
    D. V

    (Knowledge)

13. Delayed hypersensitivity is _____ hypersensitivity.

    A. anaphylactic
    B. cell-mediated
    C. cytotoxic
    D. immune complex

    (Knowledge)

14. The tuberculin skin test is an example of type _____ hypersensitivity..

    A. I
    B. II
    C. III
    D. IV

    (Knowledge)

15. The granulomatous reaction is an example of type _____ hypersensitivity.

    A. I
    B. II
    C. III
    D. IV

    (Knowledge

16. Select the grafts that, without drugs to help the recipient, lead to rejection of the graft.

    A. allograft and autograft
    B. autograft and isograft
    C. isograft and xenograft
    D. xenograft and allograft.

    (Knowledge)

17. Cyclosporine interferes

    A. mainly with B cell function.
    B. mainly with T cell function.
    C. ignificantly with B and T cell function.
    D. with neither B cell nor T cell function.

    (Knowledge)

18. SCID disables

    A. B-cell immunity only.

    B. T-cell immunity only.

    C. B-cell and T-cell immunity.

    D. neither B-cell nor T-cell immunity.

(Knowledge)

19. The HIV virus mainly attacks T

    A. helper cells.

    B. killer cells.

    C. stem cells.

    D. suppressor cells.

(Knowledge)

20. Which theory explains the transformation of cancer cells?

    A. allergic

    B. autoimmune

    C. immune surveillance

    D. immunocompetence

(Knowledge)

True/False

21. Immunodeficiencies are inadequate immune responses in the human body.

(Knowledge)

22. Allergens produce an immune response.

(Knowledge)

23. A person with blood type O has both ABO antigens but neither ABO antibodies.

(Comprehension)

24. Blood type AB can be transfused to all four ABO blood types without agglutination.

(Application)

25. An Rh positive father, who has two dominant genes for development of the Rh blood type, mates with an Rh negative female (two recessive genes). The chance to produce an Rh positive offspring for each birth is 50 percent.

(Application)

26. A person who develops SLE could find normal body movement limiting and painful.

(Comprehension)

27. A type IV hypersensitivity reaction occurs 10 to 20 minutes after exposure to an antigen.

    (Knowledge)

28. Granulomatous reactions cause body tissue damage.

    (Knowledge)

29. A person suffering with Grave's disease tends to gain weight rapidly.

    (Knowledge)

30. Rheumatoid arthritis is an example of a type II hypesensitivity.

    (Knowledge)

31. A person receives a skin graft from an identical twin. This is an example of an allograft.

    (Comprehension)

32. Xenografts introduce foreign antigens into a person's body.

    (Knowledge)

33. The eye is an organ subject to rejection reactions in the human body.

    (Comprehension)

34. The HLA is one kind of human blood type.

    (Knowledge)

35. Congenital immunodeficiencies usually develop late in a person's life.

    (Comprehension)

36. Leukemias are cancers of the blood.

    (Knowledge)

37. Acquired immunodeficiencies usually develop later in a person's life.

    (Knowledge)

38. Lymphomas are blood cancers.

    (Knowledge)

39. AIDS is a specific example of an acquired immunodeficiency.

    (Knowledge)

40. Cancers crowd out and kill neighboring cells.

    (Comprehension)

Completion

41. Histamine _____ the size of blood vessels.

    (Knowledge)

42. Hay fever is a common _____ disorder.

    (Knowledge)

43. Cytotoxic hypersensitivity is an example of type _____ hypersensitivity.

    (Knowledge)

44. When the smooth muscle of bronchioles relaxes, the diameter of the bronchioles changes by _____.

    (Comprehension)

45. Penicillin can become a potent allergen if it combines with a _____ in the body.

    (Knowledge)

46. Type II hypersensitivity occurs if IgG or _____ antibodies bind abnormally to a person's own body cells.

    (Knowledge)

Matching

Match each kind of transplant to its correct description.

47. allograft
48. autograft
49. isograft
50. xenograft

    (Knowledge)

A. between two species
B. between genetically identical individuals
C. between two body parts of the same person
D. between members of the same species

Short Essay

51. A person's blood is tested with ABO blood typing sera. One drop of the blood is combined with the anti-A serum. Another drop of blood is combined with the anti-B serum. The blood causes agglutination with only one of the two typing sera. What ABO blood types could the person have and not have?

    (Application)

52. How does a serum analysis of a person's Ig antibodies determine if an anaphylactic response is developing?

    (Analysis)

53. How is the release of histamine by injured cells advantageous for the health and survival of the cells?

    (Analysis)

54. How does the hemolytic disease of the newborn develop between a mother and offspring?

    (Analysis)

55. How does a study of agammaglobulinemia ally the concepts of genetics and immunology?

    (Synthesis)

56. How is cancer best understood by studying the human body at the cellular level?

    (Evaluation)

Correlation Questions

57. How can the field of endocrinology contribute to treatment of Grave's disease.

58. Blood type AB is often called the universal recipient for blood transfusion. How is this description accurate and not accurate?

59. How is the Rh blood typing system simpler to understand comparted to the ABO blood typing system?

60. Angiogenesis refers to the development of blood vessels to serve tissues. Recently, inhibiting this process has been explored as a cancer treatment. How can this be an effective strategy for treatment?

Answers

Multiple Choice

1. B   2. A   3. A   4. C   5. A   6. C   7. A   8. C   9. C   10. B   11. B
12. C   13. B   14. D   15. D   16. D   17. B   18. C   19. A   20. C

True/False

21. True   22. False   23. False   24. False   25. False   26. True   27. False
28. True   29. False   30. False   31. False   32. True   33. False   34. False
35. False   36. True   37. True   38. False   39. True   40. True

Completion

41. dilates   42. allergic   43. II   44. dilating   45. hapten   46. IgM

Matching

47. D   48. C   49. B   50. A

Short Essay

51. Reacting with only anti-A or anti-B, the person's blood type is either A or B. It cannot be type O or AB.

52. There will be an increase in the IgE antibodies, which are more active in allergies and in severe allergic reactions.

53. Histamine is a vasodilator. The vasodilation of blood vessels, supplying injured cells, increases the supply of substances that promote the defense and healing of the cells.

54. An Rh positive offspring from a first birth sensitizes the Rh negative mother to start producing Rh antibodies. These antibodies increase in concentration over time. With a second Rh positive birth, the antigens of this offspring can provoke a response from the mother. By this time, the mother has a sufficient concentration of antibodies for a reaction against the erythrocytes of the offspring.

55. This inherited disease is an X-linked recessive disease. Usually a mother who carries the recessive allele (e.g., Aa) of the gene passes it to a son with a probability of one-half. If the son inherits the gene from the mother, the son cannot develop antibodies and has an immunodeficiency.

56. In cancer, a person's cells multiply too rapidly. They crowd out other cells for space and other resources. Cancer cells are often eliminated by immune surveillance. Cancer cells that overcome this cellular mechanism have immunologic escape. The behavior and response of body cells must be studied to understand cancer.

Correlation Questions

57. Grave's disease develops from hyperactivity of the thyroid gland. Treatment for this disease centers on slowing down the activity of this endocrine gland and/or diminishing the concentration of the thyroid hormone secreted by this gland. Generally the thyroid hormone increases metabolism. Too much of this hormone can produce weight loss, increased apetite, etc.

58. Without any ABO antibodies, a person with blood type ABO does not have molecules to react against either the A or B antigens. However, this applies only to the ABO blood typing. There are dozens of blood type antigen-antibody systems with potential incompatibilities. All blood types must be checked for a safe blood transfusion.

59. The Rh system has only one antigen, the Rh factor. Therefore, there are only two blood types: positive (antigen present) or negative (antigen absent). The ABO system has two antigens, leading to more antigen combinations and more blood types.

60. Cancer cells can be starved if the blood supply serving them is taken away. Diminishing angiogenesis to cancer tissue uses this strategy.

Chapter 19
Diagnostic Immunology

Multiple Choice

1. Most immunologically based diagnostic tests use

    A. antigen-antibody reactions.
    B. chromatography.
    C. electrophoresis.
    D. hemolysis tests.

    (Knowledge)

2. Serum is the

    A. cellular part of the blood only.
    B. liquid part of the blood with cells.
    C. liquid part of the blood without cells.
    D. mineral part of the blood only.

    (Knowledge)

3. Select the incorrect statement about reagents in immunology.

    A. They are used in testing clinically.
    B. They cannot contain known concentrations of antibodies.
    C. They can contain known concentrations of antigens.
    D. They participate in chemical reactions.

    (Knowledge)

4. Hepatitis B is usually diagnosed by identifying antibodies the human body makes against a

    A. bacterium.
    B. fungus.
    C. protozoan.
    D. virus

    (Knowledge)

5. In a positive precipitin reaction, a precipitate is

    A. formed and the reaction mixture is cloudy.
    B. formed and the reaction mixture is not cloudy.
    C. not formed and the reaction mixture is cloudy.
    D. not formed and the reaction mixture is not cloudy.

    (Comprehension)

6. Autoimmune diseases are diagnosed by detecting abnormal

    A. antibiotics.
    B. antibodies.
    C. antigens.
    D. leukocytes.

(Knowledge)

7. For a precipitation reaction to occur, both the antigen and antibody must have as least __1__ binding sites and be present in __2__ proportions.

    A. 1 - two, 2 - near equal
    B. 1 - two, 2 - significantly unequal
    C. 1 - three, 2 - near equal
    D. 1 - three, 2 - significantly unequal

(Comprehension)

8. In a immunodiffusion test, an antibody becomes

    A. more concentrated as it moves by active transport.
    B. more concentrated as it moves by simple diffusion.
    C. less concentrated as it moves by active transport.
    D. less concentrated as it moves by simple diffusion.

(Comprehension)

9. The Ouchterlony method is a(n)

    A. alpha hemolysis method.
    B. beta hemolysis method.
    C. double diffusion method.
    D. single diffusion method.

(Knowledge)

10. In one test, the concentration of an antigen is estimated by the radial diffusion method. The sample ring with the _____ of precipitate has the greatest antigen concentration.

    A. densest red color
    B. least dense red color
    C. diameter of 1 mm
    D. diameter of 2 mm

(Application)

11. To fractionate two antigens means to _____ them.

    A. combine
    B. digest
    C. measure
    D. separate

(Knowledge)

12. In an electrophoretic field, the anode is the negative terminal of the field. The cathode is the positive terminal. In this setup a negatively-charged antigen is pulled toward the

    A. anode by opposite charges.
    B. anode by similar charges.
    C. cathode by opposite charges.
    D. cathode by similar charges.

    (Comprehension)

13. A confirmatory test for AIDS occurs through the

    A. double diffusion method.
    B. precipitin test.
    C. single diffusion method.
    D. Western blot method.

    (Knowledge)

14. In an agglutination test for ABO blood typing, antigen B binds to

    A. antibody A.
    B. antibody B.
    C. antibodies A and B.
    D. neither antibody A nor B.

    (Comprehension)

15. In the agglutination test for ABO blood typing, antibody A binds to

    A. antigen A.
    B. antigen B.
    C. antigens A and B.
    D. neither antigens A nor B.

    (Comprehension)

16. In a hemagglutination test, the agglutinins are on the surface of

    A. erythrocyte.
    B. macrophages.
    C. neutrophils.
    D. platelets.

    (Knowledge)

17. A negative agglutination test to detect a microorganism means that the microorganism is

    A. absent and infection is absent.
    B. absent and infection is not absent.
    C. present and infection is present.
    D. present and infection is not present.

    (Comprehension)

18. By an agglutination test, a recent infection is indicated if the test results change from

    A. negative to positive immediately
    B. negative to positive over time.
    C. positive to negative immediately.
    D. positive to negative over time.

    (Comprehension)

19. In a complement fixation reaction, the formation of a membrane attack complex

    A. decreases the concentration of monoclonal antibodies.
    B. increases target cell concentration.
    C. will lyse target cells.
    D. will not involve antibody presence.

    (Knowledge)

20. When a complement reaction is fixed, complement

    A. binds to antigen-antibody complexes.
    B. causes a color change.
    C. increases in concentration.
    D. stops electrophoresis in an electrical field.

    (Knowledge)

True/False

21. In diagnostic immunology, antigen-antibody reactions are used to diagnose disease.

    (Knowledge)

22. The most recently developed pregnancy test uses monoclonal antibodies.

    (Knowledge)

23. A quantitative serologic test is used to diagnose syphilis.

    (Knowledge)

24. In a precipitation reaction, the antibody concentration is one-third the concentration of the antigen. These are optimal proportions.

    (Comprehension)

25. A simple qualitative test in a precipitation reaction can be performed by mixing an antigen and antibody in a test tube.

    (Knowledge)

26. A spur is formed in the solution of a double diffusion method. The spur is where two antigens have 100 percent agreement of chemical makeup.

    (Knowledge)

27. In immunoelectrophoresis, a negative antigen is pulled toward the positive terminal of an electrophoretic field.

    (Knowledge)

28. The Western blot employs electrophoresis.

    (Knowledge)

29. Agglutination reactions have some similarities to precipitation reactions.

    (Knowledge)

30. In agglutination reactions, the antigen and antibody involved are not bound to cells.

    (Knowledge)

31. In the Coombs test, antibodies are used against antibodies.

    (Knowledge)

32. In a positive test for Rh blood typing, the agglutination of erythrocytes does not occur.

    (Comprehension)

33. Qualitative agglutination tests are usually performed in a test tube.

    (Knowledge)

34. In a positive agglutination test, agglutination occurs, but the cells involved do not clump together.

    (Knowledge)

35. Before the discovery of monoclonal antibodies, the pregnancy test was based on agglutination.

    (Knowledge)

36. In quantitative agglutination, a titer is the lowest dilution of a test serum that causes agglutination.

    (Knowledge)

37. The indicator system in a complement fixation test contains erythrocytes.

    (Knowledge)

38. Complement fixation tests cannot be quantitative.

    (Knowledge)

39. Radioimmunoassays are extremely sensitive tests.

    (Knowledge)

40. Immunofluorescence assays are more sensitive than radioimmunoassays.

    (Knowledge)

Completion

41. The range of proportions at which a lattice can form in a precipitation reaction is the _____ zone.

    (Knowledge)

42. A microgram is 1/1000 of a milligram. Agglutination tests can detect antibody concentrations as low as 1 microgram per liter. This concentration is also __(number)__ milligrams per liter.

    (Application)

43. An indirect _____ agglutination test is used to diagnose strep throat.

    (Knowledge)

44. To diagnose an infection through an agglutination reaction, a gradual _____ of antibody titer over time means that infection is present.

    (Application)

45. Immunoassays can be used to detect antigens or _____..

    (Knowledge)

46. ELISA is generally used for detecting human serum _____.

    (Knowledge)

Matching

47. complement

48. electrophoresis

49. precipitation

50. serum

    (Knowledge)

A. separation during migration

B. similar in makeup to blood plasma

C. name for a fixation assay

D. antigen combines with antibody

Short Essay

51. A person's blood type is described as AB positive. What does this labeling indicate?

    (Analysis)

52 How do you think the molecular size of antigen molecules affects the results of the immunodiffusion test?

    (Analysis)

53. How does electrophoresis differ from chromatography as a separation technique?

    (Analysis)

54. Test method A detects antibody concentrations to 0.001 milligrams per ml. Test method B detects antibody concentrations to 0.01 milligrams per ml. Express each of these concentrations in micrograms per ml. Which method is more sensitive?

   (Analysis)

55. Why is a pregnancy test based on monoclonal antibodies more reliable compared to more historical methods?

   (Evaluation)

56. How are the principles of chemistry and physics relevant to the tests described in this chapter?

   (Evaluation)

Correlation Questions

57. Autoimmunity has often been explained as the body's inability to distinguish between self and non-self. Explain.

58. Why are agglutination tests performed on a slide rather than on a test tube?

59. Can a precipitation reaction occur if the antigen and antibody involved each have only one binding site?

60. When is a qualitative diagnostic test preferable to a quantitative diagnostic test?

Answers

Multiple Choice

1. A 2. C 3. B 4. D 5. A 6. B 7. A 8. D 9. C 10. D 11. D 12. C
13. D 14. B 15. A 16. A 17. A 18. B 19. C 20. A

True/False

21. True 22. True 23. True 24. False 25. True 26. False 27. True 28. True
29. True 30. False 31. True 32. False 33. False 34. False 35. True 36. False
37. True 38. False 39. True 40. False

Completion

41. equivalence 42. 0.001 43. latex 44. increase 45. antibodies 46. antibodies

Matching

47. C 48. A 49. D 50. B

Short Essay

51. There are two different blood types being communicated. For AB, both the A and B antigens are present on a person's erythrocytes. For Rh positive, the Rh antigen is present on the red cells for a separate blood type.

52. Smaller antigen molecules probably diffuse more rapidly through the medium compared to antigen molecules with a larger molecular weight.

53. Chromatography separates molecules based on their solubility in a medium. Other factors may also be involved, such as the adsorption of molecules to the medium. Electrophoresis separates molecules by the identity and size of their electrical charge.

54. Test A detects to a concentration of 1 microgram per ml. Test B detects to only 10 micrograms per ml. Test A is more sensitive, as it can detect smaller quantities.

55. A monoclonal antibody test is more sensitive. Older test assays were based on diagnosing more inexact endocrinological changes, such as detecting the appearance of the hormone hCG when pregnancy occurs.

56. A precipitate, for example, is the product of a chemical reaction between the antigen and antibody in a precipitation reaction. As another example, electrophoresis takes advantage of the different charges of molecules as they migrate in an electrical field.

Correlation Questions

57. A healthy immune system can distinguish between a person's biochemical makeup (self) and foreign substances (nonself). This ability is lost in a person suffering from an autoimmune reaction. Part of a person's own biochemical makeup is sensed as foreign, triggering an immune reaction against the chemical makeup of the person's body.

58. The surface of a slide is sufficient to view and retain the contents from an agglutination reaction.

59. Without at least two binding sites on each kind of molecule, a molecular lattice will not form during product formation. The resulting precipitate needed for this test will not form.

60. A qualitative test is acceptable to diagnose the presence or absence of a substance (e.g., the A antigen in blood typing) or microorganisms (e.g., for the bacterium causing syphilis). Quantitative tests are necessary for evaluating the severity of a disease (e.g., concentration of antibodies developed) or trend of disease development (e.g., increasing antibody levels if a disease is progressing).

Chapter 20
Preventing Disease

Multiple Choice

1. In an epidemic, disease transmission affects __1__ members in a __2__ period of time.

   A. 1 - few, 2 - long
   B. 1 - few, 2 - short
   C. 1 - many, 2 - long
   D. 1 - many, 2 – short

   (Comprehension)

2. Select the disease has not occurred as an epidemic.

   A. cholera
   B. diphtheria
   C. polio
   D. trichinosis

   (Knowledge)

3. Pellagra is a disease that develops due to a(n)

   A. allergic reaction.
   B. bacterial infection.
   C. viral infection.
   D. vitamin deficiency.

   (Knowledge)

4. Lyme disease is transmitted through

   A. bacteria in food.
   B. the bite of a mosquito.
   C. the bite of a tick.
   D. viruses in food.

   (Knowledge)

5. Select the incorrect description about tuberculosis.

   A. It is common among the elderly.
   B. It is common among the poor.
   C. It is common among immigrants.
   D. It is common among males only.

   (Comprehension)

6. If seven people in 100,000 develop a disease, the incidence rate as a percentage is

   A. 0.7
   B. 0.07
   C. 0.007
   D. 0.0007

   (Application)

7. If 50 people in 100,000 develop a disease, the incidence rate as a percentage is

   A. 0.5
   B. 0.05
   C. 0.005
   D. 0.0005

   (Application)

8. For HIV infection the prevalence rate is __1__ compared to the overall incidence rate. For cholera, the prevalence rate is __2__ compared to the incidence rate.

   A. 1 - higher, 2 - higher
   B. 1 - higher, 2 - nearly the same
   C. 1 - lower, 2 - lower
   D. 1 - lower, nearly the same

   (Comprehension)

9. Which branch of epidemiology seeks to provide general information about a disease?

   A. descriptive
   B. field
   C. hospital
   D. surveillance

   (Knowledge)

10. Which branch of epidemiology tracks epidemic disease?

   A. descriptive
   B. field
   C. hospital
   D. surveillance

   (Knowledge)

11. Which branch of epidemiology investigates disease outbreaks?

   A. descriptive
   B. field
   C. hospital
   D. surveillance

   (Knowledge)

12. In a common source epidemic, all infected people
    A. are females.
    B. are males.
    C. share a common gathering.
    D. share a similar immune system.
    (Knowledge)

13. Food poisoning is caused by a species with sphere-shaped cells that form clusters. It is caused by a species of
    A. *Bacillus.*
    B. *Escherichia.*
    C. *Listeria.*
    D. *Staphylococcus.*
    (Comprehension)

14. Nosocomial infections are
    A. acquired at work.
    B. hereditary.
    C. hospital-acquired.
    D. nasal infections.
    (Knowledge)

15. A catheter is inserted into the
    A. bladder.
    B. kidney.
    C. ureter.
    D. urethra.
    (Knowledge)

16. Select the incorrect association.
    A. bronchoscopy/respiratory tract
    B. endoscopy/arteries and veins
    C. laparoscopy/abdominal cavity
    D. pneumonia/respiratory tract
    (Comprehension)

17. The term "prophylaxis" means
    A. bacterial.
    B. cleaning.
    C. prevention.
    D. viral.
    (Knowledge)

18. Cholera and typhoid often are spread through

    A. blood transfusions.
    B. hypodermic syringes.
    C. human sewage.
    D. sneezing.

    (Knowledge)

19. Select the incorrect statement about DDT.

    A. It first became available in the 1960s.
    B. It is an insecticide.
    C. It was effective initially.
    D. It was inexpensive.

    (Comprehension)

20. Memory B cells are one kind of

    A. erythrocyte.
    B. lymphocyte.
    C. neutrophil.
    D. monocyte.

    (Knowledge)

21. Variolation was the first vaccine against

    A. botulism.
    B. diphtheria.
    C. smallpox.
    D. tuberculosis.

    (Knowledge)

22. Select the incorrect statement about vaccines.

    A. Attenuated vaccines are usually ineffective.
    B. They contain one or more microbial antigens.
    C. Some contain live microorganisms.
    D. Some contain inactivated microorganisms.

    (Comprehension)

23. Select the incorrect association.

    A. attenuated/potent microorganisms
    B. orally/by mouth
    C. Sabin/orally
    D. subcutaneous/below the skin

    (Comprehension)

24. Toxoids were the first

    A. acellular vaccines.
    B. antibiotics.
    C. antibodies.
    D. cellular vaccines.

    (Knowledge)

25. By passive immunity administered to humans, the effectiveness lasts for __1__ with antibodies from humans and lasts __1__ with antibodies from animals.

    A. 1 - months, 2 - months
    B. 1 - months, 2 - weeks
    C. 1 - weeks, 2 - months
    D. 1 - weeks, 2 - weeks

    (Comprehension)

True/False

26. A pandemic is an epidemic that spreads worldwide.

    (Knowledge)

27. Tetanus is a sporadic disease.

    (Knowledge)

28. Morbidity in a population refers to death.

    (Knowledge)

29. Five people in a population of 100,000 die from a particular disease in one year. The annual death rate as a percentage for this disease is 0.05.

    (Application)

30. Smallpox was eradicated worldwide in 1977.

    (Knowledge)

31. *Pneumocystis carinii* is a causative agent of gastroenteritis.

    (Knowledge)

32. Food poisoning from an unknown source develops in a school. This should be investigated by an expert in surveillance epidemiology.

    (Comprehension)

33. Historically listeriosis can develop from consumption of cheese.

    (Comprehension)

34. Americans die every year from nosocomial infections.

    (Knowledge)

35. Scrubbing refers to sterilization of all microbes in an area.

    (Comprehension)

36. Tuberculosis can be transmitted through milk.

    (Knowledge)

37. A subcutaneous immunizing agent is administered below the skin.

    (Knowledge)

38. A recently-developed vaccine for whooping cough is acellular.

    (Knowledge)

39. Booster vaccines activate memory B cells.

    (Knowledge)

40. To this date, naked DNA as a vaccine has not protected any mammal against the influenza virus.

    (Comprehension)

Completion

41. An epidemic is a disease outbreak that affects _____ members in a _____ time period.

    (Knowledge)

42. From a particular disease, 9 people die per 100,000 in one year. The death rate annually as a percentage is _(number)_ .

    (Application)

43. When contaminated food is served at a common gathering, the food poisoning that develops is a _____ epidemic.

    (Comprehension)

44. By laparoscopy an instrument is introduced into the _____ cavity.

    (Knowledge)

45. Pasteur first used the process of pasteurization to prevent the spoilage of _____.

    (Comprehension)

46. Toxoids stimulate the production of antibodies called _____.

    (Knowledge)

Matching/Labeling

Label each of the following as describing active or passive immunization.

47. This involves antibody transfusion.

48. Gamma globulins are injected.

49. Microbial DNA is injected.

50. It involves administration of booster doses.

(Knowledge)

Short Essay

51. One particular disease has an incidence rate of 0.004. Explain the meaning of this rate.

(Application)

52. Outline the strategies that can decrease the incidence of tuberculosis.

(Analysis)

53. Compared to oral or intramuscular administration, describe one key factor necessary to make the absorption of an oral vaccine successful.

(Analysis)

54. Historically, what do you think have been the main problems preventing an effective vaccine for syphilis?

(Analysis)

55. Explain how the kinds of epidemiology complement one another: descriptive, surveillance, field, and hospital.

(Synthesis)

56. How do a wide variety of fields in biology (e.g., genetics, cell biology, anatomy and physiology) apply to the concepts in this chapter?

(Evaluation)

Correlation Questions

57. Prevalence rates for disease a particularly high for long-lasting diseases. Explain.

58. Ecology is a highly-relevant branch of biology to epidemiologic studies. Which branch of epidemiology depends the most on the principles of ecology?

59. Explain the advantage to the subject of active immunization compared to passive immunization.

60. Explain the advantage to the subject of passive immunization compared to active immunization.

Answers

Multiple Choice

1. D 2. D 3. D 4. C 5. D 6. C 7. B 8. B 9. A 10. D 11. B 12. C
13. D 14. C 15. D 16. B 17. C 18. C 19. A 20. B 21. C 22. A
23. A 24. A 25. B

True/False

26. True 27. True 28. False 29. False 30. True 31. False 32. False 33. True
34. True 35. False 36. True 37. True 38. True 39. True 40. False

Completion

41. many, short 42. 0.009 43. common source 44. abdominal 45. wine 46. antitoxins

Matching/Labeling

47. passive 48. passive 49. active 50. active

Short Essay

51. Four people per 100,000 people develop the disease.

52. The conditions that promote the disease must be diminished. These include poverty, malnutrition, ill health, alcoholism, and AIDS.

53. An oral vaccine cannot be destroyed by chemical digestion in the GI tract before it is absorbed into the bloodstream across the wall of the small intestine.

54. Major problems have included that the microorganism is difficult to culture. It is also a costly venture.

55. There are many examples that can be used. Surveillance epidemiology uses the general information from descriptive epidemiology. Tracking the disease can be used to investigate disease outbreaks. Hospital epidemiology draws from all of these fields.

56. Some vaccines are DNA based (genetics). In addition, a subject's genome is the blueprint for the development of one's specific immune system. This system combats all kinds of invading cells, and part of this immunity is cellular (as opposed to humoral). This ongoing struggle between invading microbes and the immune system occurs in different body regions (e.g., the lungs for tuberculosis).

Correlation Questions

57. The prevalence rate is the rate of having a certain disease at any particular time. A long-lasting disease has a long time span. Therefore, the probability (calculated as a percentage) for the disease occurring in a subject is high or very likely during that time period.

58. Field epidemiology and surveillance epidemiology depend on investigation of ecosystems and environmental factors.

59. Active immunity confers the potential for long-lasting protection, particularly if there is another exposure to an infecting microbe. However, this type of protection can require time to develop in an individual.

60. Passive immunity gives immediate defense for a subject. However, its effects are short-lived and it does not confer the potential, long-lasting protection from active immunity.

Chapter 21
Pharmacology

Multiple Choice

1. Antimicrobial drugs

    A. are made through chemical synthesis only.
    B. occur naturally only.
    C. are made through chemical synthesis and occur naturally.
    D. do not occur naturally and are not made synthetically.

    (Knowledge)

2. Systemic therapy means that a drug

    A. enter the patient's bloodstream.
    B. is administered by muscular injection.
    C. is given regularly.
    D. reaches only certain organs of the body.

    (Knowledge)

3. Drug distribution refers to

    A. when it is administered.
    B. when it is manufactured.
    C. where it is administered on a body region.
    D. where it is found in the body after administration.

    (Knowledge)

4. Drugs that are transported through the pores of the cell membrane pass through the _____ part of the membrane.

    A. carbohydrate
    B. lipid
    C. nucleic acid
    D. protein

    (Knowledge)

5. If 60 percent of a drug is protein-bound in the blood plasma at any moment, _____ percent of it is directly available to cross cell membranes.

    A. 20
    B. 40
    C. 60
    D. 100

    (Comprehension)

6. The side effects of most drugs are usually

    A. primary and usually adverse.
    B. primary and usually beneficial.
    C. secondary and usually adverse.
    D. secondary and usually beneficial.

    (Knowledge)

7. Probenecid is often administered to a subject to slow the excretion rate of

    A. erythromyocin.
    B. penicillin
    C. streptomycin.
    D. tetracycline.

    (Knowledge)

8. Narrow-spectrum, antibacterial drugs

    A. affect many microbial groups.
    B. affect only one microbial group.
    C. work over a long period of time.
    D. work over a short period of time.

    (Knowledge)

9. The origin of drug-resistant changes in bacteria occurs in their

    A. cell membranes.
    B. genetic makeup.
    C. location in the body.
    D. size and morphology.

    (Knowledge)

10. Ampicillin affects

    A. only Gram-negative bacteria.
    B. only Gram-positive bacteria.
    C. both Gram-positive and Gram-negative bacteria.
    D. neither Gram-positive nor Gram-negative bacteria.

    (Knowledge)

11. Penicillin administration is successful at treating

    A. bacterial infections only.
    B. viral infections only.
    C. bacterial and viral infections.
    D. neither bacterial nor viral infections.

    (Knowledge)

12. Four different antibiotics are compared for effectiveness against a bacterium by the Kirby-Bauer method. The antibiotic producing a halo of _____ mm thickness around its disc on agar surface is most effective.

    A. two
    B. three
    C. four
    D. five

    (Comprehension)

13. A number of different drug concentrations are compared for effectiveness against a bacterium by the broth-dilution method. Four different concentrations are found to stop growth. Which MBC indicates the most effective concentration?

    A. 2 units
    B. 4 units
    C. 6 units
    D. 8 units

    (Comprehension)

14. By the serum-killing power test, serum is

    A. cultured in a laboratory.
    B. made from sensitized animals.
    C. manufactured synthetically.
    D. withdrawn from a patient.

    (Knowledge)

15. The penicillins

    A. cause genetic amplification.
    B. cause genetic mutations.
    C. inhibit cell wall synthesis.
    D. inhibit cell membrane synthesis.

    (Knowledge)

16. Streptomycin binds to the

    A. 30S subunits of 70S ribosomes.
    B. 50S subunits of 70S ribosomes.
    C. 50S subunits of 80S ribosomes.
    D. 60S subunits of 80S ribosomes.

    (Knowledge)

17. Select the correct statement about rifampin.

    A. It is a component of the bacterial cell wall.
    B. It is an antibiotic.
    C. It selectively inhibits bacterial DNA polymerase.
    D. It selectively inhibits bacterial RNA polymerase.

(Knowledge)

18. Select the incorrect statement about the penicillins.

    A. All are naturally-occurring.
    B. The share the same basic structure.
    C. Their molecules differ with respect to their R group.
    D. They inhibit bacterial cell wall synthesis.

(Comprehension)

19. Select the incorrect statement about the cephalosporins.

    A. They are closely related to the penicillins.
    B. They do not cause allergies.
    C. They have minimal side effects.
    D. They have six-membered rings.

(Comprehension)

20. Today the sulfonamides are used most often to treat infections of the _____ tract.

    A. digestive
    B. reproductive
    C. respiratory
    D. urinary

(Knowledge)

21. Select the incorrect statement about the aminoglycosides.

    A. Amino sugar molecules are part of their structure.
    B. They are not well absorbed when taken orally.
    C. They are not effective against Gram-negative bacteria.
    D. They do not penetrate the central nervous system.

(Comprehension)

22. Select the incorrect statements about the tetracyclines.

    A. They are effective against Gram-negative bacteria.
    B. They are well absorbed orally.
    C. They are widely distributed across the body.
    D. They interfere with DNA synthesis.

(Comprehension)

23. Select the incorrect statement about the quinolones.
    A. They are effective against Gram-positive bacteria.
    B. They are narrow-spectrum agents.
    C. They are synthetic antimicrobial agents.
    D. They were derived from nalidixic acid.

    (Comprehension)

24. Select the incorrect statement about vancomycin.
    A. It acts on Gram-positive bacteria.
    B. It interferes directly with DNA synthesis.
    C. It is not absorbed well orally.
    D. It is produced by a species of *Streptomyces*.

    (Comprehension)

25. Select the incorrect statement about isoniazid.
    A. It is a synthetic drug.
    B. It is activated by a mycobacterial enzyme.
    C. It is inactivated by the kidney.
    D. It is well absorbed orally.

    (Comprehension)

True/False

26. A drug is any chemical that has a physiological effect on living things.

    (Knowledge)

27. IV administration is usually done on the brachial artery.

    (Knowledge)

28. A lipid-soluble drug can dissolve directly through the cell membrane.

    (Knowledge)

29. The symptoms of Strep throat resemble those of infectious mononucleosis.

    (Knowledge)

30. Antibiotics cause the genetic exchange in bacteria that leads to drug resistance.

    (Knowledge)

31. Combined therapy means administering two different drugs at the same time.

    (Knowledge)

32. The broth dilution method is more complicated and expensive than the disc-dilution method.

    (Knowledge)

33. If the MIC is higher than the MBC for a drug, the drug is bacteriostatic.

    (Comprehension)

34. A bacterium that loses its cell wall tends to lyse.

    (Knowledge)

35. Topoisomerases are enzymes that extend newly-forming DNA chains.

    (Knowledge)

36. Cephalosporins are less resistant to beta-lactamases than the penicillins.

    (Knowledge)

37. Kanamycin is prescribed for an infection. It must be administered by injection to be effective.

    (Knowledge)

38. Rifampin is not a semisynthetic antibiotic.

    (Knowledge)

39. Nystatin is an antifungal drug.

    (Knowledge)

40. Acyclovir is not effective against DNA viruses of the herpes family.

    (Knowledge)

Completion

41. There is risk of a superinfection when a drug is introduced into the body by _____ adminstration.

    (Knowledge)

42. A _____ antibiotic is effective against more than one microbial group.

    (Comprehension)

43. A bacterium loses its ability to produce beta-lactamase. Therefore it loses its resistance to the drug_____.

    (Knowledge)

44. The tetracycline inhibit bacterial _____ synthesis.

    (Comprehension)

45. Griseofulvin is an antibiotic effective against _____ and not effective against bacteria.

Matching

46. amantadine	A. antiviral agent
47. amphotericin	B. effective only against mycobacteria
48. chloroquine	C. polyene for systemic fungal infections
49. ethambutol	D. first isolated from *Penicillium*
50. griseofulvin	E. most effect drug against malaria

(Knowledge)

Short Essay

51. Outline an experiment to compare the effectiveness of different antibiotics against a specific bacterium using the Kirby-Bauer method.

    (Application)

52. Outline an experiment to compare drug effectiveness against a killing of a specific bacterium using the broth-dilution method.

    (Application)

53. The establishment of drug resistance by a bacterium is an excellent example of evolution. Outline this mechanism of evolution.

    (Analysis)

54. How does a person develop an allergy to a particular antibiotic?

    (Analysis)

55. How are the principles of cytology and biochemistry combined to promote the development of pharmacology as a science?

    (Synthesis)

56. Assess the value of pharmacology in promoting a better quality of human life.

    (Evaluation)

Correlation Questions

57. A drug consisting of protein molecules will not be effective in the human body if administered orally. Explain.

58. IV administration is the fastest way to introduce high levels of a drug in the body. Explain.

59. Why is a narrow-spectrum antibiotic a good choice to treat an infection if the microbe causing the infection is known?

60. If the causative agent for an infection is not known, why is treatment with a broad-spectrum antibiotic a good choice?

Answers

Multiple Choice

1. C   2. A   3. D   4. D   5. B   6. C   7. B   8. B   9. B   10. C   11. A   12. D
13. A   14. D   15. C   16. A   17. D   18. A   19. B   20. D   21. C   22. D   23. B
24. B   25. C

True/False

26. True   27. False   28. True   29. True   30. False   31. True   32. True
33. False   34. True   35. False   36. False   37. True   38. False   39. True
40. False   41. IV

Completion

42. broad-spectrum   43. penicillin   44. protein   45. fungi

Matching

46. A   47. C   48. E   49. B   50. D

Short Essay

51. In a petri dish, inoculate the agar surface with the bacterium. Impregnate each filter paper disc with a different antibiotic. Place each disc on the agar surface. After 48 hours of incubation, compare the size of the halos produced around each disc. The greater the size, the greater the effectiveness of the antibiotic.

52. Prepare nutrient broth tubes with different concentrations of the drug. Incubate the tubes for 48 hours. Check the turbidity in each tube. The lower the turbidity, the less growth of the microbe and the greater the effectiveness of the drug concentration. Test for different concentrations of the drug until discovery of the lowest level yields no turbidity (no growth).

53. Mutant strains of a bacterium may survive by a resistance to the antibiotic. The nonresistant strains will have a higher death rate. The resistant strains will have a higher survival rate and produce offspring with their superior genotypes. Fewer of the nonresistant genotypes will be passed on to the next generation. The difference in reproductive rates is the essence of natural selection. Over time the bacterial population will change.

54. The antibiotic molecule probably does not stimulate an allergic reaction by itself. However, if it combines with a protein in the human body, this can stimulate a response. One example is the combination of penicillin with a hapten in the body. An immunological line of B lymphocytes can be established that will produce a memory for a stronger response from future exposures to the antibiotic.

55. The mode of action of most drugs is understood through their molecular structure and overall shape. Each drug works against a particular aspect of cell structure (e.g., penicillin against the cell wall) or cell function (e.g., erythromycin against protein synthesis).

56. Antimicrobial drugs have added an average of 10 years to the life expectancy of Americans. Many examples can be offered. In the 1800s, infections from abscessed teeth could be fatal, as antibiotics were not available.

Correlation Questions

57. If administered orally, the protein drug passes through the digestive tract. Enzymes in the stomach (e.g., pepsin) and small intestine (e.g., trypsin) that normally degrade protein molecules in our diet can also catalyze the breakdown of the protein drug, rendering it inactive.

58. A drug administered IV does not need to clear the barriers that a drug meets by oral or intramuscular injection. By the blood the IV-administered drug reaches the affected body cells directly by circulating in the blood.

59. If the causative agent is known, a specific drug can target the vulnerable part of the microbe's structure (e.g., cell wall, ribosome, etc.).

60. If the causative agent is not known, a broad-spectrum antibiotic offers more alternatives to overcome several, possible infecting microbes.

Chapter 22
Infections of the Respiratory System

Multiple Choice

1. Select the incorrect association.

   A. aussculation/ hearing sounds.
   B. etiological agent/ cures disease
   C. symptom/ what a patient experiences
   D. trauma/ injury

   (Comprehension)

2. *Moraxella catarrhalis* is a _____ microorganism when inhabiting the upper respiratory tract.

   A. commensal
   B. mutualistic
   C. parasitic
   D. predatory

   (Knowledge)

3. Otis media in the infection of the

   A. external ear.
   B. external nose.
   C. middle ear.
   D. internal nose.

   (Knowledge)

4. *Haemophilus influenzae* is

   A. Gram-negative and coccal-shaped.
   B. Gram-negative and rod-shaped.
   C. Gram-positive and coccal-shaped.
   D. Gram positive and rod-shaped.

   (Knowledge)

5. A blood agar surface is streaked with a bacterium of unknown identity. The bacterium is also tested for its sensitivity to antibiotics. The bacterium is *Streptococcus pyrogenes* if its colonies are _1_ to bacitracin and _2_ clear halos.

   A. 1 - not sensitive, 2 - do not produce
   B. 1 - not sensitive, 2 - do produce
   C. 1 - sensitive, 2 - do not produce
   D. 1 - sensitive, 2 - do produce

   (Comprehension)

6. Each is a symptom of strep throat except
    A. a whitish exudate covering the tonsils.
    B. fever.
    C. headaches.
    D. shrunken lymph nodes.
    (Knowledge)

7. The term "erythrogenic" means
    A. red-destroying.
    B. red-producing.
    C. white-destroying.
    D. white-producing.
    (Knowledge)

8. The most serious complication of rheumatic fever is
    A. damage to the heart.
    B. damage to the skin.
    C. swollen joints.
    D. swollen lymph nodes.
    (Knowledge)

9. A patient suffers from acute glomerulonephritis. The main symptom of this disease is probably the
    A. development of a high fever.
    B. inability to control water balance in the body.
    C. persistence of a mild anemia.
    D. swelling of the joints in the body.
    (Application)

10. Select the incorrect statement about the rhinoviruses.
    A. They are extremely small.
    B. They are members of the picornavirus group.
    C. They have a hexagonal symmetry.
    D. They have single-stranded RNA.
    (Comprehension)

11. Most rhinovirus infections are transmitted by
    A. blood transfusions.
    B. contaminated food.
    C. direct hand-to-hand contact.
    D. sneezing.
    (Knowledge)

12. Select the incorrect statement about the coronaviruses.

    A. They are DNA viruses.
    B. They are extremely difficult to isolate.
    C. They are medium-sized.
    D. They cause the common cold.

    (Comprehension)

13. About _____ pneumococcal serotypes have been isolated.

    A. 20
    B. 40
    C. 60
    D. 80

    (Knowledge)

14. Today less than _____ percent of patients who receive timely and appropriate antibiotic treatment die from pneumoncoccal pneumonia.

    A. 5
    B. 4
    C. 3
    D. 1

    (Comprehension)

15. Select the genus that is not a cause of acute bacterial pneumonias.

    A. Bacillus
    B. Escherichia
    C. Haemophilus
    D. Staphylococcus

    (Knowledge)

16. *Mycoplasma pneumoniae* develops in the trachea of a young child. The best antibiotic for treatment is

    A. cephalosporin.
    B. erythromycin.
    C. penicillin.
    D. tetracycline.

    (Knowledge)

17. A microorganism is studied in the lab. It cannot generate ATP and is propagated in the yolk sac of a chick embryo. It is probably a simple

    A. bacterium.
    B. fungus.
    C. plant.
    D. protozoan.

    (Application)

18. *Coxiella burnetii* is a member of the _____ family.

    A. algal
    B. fungal
    C. protozoan
    D. rickettsia

    (Knowledge)

19. Select the incorrect characteristic of *L. pneumophila*.

    A. It is aerobic.
    B. It is nonmotile.
    C. It is rod-shaped.
    D. It is small.

    (Comprehension)

20. Pertussis is

    A. pneumonia.
    B. scarlet fever.
    C. whooping cough.
    D. yellow fever.

    (Knowledge)

21. The leading killer of humans among infectious diseases is

    A. AIDS.
    B. tuberculosis.
    C. whooping cough.
    D. yellow fever.

    (Knowledge)

22. A bacterium is studied in the lab for identification. It is resistant to lysozyme attack and can clump into cordlike masses. It grows slowly and optimally in high oxygen concentrations. It is probably a species of

    A. *Bacillus*.
    B. *Clostridium*.
    C. *Escherichia*.
    D. *Mycobacterium*.

    (Application)

23. Caseation necrosis is

    A. cell pigmentation.
    B. cheeselike death.
    C. rapid cell division.
    D. the spreading of cells.

    (Knowledge)

24. BCG is a(n)
    A. antibiotic against Gram-negative bacteria.
    B. antibiotic against Gram-positive bacteria.
    C. vaccine for tuberculosis.
    D. vaccine for whooping cough.

    (Knowledge)

25. *M. bovis* usually enters the human body through the _____ system.
    A. circulatory
    B. gastrointestinal
    C. respiratory
    D. urinary

    (Knowledge)

26. Use of a humidifier in a child's bedroom will help to control the symptoms caused by the
    A. bacterium that causes the croup.
    B. bacterium that causes strep throat.
    C. virus that causes the croup.
    D. virus that causes strep throat.

    (Comprehension)

27. The respiratory symptoms of the hantavirus include
    A. capillaries leaking and dry air spaces.
    B. capillaries leaking and fluid in the air spaces.
    C. capillaries not leaking and dry air spaces.
    D. capillaries not leaking and no air spaces.

    (Knowledge)

28. Histoplasmosis is caused by a
    A. bacterium.
    B. fungus.
    C. protozoan.
    D. virus.

    (Knowledge)

29. Arthrospores are associated with
    A. blastomycosis.
    B. coccidioidomycosis.
    C. pneumonia.
    D. strep throat.

    (Knowledge)

30. The RNA sequence of *P. carinii* reveals that it is a
    A. bacterium.
    B. fungus.
    C. protozoan.
    D. virus.
    (Knowledge)

True/False

31. In the human body, bronchioles are smaller and more numerous than secondary bronchi; secondary bronchi are smaller and more numerous that primary bronchi.

    (Comprehension)

32. Each lung is surrounded by a smooth membrane called the pleura.

    (Knowledge)

33. Ampicillin is effective at treating the disease epiglottitis.

    (Knowledge)

34. The skin cannot be infected by *C. diphtheriae*.

    (Knowledge)

35. The rhinovirus is named by its viral shape.

    (Knowledge)

36. A bacterium is tested for identification in the laboratory. Its colonies on a nutrient agar surface are flooded with a dilute solution of hydrogen peroxide. Bubbles are formed on the surface immediately. This shows that the bacterium could be *Streptococcus pneumoniae*.

    (Application)

37. Aspirating means to reduce swelling by adding a cold compress to the swollen area of the body.

    (Knowledge)

38. A young, adult population is studied for the incidence of bacterial pneumonias. Out of 120 reported cases, at least 30 of these are probably caused by *Klebsiella* species.

    (Application)

39. Pneumococcal sepsis is a life-threatening disease.

    (Knowledge)

40. A tubercle is an inflammatory lesion.

    (Knowledge)

Completion

41. Exhaled air normally passes from the alveoli through the _____ to the tertiary bronchi to the _____ bronchi to the primary bronchi to the trachea to the _____ to the _____ to the nose.

    (Comprehension)

42. The normal, adult breathing rate is in the range of 12 to 18 cycles per minute. One example of tachypnea (rapid breathing rate) is _____ cycles per minute.

    (Application)

43. Cutaneous diptheria is an infection of the _____.

    (Knowledge)

44. *C. psittaci* commonly infects all types of _____ species.

    (Knowledge)

45. *Bordetella pertussis* is Gram-_____.

    (Knowledge)

Matching

46. *Corynebacterium*   A. dimorphic fungus

47. *Histoplasma*   B. it causes the common cold

48. *Mycobacterium*   C. a species causes pneumonia

49. *Pneumocysti*   D. a species causes tuberculosis

50. rhinovirus   E. *diphtheriae* is a species member

(Knowledge)

Short Essay

51. A person suffers a loss of the cilia lining the mucous membranes of the upper respiratory tract. What may develop in the person from this change?

    (Application)

52. Erythromycin is prescribed for a viral infection of the respiratory tract. Will this prescription be effective?

    (Application)

53. The trachea and bronchi have walls that are reinforced with rings of cartilage. Often an infection or inflammation of the bronchioles can cause these passageways to collapse. Why?

    (Analysis)

54. What are several adaptations that promote the exchange of oxygen and carbon dioxide at the alveoli?

    (Analysis)

55. Often a person recovering from the common cold has immunity to this condition for five to six weeks? Can you offer a reason for this?

    (Synthesis)

56. A person suffers from laryngitis. One suggestion for treatment is to gargle with a medication. Another treatment is to inhale small droplets of a medication. Which treatment do you think will be more effective?

    (Evaluation)

Correlation Questions

57. Why are smokers more susceptible to pneumococcal pneumonia?

58. Removal of tonsils surgically can potentially be harmful to a person's health. Why?

59. Upper respiratory infections can sometimes spread to the middle ear. How?

60. A person suffers from a throat infection. He is treated for laryngitis. Is this the correct strategy for treatment?

Answers

Multiple Choice

1. B   2. A   3. C   4. B   5. D   6. D   7. B   8. A   9. B   10. C   11. C   12. A
13. D   14. A   15. A   16. B   17. A   18. D   19. B   20. C   21. B   22. D
23. B   24. C   25. B   26. C   27. B   28. B   29. B   30. B

True/False

31. True   32. True   33. False   34. False   35. False   36. False   37. False
38. False   39. True   40. True

Completion

41. alveoli - bronchioles - tertiary bronchi - secondary bronchi - primary bronchi - trachea - larynx - pharynx - nose   42.   a rate greater than 18 breathing cycles per minute   43. skin   44. bird   45. negative

Matching

46. E   47. A   48. D   49. C   50. B

Short Essay

51. The cilia beat opposite to the inflow of air, serving as a filter for foreign bacteria that may invade the body. Losing this first line of defense, the body is more vulnerable to an invading microbe and infection.

52. Erythromycin, and most antibiotics, blocks ribosome activity during protein synthesis. Viruses lack ribosomes.

53. The rings of cartilage are lost at the level of the bronchioles, making them vulnerable to collapsing. The larger passageways of the respiratory tract have this reinforcement.

54. The alveoli have thin, moist membranes. These are advantages for the simple diffusion of gases. Also, collectively the alveoli offer a tremendous surface area for gas exchange.

55. Many theories can be advanced. Perhaps the virus causing the common cold stimulates an immunological memory as it is destroyed by lymphocyte and antibody attack. The memory cell line established, however, is not permanent.

56. A gargled substance will mainly affect the throat or pharynx and not reach the larynx, the next region of the respiratory tract. An inhaled mist, however, will reach the larynx and perhaps reduce the inflammation.

Correlation Questions

57. The chemicals and irritants from smoking destroy some of the major lines of defense in the respiratory tract, damaging mucous membranes and removing the cilia lining the tract.

58. The tonsils are lymphoid tissue, representing a part of the immune system in the human body. Loss of this line of defense can make the body more susceptible to infection.

59. The eustachian tube connects the throat to the middle ear. This tube serves as an avenue to move air from the throat to the middle ear to balance air pressure on the tympanum or ear drum. However it is also an avenue for a microorganism to spread from the throat into the middle ear.

60. Laryngitis is the inflammation of the laryngitis, a part of the respiratory tract. Pharyngitis is the inflammation of the throat, serving the respiratory and digestive tracts. This is a different region of human body structure.

Chapter 23
Infections of the Digestive System

Multiple Choice

1. Peristalsis refers to the
   A. absorption of food molecules.
   B. chemical digestion of food.
   C. elimination of food from the digestive tract.
   D. intestinal movement propelling food.
   (Knowledge)

2. *E. coli* is named in part by the fact that it inhabits the _____ of the human body.
   A. large intestine
   B. oral cavity
   C. small intestine
   D. stomach
   (Comprehension)

3. A patient has the symptoms of diarrhea, nausea, vomiting, and cramps from abdominal pain. This patient probably suffers from
   A. gastroenteritis.
   B. peristalsis.
   C. parotitis.
   D. pleurisy.
   (Knowledge)

4. A patient has some destruction of the enamel covering the teeth. This is probably caused by the activity of
   A. *B. subtilis.*
   B. *H. pylori.*
   C. *S. aureus.*
   D. *S. mutans.*
   (Comprehension)

5. A patient suffers from peridontal disease. Isolation of one bacterium from this person's oral cavity reveals an anaerobe that is Gram-negative. This bacterium is probably a member of the genus
   A. *Aerobacter.*
   B. *Porphyromonas*
   C. *Staphylococcus.*
   D. *Streptococcus.*
   (Application)

6. The mineral that helps to prevent tooth decay is

   A. bromide.
   B. chloride.
   C. fluoride.
   D. iodide.

   (Knowledge)

7. Mumps is caused by a

   A. bacterium.
   B. fungus.
   C. protozoan.
   D. virus.

   (Knowledge)

8. Select the incorrect characteristic about the *Shigella* species.

   A. They are Gram-negative.
   B. They belong to the Enterobacteriaceae.
   C. They cause bacillary dysentery.
   D. They have a coccus shape.

   (Comprehension)

9. A person suffers from dysentery. Isolation of one bacterium from this person's small intestine reveals a Gram-negative, rod-shaped bacterium. This bacterium is probably a species of

   A. *Bacillus.*
   B. *Clostridium.*
   C. *Shigella.*
   D. *Streptococcus.*

   (Application)

10. A person with a normal body weight of 150 pounds suffers from dehydration by bacterial infection. The minimal loss of _____ pounds through dehydration will probably be fatal to this person.

    A. 6
    B. 8
    C. 12
    D. 24

    (Application)

11. Select the characteristic that is not a symptom of typhoid fever.

    A. Fatigue develops.
    B. High fever is produced.
    C. Patients develop an increased appetite.
    D. Patients develop rose spots.

    (Knowledge)

12. Salmonellosis is

   A. food poisoning.
   B. schistosomiasis.
   C. spotted fever.
   D. typhoid fever.

   (Knowledge)

13. If an antibiotic is contraindicated, it is

   A. allergic.
   B. medically advisable.
   C. medically inadvisable.
   D. nonallergic.

   (Knowledge)

14. _____ strains of *E. coli* are the primary cause of traveler's diarrhea.

   A. Enterohemorrhagic
   B. Enteroinvasive
   C. Enteropathogenic
   D. Enterotoxigenic

   (Comprehension)

15. An antibiotic that might be recommended to treat traveler's diarrhea is

   A. ampicillin.
   B. ciprofloxacin.
   C. erythromycin.
   D. tetracycline.

   (Knowledge)

16. A species of *Vibrio* causes

   A. cholera.
   B. food poisoning.
   C. typhoid fever.
   D. spotted fever.

   (Knowledge)

17. If chloride ions are excreted by epithelial cells, __1__ ions follow because their charge is __2__ .

   A. 1 - bromide, 2 - the same
   B. 1 - fluoride, 2 - the same
   C. 1 - iodide, 2 - opposite
   D. 1 - sodium, 2 - opposite

   (Comprehension)

18. The fluids used for ORT usually contain

    A. calcium and chloride.
    B. chloride and iodide.
    C. glucose and calcium.
    D. glucose and sodium.

    (Knowledge)

19. *Vibrio parahaemolyticus* causes

    A. blood septicemia.
    B. dental caries.
    C. mild diarrhea.
    D. stomach ulcers.

    (Knowledge)

20. Select the incorrect characteristic about *Yersinia enterocolitica*.

    A. It grows best at room temperature.
    B. It is Gram-positive.
    C. It is usually found in animals.
    D. It produces an enterotoxin.

    (Comprehension)

21. Select the incorrect characteristic about *Campylobacter species*.

    A. They are Gram-negative.
    B. They are cultivated in microaerophilic conditions.
    C. They can be human pathogens.
    D. They have coccal-shaped cells.

    (Comprehension)

22. Stomach ulcers are caused by a species of

    A. *Bacillus.*
    B. *Escherichia.*
    C. *Helicobacter.*
    D. *Staphylococcus.*

    (Knowledge)

23. Select the incorrect characteristic about *S. aureus*.

    A. It causes food poisoning.
    B. It does not retain Gentian violet when decolorized.
    C. It forms grapelike clusters of spherical cells.
    D. It produces a heat-stabile enterotoxin.

    (Comprehension)

24. Select the incorrect characteristic about *Clostridium perfringens*.

    A. It can metabolize in the absence of oxygen.
    B. It causes foodborne intoxication.
    C. It does not retain Gentian violet when decolorized.
    D. It is resistant to harsh conditions.

    (Comprehension)

25. The rotavirus causing gastroenteritis mainly damages

    A. intestinal epithelial cells.
    B. smooth muscle tissue.
    C. valves of the intestinal tract.
    D. white blood cells.

    (Knowledge)

26. *Entamoeba histolytica* is a

    A. bacterium.
    B. fungus.
    C. protozoan.
    D. virus.

    (Knowledge)

27. *Giardia lamblia* moves by the action of

    A. cilia.
    B. flagella.
    C. pseudopodia.
    D. trichocysts.

    (Knowledge)

28. *Balantidium coli* moves by the action of

    A. cilia.
    B. flagella.
    C. pseudopodia.
    D. trichocysts.

    (Knowledge)

29. Select the incorrect characteristic about *Ascaris lumbricoides*.

    A. It has a simple life cycle.
    B. It is a roundworm parasite.
    C. It is common in regions with poor sanitation.
    D. It sheds eggs in human feces.

    (Comprehension)

30. Select the incorrect characteristic about the hepatitis A virus.

    A. It contains single-stranded RNA.
    B. It has an envelope.
    C. It multiplies in the liver.
    D. It is a small virus.

    (Comprehension)

True/False

31. During vomiting, swallowed food passes from the esophagus into the oral cavity.

    (Comprehension)

32. A cholecystectomy is the surgical removal of the gallbladder. After this procedure, a person may lose some ability to chemically digest proteins.

    (Application)

33. Shiga toxin produces dysentery.

    (Knowledge)

34. Enteropathogenic strains of *E. coli* cause diarrhea in newborn infants.

    (Knowledge)

35. A researcher is studying ways to control a bacterial population of *Vibrio cholerae*. One possible biological control is to eradicate the local population of mosquitoes.

    (Application)

36. Campylobacter species are coccus-shaped bacteria.

    (Knowledge)

37. A protozoan is studied for identification. It moves by cilia. It is a harmless commensal. These characteristics means it could be *G. lamblia*.

    (Comprehension)

38. Pinworms cause the most common helminthic infection in the U.S.

    (Knowledge)

39. The hepatitis B virus is a DNA-containing virus.

    (Knowledge)

40. Hepatitis E is usually benign and self-limited.

    (Knowledge)

Completion

41. The three regions of the small intestine are:

    (Knowledge)

42. Human caries is more likely to develop if a person consumes the sugar _____.

    (Comprehension)

43. *Salmonella* species have Gram-_____ rods.

    (Knowledge)

44. *H pylori* is Gram-_____.

    (Knowledge)

45. Hepatocytes are cells of the _____.

    (Knowledge)

Matching

Each letter is used only once.

46. *Ascaris*   A. hookworm
47. *Balantidium*   B. protozoan
48. *Taenia*   C. roundworm
49. *Trichinella*   D. tapeworm
50. *Trichuris*   E. whipworm

    (Knowledge)

Short Essay

51. An antibiotic is taken by a patient to treat a bacterial infection. Could this have effects on the normal floral population of bacteria in the human body?

    (Application)

52. How could a commensal living in the human GI tract become a pathogen?

    (Application)

53. *Vibrio cholerae* infection stimulates the secretion of chloride ions into the human intestine. How does this promote dehydration in the infected subject?

    (Analysis)

54. Why do the fluids given in ORT contain glucose and sodium?

    (Analysis)

55. How do you think the mumps virus causes widespread damage throughout the body (e.g., pancreas, thyroid, inner ear) after originally entering the body through the respiratory or digestive tracts? Why does the virus leave some body regions unharmed?

    (Synthesis)

56. *E. coli* has been used extensively in recombinant DNA studies. What advantages does it offer for this type of research?

    (Evaluation)

Correlation Questions

57. The mucous membrane (inner lining) of the small intestine contains villi. How is this an advantage to the functioning of the small intestine?

58. Once thought to be caused by stress, stomach ulcers are caused by a bacterium (*Helicobacter*). However, stress can still play a factor in the development of ulcers as well as the development of other infections. How?

59. How is the concept of pH related to dental caries?

60. What conditions in the digestive tract make it vulnerable to various kinds of microbial infections?

Answers:

Multiple Choice

1. D   2. A   3. A   4. D   5. B   6. C   7. D   8. D   9. C   10. C   11. C   12. A
13. C   14. D   15. B   16. A   17. D   18. D   19. C   20. B   21. D   22. C
23. B   24. C   25. A   26. C   27. B   28. A   29. A   30. B

True/False

31. True   32. False   33. True   34. True   35. False   36. False   37. False
38. True   39. True   40. True

Completion

41. duodenum, jejunum, ileum   42. sucrose   43. negative   44. negative   45. liver

Matching

46. A   47. B   48. D   49. C   50. E

Short Essay

51. If the antibiotic is somewhat nonspecific, it could also reduce the concentrations of normal floral bacteria in the body.

52. A normal floral bacterium, that was preventing it from being harmful, could be eliminated. This could change the role of the pathogen. Also, the commensal could mutate into a pathogenic form.

53. Sodium ions, which are positive, follow the negative chloride ions into the intestine. By osmosis, water follows the sodium chloride into the intestine, leading to water elimination from the body.

54. They increase the solute concentration in the blood, attracting water into the blood from the small intestine by osmosis. Water is absorbed from the small intestine into the blood by the developing osmotic gradient.

55. There are several possible explanations. Perhaps there is a protein common to these several body regions that is attacked and destroyed by the mumps virus as it spreads through the body. Other body regions may not be attacked if they lack this protein.

56. *E. coli* is a simple haploid organism. It has one circular chromosome and can be cultured easily in the lab. It multiplies rapidly for statistical analysis. Also, much is known about this bacterium from previous research.

Correlation Questions

57. Macromolecules (e.g. starch, proteins, fats) are chemically digested into their subunits in the oral cavity, stomach, and small intestine. These subunits (glucose, amino acids, fatty acids) are absorbed into the blood across the mucosal lining of the small intestine. The villi increase the surface area of this membrane to facilitate the process of absorption.

58. Stress can weaken the immune system, making the body more susceptible to microbial attack.

59. Normally the pH of the oral cavity is neutral--a safe environment for the teeth. The metabolism of sugars produces acids in the oral cavity. These acids erode away the enamel of the teeth.

60. The digestive tract is a warm, dark, moist environment with a favorable pH to support a variety of infectious microbes.

Chapter 24
Infections of the Genitourinary System

Multiple Choice

1. A blockage in the ureter prevents the normal transport of urine from the

    A. bladder to the kidney.
    B. bladder to the urethra.
    C. kidney to the bladder.
    D. urethra to the bladder.

    (Comprehension)

2. The cervix is the

    A. last region of the urinary tract.
    B. microscopic unit of the kidney.
    C. necklike extension of the uterus.
    D. upper urinary tract.

    (Knowledge)

3. An infection of the fallopian tubes is

    A. endometritis.
    B. oophoritis.
    C. salpingitis.
    D. UTI.

    (Knowledge)

4. The most common microbe causing urinary tract infections is

    A. *B. subtilis.*
    B. *E. coli.*
    C. *P. aeruginosa.*
    D. *S. aureus.*

    (Knowledge)

5. Select the substance that, if present in the urine, does not indicate a urinary tract infection.

    A. blood cells
    B. leukocyte esterase
    C. nitrite
    D. sodium

    (Knowledge)

6. Select the bacterium not known to cause UTIs.

    A. *Bacillus*
    B. *Escherichia*
    C. *Klebsiella*
    D. *Pseudomonas*

    (Knowledge)

7. Select the incorrect statement about *Leptospira interrogans*.

    A. It can be treated with penicillin.
    B. It enters humans through mucous membranes.
    C. It is a member of the spirochete family.
    D. Its presence is easy to diagnose.

    (Comprehension)

8. A diagnostic test is designed to detect gonorrhea in a male. The simplest way to detect gonorrhea from this person's urine is if it

    A. grows on Thayer-Martin medium with antibiotics.
    B. grows on Thayer-Martin medium without antibiotics.
    C. has Gram-negative diplococci.
    D. has Gram-positive diplococci.

    (Application)

9. Select the incorrect statement about *Neisseria gonorrhoeae*.

    A. It is a diplococcus.
    B. It is a highly adapted pathogen.
    C. It is easily cultured on a simple medium.
    D. It is easily killed by sunlight.

    (Comprehension)

10. About _____ percent of men contract gonorrhea after a single exposure.

    A. 5
    B. 20
    C. 50
    D. 75

    (Knowledge)

11. The discovery of _____ was a major step toward the control of gonorrhea.

    A. erythromycin
    B. penicillin
    C. streptomycin
    D. tetracycline

    (Knowledge)

12. An unknown bacterium is studied for identification. It is highly motile and does not form endospores. Its cells are neither bacilli nor cocci. The bacterium belongs to the genus
    A. *Clostridium.*
    B. *Neisseria.*
    C. *Pseudomonas.*
    D. *Treponema.*
    (Application)

13. Select the incorrect statement about *Treponema pallidum.*
    A. It forms chains of bacilli.
    B. It is a bacterium.
    C. It is difficult to culture.
    D. It infects only human beings.
    (Comprehension)

14. Select the disease that has been called the great pox.
    A. anthrax
    B. gonorrhea
    C. smallpox
    D. syphilis
    (Knowledge)

15. Secondary syphilis usually appears _____ weeks after the appearance of the chancre.
    A. 1 to 20
    B. 2 to 4
    C. 6 to 8
    D. 10 to 12
    (Knowledge)

16. Select the incorrect statement about *Chlamydia trachomatis.*
    A. It is the most prevalent STD worldwide.
    B. It can cause ectopic pregnancy.
    C. Its disease is easy to diagnose.
    D. Its infection is the major source of female infertility.
    (Comprehension)

17. *Ureaplasma urealyticum* causes
    A. gonococcal urethritis.
    B. lymphogranuloma venereum.
    C. nongonococcal urethritis.
    D. nonlymphogranuloma venereum.
    (Knowledge)

18. Chancroid is caused by a member of the genus

    A. *Escherichia.*
    B. *Haemophilus.*
    C. *Mycobacterium.*
    D. *Staphylococcus.*

    (Knowledge)

19. Granuloma inguinale is an infection of the

    A. blood.
    B. lower respiratory tract.
    C. pyloric region of the stomach.
    D. skin and mucous membranes.

    (Knowledge)

20. Select the incorrect statement about HSV.

    A. It degrades the DNA of the host cells.
    B. It has a latent phase.
    C. It has an active phase.
    D. It is not a DNA virus.

    (Comprehension)

21. The herpes simplex virus directly affects human cells that

    A. carry oxygen and carbon dioxide.
    B. contract to produce movement.
    C. send messages through the body.
    D. wander through the body by phagocytosis.

    (Comprehension)

22. Vidarabine is an

    A. antibacterial agent used to treat herpes simplex.
    B. antibacterial agent used to treat syphilis.
    C. antiviral agent used to treat herpes simplex.
    D. antiviral agent used to treat syphilis.

    (Knowledge)

23. Select the incorrect statement about HPV.

    A. It appears on cutaneous membranes.
    B. It can be cultivated in the laboratory.
    C. It is not an RNA virus.
    D. It is a papovavirus.

    (Comprehension)

24. Select the incorrect statement about *Gardnerella vaginalis*.

    A. It is not decolorized in the Gram stain steps.
    B. It discharges amines.
    C. It is nonmotile.
    D. Its incidence is high in women with vaginitis.

(Comprehension)

25. Toxic shock is caused by strains of

    A. *Bacillus*.
    B. *Enterobacter*.
    C. *Staphylococcus*.
    D. *Streptococcus*.

(Knowledge)

26. *Candida albicans* is a

    A. bacterium.
    B. fungus.
    C. protozoan.
    D. virus.

(Knowledge)

27. Select the incorrect statement about *Candida albicans*.

    A. It can be a harmless inhabitant of the vagina.
    B. It causes inflammation of the vagina.
    C. It is treated with antifungal medications.
    D. It resembles yeasts.

(Comprehension)

28. *Trichomonas* is a

    A. ciliated bacterium.
    B. ciliated protozoan.
    C. flagellated bacterium.
    D. flagellated protozoan.

(Knowledge)

29. *L. monocytogenes* is a(n)

    A. nonopportunistic commensal.
    B. nonopportunistic pathogen.
    C. opportunistic commensal.
    D. opportunistic pathogen.

(Knowledge)

30. Rubella is a
    A. bacterium.
    B. fungus.
    C. protozoan.
    D. virus.
    (Knowledge)

True/False

31. An enlarged prostate gland blocks the passage of urine from the bladder through the urethra.
    (Comprehension)

32. *L. interrogans* can be treated early with tetracycline.
    (Knowledge)

33. In the lab, a gonococcus is found to have an outer membrane protein, Protein II. It can bind to epithelial cells in clumps. This species belongs to *Escherichia* but does not belong to *Neisseria*.
    (Application)

34. *N. gonorrhea* infects only humans.
    (Knowledge)

35. *T. pertenue* causes syphilis.
    (Knowledge)

36. Primary syphilis begins a few weeks to a month after the chancre appears.
    (Knowledge)

37. HSV affects epithelial cells and neurons.
    (Knowledge)

38. Genital herpes can be cured.
    (Knowledge)

39. A population of lactobacilli in the female reproductive tract tends to change the pH from 6 to 3 in this structure.
    (Comprehension)

40. Male urethritis is caused by a species of *Neisseria*.
    (Knowledge)

Completion

41. _____ is the term that means "around birth."

    (Knowledge)

42. A mutated form of *E. coli* increases its adhesion-bearing capability by increasing its number of _____ among its cellular structures.

    (Comprehension)

43. _____ are soft granulomas that replace skin or bone.

    (Knowledge)

44. A chlamydia infection causes an _____ pregnancy, meaning that the fetus does not develop in its normal location.

    (Comprehension)

45. Chancroid is fairly common in _____ countries.

    (Knowledge)

Matching

46. bladder

47. embryo

48. gamete

49. testis

50. urethra

    (Comprehension)

A. longer structure in the male compared to the female

B. develops in the uterus

C. contained in the scrotum

D. voids urine into the urethra

E. ovum or sperm

Short Essay

51. A urine sample is highly acidic. What does this indicate about body metabolism and the function of the kidneys?

    (Application)

52. How does a change in pilus structure promote the survival of the gonococcus *Neisseria gonorrhoeae*?

    (Application)

53. How does an enlarged prostate gland affect the function of the urinary tract? How could this lead to a bacterial infection?

    (Analysis)

54. Why does the appearance of leukocyte esterase in a urine sample indicate a urinary tract infection?

    (Analysis)

55. How does the makeup of the human body promote latent infections of HSV?

    (Synthesis)

56. How does a knowledge of human body structure and function promote understanding of the content of this chapter?

    (Evaluation)

Correlation Questions

57. A person experiences loss of skeletal muscle control two years after being diagnosed with an HSV infection. How can this infection produce this symptom?

58. What conditions in the female reproductive tract promote the growth of microbes?

59. How can an infection of the urinary tract produce dysuria?

60. Why are blood tests necessary as part of the diagnosis for many of the infections of the urinary and reproductive systems?

Answers

Multiple Choice

1. C 2. C 3. C 4. B 5. D 6. A 7. D 8. C 9. C 10. B 11. B
12. D 13. A 14. D 15. C 16. C 17. C 18. B 19. D 20. D
21. C 22. C 23. B 24. C 25. C 26. B 27. A 28. D 29. D 30. D

True/False

31. True 32. True 33. False 34. True 35. False 36. True 37. True
38. False 39. False 40. True

Completion

41. Perinatal 42. pili 43. gummas 44. ectopic 45. tropical

Matching

46. D 47. B 48. E 49. C 50. A

Short Essay

51. The body is producing high concentrations of acid, perhaps through exercise, and/or producing acids metabolically. To prevent acidosis in the blood, the kidneys remove and eliminate this buildup of hydrogen ions.

52. A different pilus allows the bacterium to adhere to a different kind of epithelial cell. For example, the bacterium could adhere to a cell of the GI tract instead of adhering to the urinary tract.

53. The urethra passes through the prostate gland. This donut-shaped gland encircles the urethra under the bladder. The enlargement of the gland blocks the urethra and elimination of urine from the bladder. Retention of urine and bacteria in the bladder could lead a buildup of bacteria normally eliminated, leading to bacterial infection.

54. The enzyme indicates the presence of white blood cells. They have migrated to the urinary tract to fight an infection there.

55. Viruses enter the neurons of the body and stay there in latent form. The intracellular makeup of the neurons provides an optimal environment. Otherwise the surrounding environment of the body is optimal for other factors such as pH and temperature.

56. The microbes described infect specific sites in the urinary and reproductive systems.

Correlation Questions

57. HSV infects neurons, the signal-sending cells of the body. The contractions of skeletal muscles, necessary for movement, depend on the signaling from nerve cells in order to contract. Viral infection of nerve cells can inhibit their signaling function.

58. The environmental conditions for pH, temperature, and absence of light are optimal for many infecting microorganisms.

59. The infecting microbe can create chemical conditions in the mucous membranes of the urinary tract, leading to inflammation. One symptom of inflammation is pain from the affected area of the body.

60. Part of the immune response of the body toward infection is an increase in the number of white blood cells to fight the infection. Sometimes a product of these more numerous, active cells (e.g., leukocyte esterase) is indicative of the immune response. In some cases, an increase in one particular white blood cell type (e.g., neutrophil) indicates the presence of a particular microbe, pinpointing the diagnosis.

Chapter 25
Infections of the Nervous System

Multiple Choice

1. Select the largest organ of the nervous system.

   A. brain
   B. heart
   C. kidney
   D. spinal cord

   (Knowledge)

2. Select the substances that cannot pass through the blood brain barrier.

   A. amino acids
   B. antibiotics
   C. carbon dioxide molecules
   D. glucose molecules

   (Knowledge)

3. Encephalitis is an inflammation of the

   A. brain.
   B. heart.
   C. kidney.
   D. skeletal muscles.

   (Knowledge)

4. Select the incorrect statement about *Neisseria meningitidis*.

   A. It is a disease-causing microorganism.
   B. It is decolorized in the Gram-staining procedure.
   C. It is grown in lab on a minimal medium.
   D. Its only natural reservoir is the human body.

   (Comprehension)

5. The meningococcus is transmitted from person to person by

   A. blood transfusion.
   B. contaminated food.
   C. respiratory droplets.
   D. urinary tract infections.

   (Knowledge)

6. A mutated strain of *N. meningitidis* loses its ability to bind to proteins and steal iron. This prevents it from obtaining iron from

    A. lactoferrin only.
    B. transferrin only.
    C. lactoferrin and transferrin.
    D. neither lactoferrin nor transferrin.

    (Comprehension)

7. The antibiotic of choice to treat systemic meningococcal infections is

    A. erythromycin.
    B. penicillin G.
    C. rifampin.
    D. tetracycline.

    (Knowledge)

8. Select the incorrect statement about *Haemophilus influenzae*.

    A. It can be treated with rifampin.
    B. It is a disease-causing bacterium.
    C. It is transmitted by asymptomatic carriers.
    D. It lacks a carbohydrate capsule.

    (Comprehension)

9. A comprehensive study of bacterial meningitis is completed from a large geographical area. Out of 500 cases, *E. coli* probably caused about _____ of these infections.

    A. 25
    B. 75
    C. 125
    D. 500

    (Application)

10. Cryptococcal meningitis is caused by a

    A. bacterium.
    B. fungus.
    C. protozoan.
    D. virus.

    (Knowledge)

11. The growth of a culture of *Clostridium tetani* can be inhibited significantly by placing it in an environment

    A. of 25 degrees Celsius.
    B. of 37 degrees Celsius.
    C. with oxygen.
    D. without oxygen.

    (Application)

12. Tetanospasmin is a(n)

    A. antibiotic.
    B. antibody.
    C. antigen.
    D. toxin.

    (Knowledge)

13. Select the incorrect statement about *Clostridium botulinum*.

    A. It forms endospores.
    B. It is aerobic.
    C. It is motile.
    D. It is rod-shaped.

    (Knowledge)

14. Botulinum toxin will directly block the function of human body cells that

    A. carry oxygen.
    B. cover the surfaces of the body.
    C. fight infection.
    D. send a signal.

    (Comprehension)

15. Rabies is caused by a

    A. bacterium.
    B. fungus.
    C. protozoan.
    D. virus.

    (Knowledge)

16. The final phase of rabies is the _____ phase.

    A. excitation
    B. inhibition
    C. paralytic
    D. prodromal

    (Knowledge)

17. The Pasteur treatment for rabies involves injections into the _____ wall.

    A. abdominal
    B. pericardial
    C. pleural
    D. urinary

    (Knowledge)

18. The last case of polio in the Western hemisphere occurred in Peru in
    A. 1986.
    B. 1988.
    C. 1991.
    D. 1994.
    (Knowledge)

19. OPV is a _____ vaccine.
    A. bivalent
    B. trivalent
    C. tetravalent
    D. octavalent
    (Knowledge)

20. To eradicate the arbovirus from an environment, a biological control strategy should target a population of
    A. arachnids.
    B. fish.
    C. insects.
    D. reptiles.
    (Comprehension)

21. Each of the following is caused by a viral pathogen except
    A. botulism.
    B. chickenpox.
    C. measles.
    D. rubella.
    (Knowledge)

22. Kuru is caused by
    A. exons.
    B. introns.
    C. prions.
    D. protozoans.
    (Knowledge)

23. A population of trypanosomes can lose their ability to cause disease if a mutation blocks their ability to develop
    A. cell walls.
    B. cilia.
    C. flagella.
    D. pseudopodia.
    (Comprehension)

24. African trypanosomiasis is

    A. malaria.
    B. meningitis.
    C. sleeping sickness.
    D. tetanus.

    (Knowledge)

25. An autopsy is conducted on a person who died from trypanosomiasis. By this procedure these protozoans are found localized in the

    A. brain and spinal cord.
    B. muscles and bones.
    C. pericardium.
    D. ureters and urinary bladder.

    (Comprehension)

True/False

26. The function of the cerebrospinal fluid is to send impulses.

    (Knowledge)

27. A person suffers from myelitis. One symptom of this is a swelling of the skeletal muscles.

    (Comprehension)

28. *N. meningitidis* can ferment maltose.

    (Knowledge)

29. Petechiae are purplish spots.

    (Knowledge)

30. A mutated form of *Streptococcus pneumoniae* loses its ability to develop a capsule. This change increases its ability to produce disease.

    (Comprehension)

31. Bacteria usually enter the CNS from the bloodstream.

    (Knowledge)

32. Viral meningitis is rare among children.

    (Knowledge)

33. *Cryptococcus neoformans* is a yeast with a thick polysaccharide capsule.

    (Knowledge)

34. A researcher attempts to inhibit the growth of a population of *Clostridium tetani* through a pH change in the environment. This can be accomplished by changing the pH to from 7.5 to 5.5.

   (Application)

35. A person develops trismus. As a result, this person's skeletal muscles increase their speed of contraction.

   (Comprehension)

36. The endospores of *C. botulinum* are confined to certain, select environments.

   (Knowledge)

37. The average time for the symptoms of rabies to appear after the infecting animal bite is two months.

   (Knowledge)

38. The poliovirus has seven different serotypes.

   (Knowledge)

39. Polio appears to be on schedule for worldwide eradication during the current decade.

   (Knowledge)

40. An autopsy is conducted on a person who died from spongiform encephalopathy. This autopsy reveals holes in the heart and skeletal muscles as the cause of death.

   (Comprehension)

Completion

41. There are five lumbar vertebrae in the human body. The spinal cord normally ends at L1 or L2. These are the first and second lumbar vertebrae. L3 is very close to the end of the spinal cord. To collect CSF safely, the lumbar puncture must be between the _____ and _____ or the _____ and _____ lumbar vertebrae.

   (Application)

42. A mutation in *N. meningitidis* inhibits its ability to develop adhesins. This interferes with its ability to _____ to _____ cells in the human body and cause infection.

   (Comprehension)

43. Both botulism and tetanus are caused by species of the genus _____.

   (Knowledge)

44. The earliest symptoms of rabies are in the _____ phase.

   (Knowledge)

45. The polio virus is a _____ strand RNA virus.

    (Knowledge)

Matching

46. antibiotic   A. endospores

47. *Clostridium*   B. fungus

48. *Cryptococcus*   C. protozoan

49. rabies   D. rhabdovirus

50. trypanosome   E. rifampin

    (Knowledge)

Short Essay

51. Why does penicillin destroy certain bacteria but not harm human cells?

    (Application)

52. During the winter, how do heated college classrooms often offer the perfect environment for the spread of bacterial infections?

    (Application)

53. What advantages do capillaries offer to promote an exchange function to serve the body?

    (Analysis)

54. *N. meningitidis* can ferment maltose. Relate this capability to its genetic structure.

    (Analysis)

55. What characteristics allow a microbe to be invasive to the human body?

    (Synthesis)

56. The development of a fever can be viewed as a protective mechanism in the human body. How?

    (Evaluation)

Correlation Questions

57. The CNS (central) is composed of the brain and spinal cord. The PNS (peripheral) is composed of the cranial and spinal nerves attached to the brain and spinal cord respectively. Explain the naming of each branch of the nervous system.

58. Brain cells require a constant supply of glucose from the blood. What does this indicate about their carbohydrate chemistry?

59. The spinal nerves are all mixed nerves. Explain.

60. Can meningitis and encephalitis be distinguished on the basis of brain function?

Answers

Multiple Choice

1. A 2. B 3. A 4. C 5. C 6. C 7. B 8. D 9. A 10. B 11. C
12. D 13. B 14. D 15. D 16. C 17. A 18. C 19. B 20. C
21. A 22. C 23. C 24. C 25. A

True/False

26. False 27. False 28. True 29. True 30. False 31. True
32. False 33. True 34. True 35. False 36. False 37. True
38. False 39. True 40. False

Completion

41. third and fourth or fourth and fifth 42. adhere to epithelial cells
43. *Clostridium* 44. prodromal 45. plus

Matching

46. E 47. A 48. B 49. D 50. C

Short Essay

51. Penicillin destroys the bacterial cell wall. This structure is absent in human cells.

52. A large number of people can be concentrated in a small space. Often, during the winter, heating systems can dry out the mucous membranes of the upper respiratory tract. This increases the chance for a person to be infected.

53. They have thin membranes and pores to promote transport. Large numbers of capillaries supply any small region of the body.

54. A genetic mutation could have led to the production of an enzyme system to establish this ability. Another explanation is that most bacteria lost this ability through mutation and *Neisseria* has not been affected by this mutation.

55. The bacterium must have a portal of entry to invade the body. It must also overcome the first and second lines of defense protecting the body. If a microbe can overcome these protective mechanisms, it must find an environment in the body presenting optimal physical and chemical conditions for survival and reproduction.

56. The higher temperature in the body from a fever may be incompatible for the survival of many microbes. This higher temperature may be outside their temperature range for survival. Therefore, a fever may eliminate these microbes.

Correlation Questions

57. The brain and spinal cord resemble the central trunk of a tree. The peripheral nerves resemble the branches attached to the trunk of that tree.

58. Brain cells cannot convert large amounts of glucose into glycogen. Glycogen is a polysaccharide that stores energy. It can be broken down into glucose for immediate energy. Without the capacity to store glycogen and convert it to glucose, brain cells need a constant outside input of glucose.

59. The spinal nerves contain both sensory neurons (send signals toward the CNS) and motor neurons (send signals away from the CNS).

60. Encephalitis affects brain function, arising from inflammation of the brain tissue. Meningitis is an inflammation of the coverings around the brain. Symptoms are different for each disease. For example, the CSF becomes cloudy in meningitis. Fever develops in encephalitis.

Chapter 26
Infection of the Body's Surfaces

Multiple Choice

1. The dermis of the skin is highly vascular. However, the epidermis lacks a blood supply. The epidermal cells that are most distant from the blood supply belong to the stratum

    A. basale.
    B. corneum.
    C. germinativum.
    D. lucidum.

    (Comprehension)

2. Lysozyme is an enzyme that

    A. destroys Gram-negative bacteria.
    B. destroys Gram-positive bacteria.
    C. inhibits skin regeneration.
    D. stimulates skin regeneration.

    (Knowledge)

3. Keratitis is inflammation of the

    A. cornea.
    B. dermis.
    C. epidermis.
    D. sclera.

    (Knowledge)

4. Erysipelas affects

    A. the dermis only.
    B. the epidermis only.
    C. the dermis and epidermis.
    D. neither the epidermis nor dermis.

    (Knowledge)

5. Select the incorrect statement about *Streptococcus pyrogenes*.

    A. It is protected from phagocytosis.
    B. Its M protein can be neutralized by an antibody.
    C. Its streptokinase kills leukocytes.
    D. There are more than 80 different serotypes.

    (Comprehension)

6. A bacterium is studied in lab for identification. It does not decolorize by the second step of the Gram staining procedure. Its cells are not rod-shaped. They do appear in clusters under the microscope. Among the following choices the bacterium is

   A. *Bacillus subtilis*
   B. *Escherichia coli*
   C. *Staphylococcus aureus*
   D. *Streptococcus pyrogenes*

   (Application)

7. Alpha and delta toxins

   A. build bacterial cell walls.
   B. damage cell membranes.
   C. inactivate kinases.
   D. promote protein synthesis.

   (Knowledge)

8. A bacterium is studied in lab for identification. Its cells have a blue-green pigment. Its cells also contain pili and have an extracellular slime layer. This bacterium is

   A. *Clostridium botulinum.*
   B. *Escherichia coli.*
   C. *Pseudomonas aeruginosa.*
   D. *Staphylococcus aureus.*

   (Application)

9. Gas gangrene is caused by

   A. *Clostridium botulinum.*
   B. *Clostridium perfringens.*
   C. *Staphylococcus aureus.*
   D. *Staphylococcus epidermidis.*

   (Knowledge)

10. A person first develops an infection in the nasopharynx. This can lead to an infection caused by *Pseudomonas* called

   A. neuralgia.
   B. osteomyelitis.
   C. otitis externa.
   D. pericarditis.

   (Comprehension)

11. Acne is caused by an inflammatory response to a

    A. bacterium.
    B. fungus.
    C. protozoan.
    D. virus.

    (Knowledge)

12. Leprosy is caused by a species of the genus

    A. *Bacillus.*
    B. *Clostridium.*
    C. *Mycobacterium.*
    D. *Pseudomonas.*

    (Knowledge)

13. Select the incorrect characteristic about indeterminate leprosy.

    A. It develops two to six months after infection.
    B. Its symptoms include skin lesions.
    C. Skin biopsies reveal the presence of nerve damage.
    D. Untreated cases progress to tuberculoid leprosy.

    (Comprehension)

14. Chicken pox is caused by a

    A. bacterium.
    B. fungus.
    C. protozoan.
    D. virus.

    (Knowledge)

15. The pattern of shingles corresponds to the outline of the dermatomes of the body. A dermatome is region of the skin supplied as a single sensory nerve. A dermatome probably appears as a _____ on the skin.

    A. blister
    B. lack of pigmentation
    C. mole
    D. segmental area

    (Comprehension)

16. The most common clinical syndrome of primary HSV-1 infection is

    A. gingivostomatitis.
    B. keratitis.
    C. neuralgia.
    D. septicemia.

    (Knowledge)

17. Herpetic whitlow is an infection of the

   A. brain.
   B. heart.
   C. kidney
   D. skin.

(Knowledge)

18. Select the incorrect statement about the measles virus.

   A. It belongs to the paramyxovirus family.
   B. It can cause red blood cells to clump together.
   C. It has a coiled RNA nucleocapsid.
   D. It survives outside the body for long periods.

(Comprehension)

19. Select the incorrect statement about variola.

   A. It belongs to the poxvirus family.
   B. It is an RNA virus.
   C. It is closely related to vaccinia.
   D. It is the smallpox virus.

(Comprehension)

20. Select the incorrect statement about HPV.

   A. It causes skin elevations.
   B. It has a known means of transmission.
   C. It is an RNA virus.
   D. It is a member of the papovavirus family.

(Comprehension)

21. The dermatophytes are a group of

   A. algae.
   B. bacteria.
   C. fungi.
   D. protozoans.

(Knowledge)

22. *Candida albicans* is a(n) _1_ that can become a(n) _2_ .

   A. 1 - opportunist, 2 - mutualistic species
   B. 1 - opportunist, 2 - pathogen
   C. 1 - mutualistic species, 2 - pathogen
   D. 1 - pathogen, 2 - opportunist

(Comprehension)

23. *Candida* species normally colonize each of the following regions of the human body except the

    A. blood.
    B. gastrointestinal tract.
    C. mucous membranes.
    D. skin.

    (Knowledge)

24. Scabies is an infection of the

    A. heart.
    B. mucous membranes.
    C. skin.
    D. spinal nerves.

    (Knowledge)

25. Scabies infects the human body by the bite of a(n)

    A. annelid.
    B. arthropod.
    C. crustacean.
    D. flatworm.

    (Knowledge)

26. Select the genus not known to cause bacterial inflammation of the conjunctiva.

    A. *Escherichia*
    B. *Haemophilus*
    C. *Staphylococcus*
    D. *Streptococcus*

    (Knowledge)

27. *Chlamydia trachomatis* infects the __1__ and __2__ transmitted to infants at birth.

    A. 1 - eye, 2 - can be
    B. 1 - eye, 2 - cannot be
    C. 1 - ear, 2 - can be
    D. 1 - ear, 2 - cannot be

    (Comprehension)

28. Neonatal gonorrheal ophthalmia is caused by a species of

    A. *Bacillus*
    B. *Clostridium*
    C. *Neisseria*
    D. *Treponema*

    (Knowledge)

29. Herpetic keratitis is an ulceration of the
    A. cornea.
    B. dermis.
    C. liver.
    D. reproductive tract.

    (Knowledge)

30. A researcher wants to eradicate the infection caused by *Loa loa* through a biological control. This researcher should concentrate on a species from the local population of
    A. annelids.
    B. crustaceans.
    C. insects.
    D. mollusks.

    (Application)

True/False

31. The dermis is a thicker, deeper layer of the skin compared to the epidermis.

    (Comprehension)

32. A researcher in the lab is testing for the presence of *S. aureus*. Test results reveal that one bacterium cannot ferment mannitol and is decolorized by the second step of the Gram stain procedure. The researcher can conclude that the bacterium is not *S. aureus*.

    (Application)

33. A researcher in the lab is testing for the presence of *C. perfringens*. Test results reveal that one bacterium is a normal floral species of the human skin and is decolorized by the second step of the Gram stain procedure. The researcher can conclude that the bacterium is *C. perfringens*.

    (Application)

34. A scientist conducts research to find a cure for acne. One avenue for this cure is to study the mechanisms of the endocrine system.

    (Comprehension)

35. Acyclovir is used routinely to treat primary genital herpes.

    (Knowledge)

36. Koplik spots appear on the surface of the skin as an initial indication of measles.

    (Knowledge)

37. SSPE is a rare form of chickenpox.

    (Knowledge)

38. A person is suffering from warts. For relief, this person should use an antifungal medication.

    (Comprehension)

39. *Candida* is an opportunistic pathogen. This means it is a microorganism that does not cause infection but can cause an infection if conditions change.

    (Comprehension)

40. Onchocerciasis is a disease of the nervous system.

    (Knowledge)

Completion

41. The conjunctiva does not cover the _____ of the eye.

    (Knowledge)

42. Cystic fibrosis is a genetic disease of the _____.

    (Knowledge)

43. A teratogen is a producer of _____.

    (Knowledge)

44. Most children developing Reye's syndrome have taken _____ prior to a viral illness.

    (Knowledge)

45. Dermatophyte infections are usually treated orally with _____.

    (Knowledge)

Matching

46. conjunctiva
47. keratin
48. hyaluronidase
49. leukocidin
50. lysozyme

    (Comprehension)

A. cements cells together
B. found in the tear fluid
C. kills neutrophils
D. consists of two layers
E. found in stratum corneum

Short Essay

51. Erysipelas is an infection that spreads quickly through the body. Explain the reason for this.

    (Application)

52. *Staphylococcus aureus* can be a commensal living on the surface of the skin. Explain how its role can change from a commensal to a pathogen.

    (Application)

53. The human body is covered by a layer of dead cells. Explain this statement.

    (Analysis)

54. A dermatome, labeled C4, lies over the deltoid muscle of the body. Due to a shingles infection, blisters appear over this area. What sensory and motor functions may be affected by this infection?

    (Analysis)

55. Describe a series of experiments that can be used to identify *S. aureus*.

    (Synthesis)

56. The skin is often underestimated as an important organ in the human body. Why? What makes it an organ?

    (Evaluation)

Correlation Questions

57. The epidermis of the skin is stratified (many layered) epithelium as opposed to simple (one layer) epithelium. How is this stratification adaptive?

58. How is the production of sebum by the skin adaptive?

59. Red spots develop on the skin through bacterial infection. How do you know that this infection has spread to the dermis?

60. An infecting microorganism produces a streptokinase in the body. How is this dangerous to the health of the body?

Answers

Multiple Choice

1. B   2. B   3. A   4. C   5. C   6. C   7. B   8. C   9. B   10. C   11. A   12. C
13. A   14. D   15. D   16. A   17. D   18. D   19. B   20. C   21. C   22. B
23. A   24. C   25. B   26. A   27. A   28. C   29. A   30. C

True/False

31. True   32. True   33. False   34. True   35. True   36. False   37. False
38. False   39. True   40. False

Completion

41. cornea 42. lungs 43. birth defects 44. aspirin 45. griseofulvin

Matching

46. D 47. E 48. A 49. C 50. B

Short Essay

51. The bacterium causing this disease penetrates deep into the dermis of the skin. The dermis is highly vascular. From the site where a bacterium penetrates the body, the circulating blood is a vehicle for distributing the microbe throughout the body.

52. The skin is a first line of defense that prevents this bacterium from entering the body. However, if there is a break in the skin this bacterium can enter the bloodstream and circulate throughout the body.

53. The more external cells of the epidermis are too far removed from the underlying blood supply to be maintained. These cells are constantly dying and being replaced by underlying skin layers through mitosis.

54. C4 reveals to the area of the skin and underlying skeletal muscles served by the fourth cervical nerve pair. Spinal nerves are mixed, having both sensory and motor neurons. By an infection the sensory and motor ability is lost in the region of the deltoid muscle. A tap of the skin there will not be sensed. The motor ability of the deltoid is lost. It cannot contract to pull the humerus away from the midline of the body (abduction).

55. Include information about its Gram-staining results, cell morphology, nutritional requirements, and metabolic abilities.

56. The skin is an organ, as it consists of several tissue types integrated to perform a common function. Consider its role as a first line of defense to prevent the invasion of microorganisms. Further study reveals its role in body temperature control.

Correlation Questions

57. Stratification of the epithelium provides a thicker covering, which is more protective.

58. Sebum is a waterproofing chemical, offering another line of defense to protect the body.

59. The red spots develop from the bursting of blood vessels. The epidermis lacks a blood supply. The dermis is vascular.

60. Streptokinase destroys blood clots. The formation of blood clots is a protective mechanism in the body, either to plug wounds or to repair small blood vessels that are always breaking through minor injuries or aging.

Chapter 27
Systemic Infections

Multiple Choice

1. The direct function of the heart valves is to
    A. prevent the back flow of blood.
    B. pump blood through the arteries.
    C. reinforce the walls of the heart.
    D. transmit signals through the heart.
    (Knowledge)

2. After leaving the heart, blood passes from the
    A. arteries to the capillaries to the veins.
    B. arteries to the veins to the capillaries.
    C. capillaries to the veins to the arteries.
    D. capillaries to the arteries to the veins.
    (Knowledge)

3. Select the incorrect association.
    A. endocardium/inner lining
    B. myocardium/heart muscle
    C. pericardium/surrounding membrane
    D. systemic circulation/lungs
    (Comprehension)

4. Vegetations of the heart are
    A. breakages in the heart wall.
    B. inflammations of the heart lining.
    C. masses of bacteria and clots.
    D. ruptured blood vessels in the organ.
    (Knowledge)

5. Acute bacterial endocarditis is
    A. slow in developing and progresses rapidly.
    B. slow in developing and progresses slowly.
    C. sudden in developing and progresses rapidly.
    D. sudden in developing and progresses slowly.
    (Knowledge)

6. Select the incorrect statement about subacute bacterial endocarditis.

    A. It is fatal without treatment.
    B. It progresses rapidly.
    C. It starts gradually.
    D. It usually occurs in people with abnormal hearts.

    (Comprehension)

7. Select the incorrect statement about *Trypanosoma cruzi*.

    A. It has a complicated life cycle.
    B. It is a ciliated microorganism.
    C. It is a protozoan.
    D. It is transmitted to humans by an insect bite.

    (Comprehension)

8. Pericardial tamponade is the _____ of the heart.

    A. compression
    B. contraction
    C. enlargement
    D. relaxation

    (Knowledge)

9. Septicemia is a bacterial invasion that is

    A. persistent and not serious.
    B. persistent and serious.
    C. short-lived and not serious.
    D. short-lived and serious.

    (Knowledge)

10. Select the incorrect statement about *Yersinia pestis*.

    A. It is a virulent pathogen.
    B. It is a coccobacillus.
    C. It is Gram-positive.
    D. It is transmitted between human hosts by flea bites.

    (Comprehension)

11. Select the incorrect statement about *Francisella tularensis*.

    A. It frequently infects human beings.
    B. It is a coccobacillus.
    C. It is Gram-negative.
    D. Its disease occurs worldwide among wild mammals.

    (Comprehension)

12. Occuloglandular disease begins in the

    A. brain.
    B. eye.
    C. heart.
    D. lymph nodes.

    (Knowledge)

13. Select the incorrect statement about *Brucella* species.

    A. Their species are distinguished by surface antigens.
    B. They are coccobacilli.
    C. They infect different kinds of mammals.
    D. They retain Gentian violet after the Gram counterstain.

    (Comprehension)

14. Lyme disease is caused by a species of

    A. *Bacillus.*
    B. *Borrelia.*
    C. *Brucella.*
    D. *Mycobacterium.*

    (Knowledge)

15. Anthrax is caused by a species of

    A. *Bacillus.*
    B. *Borrelia.*
    C. *Brucella.*
    D. *Pseudomonas.*

    (Knowledge)

16. The most common form of anthrax is

    A. circulatory.
    B. cutaneous.
    C. gastrointestinal.
    D. respiratory.

    (Knowledge)

17. Select the incorrect statement about *Rickettsia rickettsii.*

    A. It can be passed between ticks transovarially.
    B. It causes RMSF.
    C. It multiplies in the smooth lining of blood vessels.
    D. It is a Gram-positive bacterium.

    (Comprehension)

18. Another name for murine typhus is _____ typhus.

    A. airborne
    B. arthropod
    C. circulatory
    D. fleaborne

    (Knowledge)

19. Yellow fever is caused by a

    A. bacterium.
    B. fungus.
    C. protozoan.
    D. virus.

    (Knowledge)

20. Select the incorrect statement about dengue fever.

    A. It appears frequently in temperate climates.
    B. It is transmitted by a mosquito.
    C. It resembles yellow fever in many ways.
    D. It is caused by closely related viruses.

    (Knowledge)

21. Select the incorrect statement about infectious mononucleosis.

    A. It is caused by EBV.
    B. It often occurs in humans from 15 to 25 years old.
    C. Its symptoms appear about one year after infection.
    D. Its virus produces latent and active infections.

    (Comprehension)

22. Nasopharyngeal carcinoma is common in

    A. Canada.
    B. China.
    C. England.
    D. the United States.

    (Knowledge)

23. Select the earliest stage in the infection by the AIDS virus.

    A. fusion of dendritic cells to CD4 lymphocytes
    B. killing of virus-producing cells by CD8 T cells
    C. outbreak of a skin rash
    D. spreading of the virus to the brain

    (Knowledge)

24. Select the genus of bacterium that is not among the most threatening to AIDS patients.

    A. *Cryptococcus*
    B. *Histoplasma*
    C. *Pneumocystis*
    D. *Pseudomonas*

    (Knowledge)

25. Select the choice that is not a main mode of AIDS transmission.

    A. contaminated food
    B. infected blood
    C. mother to infant
    D. sexual contact

    (Knowledge)

26. When AIDS was first recognized in the United States, it occurred almost exclusively among

    A. heterosexual females.
    B. heterosexual males.
    C. homosexual females.
    D. homosexual males.

    (Knowledge)

27. The disease Ebola is caused by a

    A. bacterium.
    B. fungus.
    C. protozoan.
    D. virus.

    (Knowledge)

28. Merozoites invade

    A. muscle cells.
    B. nerve cells.
    C. red blood cells.
    D. white blood cells.

    (Knowledge)

29. Toxoplasmosis occurs in each of the following except

    A. birds.
    B. fish.
    C. mammals.
    D. reptiles.

    (Knowledge)

30. Select the incorrect statement about schistosomiasis.
    A. It is caused by a helminth.
    B. It is prevalent in Asia.
    C. Its treatment is relatively inexpensive.
    D. Schistosomes have complex life cycles.

    (Comprehension)

True/False

31. The systemic circulation is between the heart and the lungs.

    (Knowledge)

32. Most cases of endocarditis are caused by bacteria.

    (Knowledge)

33. An embolus is a clot that becomes dislodged and travels through the circulation.

    (Comprehension)

34. Chagas' disease is an acute, chronic illness in humans.

    (Knowledge)

35. Significant fluid buildup from pericarditis can interfere with the efficient pumping action of the heart.

    (Comprehension)

36. Brucella species can be cultivated in lab under concentrations of diminished carbon dioxide.

    (Comprehension)

37. A large population suffering from yellow fever is studied. Among this group of 1000, probably 500 suffer the symptoms of the disease.

    (Application)

38. Yellow fever is also called breakbone fever.

    (Knowledge)

39. The most common means of HIV infections is sexual transmission.

    (Knowledge)

40. Babesiosis is caused by a virus.

    (Knowledge)

Completion

41. Wild _____ are the animals that must be eliminated from human housing to prevent the outbreak of the bubonic from an area.

   (Knowledge)

42. _____ are the mammals that must be eliminated from an area to eradicate Lyme disease.

   (Knowledge)

43. Variation in the _____ molecules of *Borrelia* species explains the pattern of appearance and disappearance of Lyme disease.

   (Knowledge)

44. *Bartonella henselae* is pleomorphic, meaning that it can change its _____.

   (Comprehension)

45. Removing _____ through insecticides will prevent the development of epidemic typhus.

   (Comprehension)

46. Through a viral infection, a person complains of fatigue. Possible anemia can be diagnosed by measuring the concentration of _____ in the body.

   (Application)

Matching

47. Epstein-Barr   A. causes malaria
48. *Plasmodium*   B. causes filariasis
49. *Schistosoma*   C. helminth
50. *Wuchereria*   D. virus

   (Knowledge)

Short Essay

51. How can a measurement of the percentages of different leukocytes lead to the correct diagnosis of infectious diseases?

   (Application)

52. Blood tends not to clot in vessels that have a smooth inner surface. How does *Rickettsia rickettsii* activity lead to the clotting of the blood in an infected subject?

   (Analysis)

53. What characteristics distinguish the different kinds of bacteria that cause the different kinds of anthrax?

    (Synthesis)

54. What is the key to eradicating malaria through a biological control?

    (Synthesis)

55. How will a cure for AIDS require advancement from several lines of research?

    (Synthesis)

56. A tissue is a group of similar cells integrated to perform a common function. Blood is usually classified as one kind of connective tissue. How well do you think blood fits the definition of a typical tissue?

    (Evaluation)

Correlation Questions

57. Cystic fibrosis is an autosomal recessive disease. What is the probability that two parents, each with the genotype Cc, produce an offspring with this disease?

58. The myocardium in the left ventricle of a human heart is thicker than the myocardium in the right ventricle. Explain.

59. The blood pressure is higher in systemic arteries compared to systemic veins. Explain.

60. Why are systemic infections difficult to diagnose?

Answers

Multiple Choice

1. A 2. A 3. D 4. C 5. C 6. B 7. B 8. A 9. B 10. C 11. A
12. B 13. D 14. B 15. A 16. B 17. D 18. D 19. D 20. A
21. C 22. B 23. A 24. D 25. A 26. D 27. D 28. C 29. B 30. C

True/False

31. False 32. True 33. True 34. True 35. True 36. False
37. False 38. False 39. True 40. False

Completion

41. rodents 42. deer 43. antigens 44. shape 45. lice 46. red blood cells

Matching

47. D 48. A 49. C 50. B

Short Essay

51. The percentages of the different kinds of white blood cells change in response to different diseases. In the case of infectious mononucleosis, the percentage of neutrophils and monocytes will increase. The percentage of eosinophils will increase in response to parasitic infections. Lymphocytes often increase in response to viral infections.

52. This bacterium damages the inside surface of blood vessels. Platelets in the blood tend to be attracted to these rough, abnormal surfaces. The activity of platelets initiates the process of blood clotting.

53. Different kinds of anthrax bacteria produce different kinds of protein endotoxins. These different proteins can be traced to genetic and metabolic differences among the different kinds of bacteria.

54. Possibilities include preventing the mating and reproduction of the mosquito host that transmits the protozoan causing malaria.

55. Research in metabolism, genetic systems, and immunology hold the key for a cure. HAART is highly active antiretroviral therapy. Protease inhibitors block the assembly of viral particles. Other inhibitors center on genetic mechanisms, blocking the reverse transcription in the virus. Study of the human immune system could lead to a vaccine.

56. The cells of blood are not similar. There are many different kinds of white blood cells with different functions. Red blood cells carry oxygen. Thrombocytes initiate the clotting of the blood. These distinctions make blood a complex tissue with many different abilities.

Correlation Questions

57. This is a monohybrid cross from genetics. From the Cc x Cc mating, the possible genetic recombinations among offspring are: CC, Cc,Cc, and cc. The chance to produce the genotype cc, causing cystic fibrosis, is one-fourth.

58. The left ventricle pumps blood through the systemic circulation of the body. Through this route, it pumps blood to more distant sites compared to the shorter trip between the right ventricle and lungs (pulmonary circulation). The longer systemic trip requires more pumping pressure supplied by the thicker wall of the left ventricle. The thick myocardium of the left ventricle is an adaptation.

59. Arteries transport blood away from the heart. They are closer to the pressure developed by the heart, which is a pump. Veins return blood to the heart. Further away from the heart's pumping pressure, they are at the end of the circulatory trip and have a lower pressure.

60. When a given body region is infected, the entire body can become infected. The circulating blood serves as a transport vehicle to spread the infecting microbe throughout the body.

Chapter 28
Microorganisms and the Environment

Multiple Choice

1. Each of the following is a major biological element except

   A. hydrogen.
   B. magnesium.
   C. phosphorus.
   D. sulfur.

   (Knowledge)

2. In a five liter sample of the atmosphere, the sample contains about _____ liters of oxygen.

   A. 0.3
   B. 1.0
   C. 2.5
   D. 3.0

   (Application)

3. Lignin is a(n)

   A. enzyme breaking down organic molecules.
   B. mineral that cycles in the environment.
   C. stable component of woody plants.
   D. vital component of cell membranes.

   (Knowledge)

4. Select the incorrect statement about a member of the Actinomycetes.

   A. It forms mycelia.
   B. It is an aerobic bacterium.
   C. It is Gram-positive.
   D. It represents more than 100 genera.

   (Comprehension)

5. Select the bacterium that causes human disease but is not found commonly in the soil.

   A. *Clostridium botulinum*
   B. *Clostridium tetani*
   C. *Pseudomonas aeruginosa*
   D. *Staphylococcus aureus*

   (Knowledge)

6. Five grams of soil are collected. The number of protozoan cells in this amount is probably about
   A. 500
   B. 1000
   C. 50,000
   D. 1,500,000
   (Application)

7. The mycorrhizae are a symbiotic association of
   A. bacteria and plants.
   B. fungi and plants.
   C. fungi and protozoa.
   D. protozoa and bacteria.
   (Knowledge)

8. The rhizosphere is the part of the soil
   A. around plant roots.
   B. in crevices near rocks.
   C. in the air above the surface.
   D. in the depths beneath the surface.
   (Knowledge)

9. About _____ of the surface of the Earth is covered with water.
   A. 1/3
   B. 1/2
   C. 3/4
   D. 9/10
   (Application)

10. Eutrophic waters change color from
    A. blue to green.
    B. blue to red.
    C. green to blue.
    D. red to blue.
    (Knowledge)

11. Aerosols are
    A. large groups of bacteria.
    B. large particles of liquid.
    C. small groups of bacteria.
    D. tiny particles of liquid.
    (Knowledge)

12. In a five liter sample of the atmosphere, about _____ liters of this sample is nitrogen.

    A. 1.5
    B. 2.5
    C. 3.0
    D. 4.0

    (Application)

13. By nitrogen fixation, nitrogen gas in the soil is first converted to

    A. ammonia.
    B. nitrate.
    C. nitrite.
    D. protein.

    (Knowledge)

14. Denitrification converts

    A. nitrate to nitrogen gas.
    B. nitrite to nitrogen gas.
    C. nitrogen gas to nitrate.
    D. nitrogen gas to nitrite.

    (Knowledge)

15. In a 100 liter sample of the atmosphere, about _____ liters of this sample is carbon dioxide.

    A. 0.003
    B. 0.03
    C. 0.3
    D. 3.0

    (Application)

16. Carbon dioxide is __1__ by photosynthesis and __2__ by respiration.

    A. 1 - produced, 2 - produced
    B. 1 - produced, 2 - used
    C. 1 - used, 2 - produced
    D. 1 - used, 2 - used

    (Comprehension)

17. The main inorganic supply of phosphorus is in the

    A. atmosphere.
    B. ocean.
    C. rocks.
    D. streams.

    (Knowledge)

18. *Acinetobacter* is a(n)

    A. facultative anaerobe.
    B. obligate aerobe.
    C. obligate anaerobe.
    D. microaerophilic organism.

    (Knowledge)

19. Desulfurylation produces

    A. hydrogen sulfide.
    B. sulfate ions.
    C. sulfric acid.
    D. sulfuric acid.

    (Knowledge)

20. Which metal is often trapped in iron pyrite?

    A. copper
    B. gold
    C. platinum
    D. zinc

    (Knowledge)

21. BOD classifies

    A. the atmosphere.
    B. the soil.
    C. pure water.
    D. waste water.

    (Knowledge)

22. Most tertiary treatments of water are

    A. biological.
    B. chemical.
    C. enzymatic.
    D. mechanical.

    (Knowledge)

23. Select the incorrect statement about coliform bacteria.

    A. They are aerobic and facultative anaerobic.
    B. They are unique with sphere-shaped cells.
    C. They are Gram-negative.
    D. They are nonspore-forming.

    (Comprehension)

24. The first step of the MPN is the _____ test
    A. aerobic
    B. completed
    C. confirmed
    D. presumptive
    (Knowledge)

25. Recalcitrant compounds are
    A. easily decomposed.
    B. high in calcium concentration.
    C. high in iron concentration.
    D. resistant to microbial attack.
    (Knowledge)

True/False

26. A sample of soil is heated at 70 degrees Celsius for 15 minutes. An analysis of this soil reveals living bacteria. This proves that the soil sample lacks thermophiles.

    (Comprehension)

27. Most fungi are obligate anaerobes.

    (Knowledge)

28. Algae are usually abundant in most soils.

    (Knowledge)

29. The rhizosphere is the layer of air within three feet from ground surface.

    (Knowledge)

30. One species of bacterium requires high concentrations of oxygen to survive. It will probably thrive in heavily polluted water.

    (Comprehension)

31. Humans incorporate nitrogen into their metabolism by inhaling it.

    (Comprehension)

32. By denitrification nitrate is converted to nitrogen gas.

    (Knowledge)

33. Ammonification converts ammonia to ions.

    (Knowledge)

34. A twenty-liter air sample from the atmosphere is analyzed. One of the gases makes up about four liters of this mixture. This gas is probably nitrogen.

    (Application)

35. Carbon monoxide is the major greenhouse gas.

    (Knowledge)

36. The supply of phosphorus in the Earth is immense.

    (Knowledge)

37. Sulfur is the third most common element on the Earth.

    (Knowledge)

38. Hydrogen sulfide is produced by desulfurylation.

    (Knowledge)

39. A bacterium is studied in the lab. It retains Gentian violet after the decolorization step of the Gram-staining procedure. It has spherical cells that occur in clusters. It is a coliform bacterium.

    (Comprehension)

40. Humans have learned to make organic matter that is not biodegradable.

    (Knowledge)

Completion

41. By the process of mineralization microorganisms convert _____ material to _____ material.

    (Knowledge)

42. Most mutualistic relationships in the soil are between bacteria and _____.

    (Knowledge)

43. A prokaryote fixes 20 molecules of nitrogen gas. This requires _(number)_ molecules of ATP.

    (Knowledge)

44. The root _____ is an extension of the surface cell of a root.

    (Knowledge)

45. The MPN test is used to test for the presence of _____ bacteria.

    (Knowledge)

Matching

46. carbon	A. element in the amino group
47. nitrogen	B. a component of rotten egg gas
48. oxygen	C. limiting nutrient in many soils
49. phosphorus	D. element forming four covalent bonds
50. sulfur	E. gas produced by photosynthesis

(Comprehension)

Short Essay

51. What makes a synthetic plastic nonbiodegradable?

    (Application)

52. A soil plot loses its normal population of protozoa. Predict the biological consequence of this change.

    (Application)

53. How has the increased combustion of fossil fuels on the Earth affected the carbon cycle?

    (Analysis)

54. How can the activity of microorganisms compensate for any changes that could develop in the nitrogen cycle on the Earth?

    (Analysis)

55. How have changes in the phosphorus cycle affected the variety of life forms in ponds and streams?

    (Synthesis)

56. Compare the BOD produced by anaerobic and aerobic microorganisms in sewage plants.

    (Evaluation)

Correlation Questions

57. Farmers rotate crops in their fields, year by year. During some years, leguminous (nitrogen-fixing) plants are part of that rotation. These plants work in a mutualistic association with bacteria. Why is this crop rotation necessary?

58. The layers of a soil sample are studied by a biologist. The surface layer has a dark, moist appearance. What is its probable composition?

59. The buildup of carbon dioxide in the atmosphere produces a greenhouse effect on the Earth. Explain.

60. Consider this levels-of-organization scheme: population (smaller)-community-ecosystem (larger). Where should the biosphere be placed in this hierarchy?

Answers

Multiple Choice

1. B   2. B   3. C   4. D   5. D   6. C   7. B   8. A   9. C   10. A   11. D
12. D   13. A   14. A   15. B   16. C   17. C   18. B   19. A   20. B
21. D   22. B   23. B   24. D   25. D

True/False

26. False   27. True   28. False   29. False   30. False   31. False
32. True   33. False   34. False   35. False   36. True   37. False   38. True
39. False   40. True

Completion

41. organic to inorganic   42. plant   43. three hundred and twenty
44. hair   45. coliform

Matching

46. D   47. A   48. E   49. C   50. B

Short Essay

51. A microorganism, with the necessary enzyme system, is needed to break down the molecules in the substance through metabolic activity. If a substance is not biodegradable, such a microorganism is absent in the environment.

52. Bacterial populations in the soil will increase, as their protozoan predators are absent.

53. The level of carbon dioxide in the atmosphere has increased through this combustion. Increased photosynthetic activity by phytoplankton and other photosynthetic microbes could perhaps remove some of this carbon dioxide.

54. If the nitrogen increases in the atmosphere, there must be increased activity from the nitrogen fixers to remove it. If the level of nitrogen decreases in the air, more activity from the denitrifiers will be needed to release nitrogen.

55. Phosphorus is often a limiting factor in waterways. Its increased concentration in lakes and ponds has promoted algal blooms. The activity of the algae has depleted oxygen from the water, affecting fish populations and other species in the ponds and streams.

56. To decompose a given mass of organic matter, anaerobic microbes should create less of an oxygen demand than aerobic microbes.

Correlation Questions

57. Certain crops deplete nitrogen from the soil. Through a substitution with a leguminous plant, the nitrogen can be replaced in the soil by nitrogen fixation.

58. The dark, moist layer is humus. Humus is decaying organic matter.

59. The layer of carbon dioxide traps heat onto the surface of the earth. The shell of gas holds the heat on the planet, similar to how a greenhouse keeps heat trapped inside.

60. The biosphere is the largest, most encompassing ecosystem.